Contents

Author acknowledgements

Anthony Bush

To Beatrice, Charlotte, Nicolas, John, Patricia, Peter, Maria, Camilla and Hanna. Thank you.

Max Garrard

There are numerous people who have guided, supported and advised me, thank you all. Most significantly, I thank the most important person in my life, my wife Rachael, for her eternal tolerance and support. Sometimes the simplest advice is indeed the best.

Adam Gledhill

Thank you to my family and Amy for all their support and patience throughout my writing of this book, and thank you to my nephew Jack whose smiles and giggles were a very welcome distraction.

Nikki Mackay

Thank you to my fiancé for his continued support and patience during my writing ventures. To my nephews who never fail to make me smile, may this inspire you, too, to achieve great things in life. Also to my clients who enable me to continually learn and reflect on my own practice and drive their performance forward.

Louise Sutton

To all those that have inspired my work, especially my students who continue to provide the challenge and enthusiasm for what I do.

Acknowledgements

The authors and publisher would like to thank the following for their kind permission to reproduce their material:

Dorling Kindersley (p.25); Blazevich, A.J. Sports Biomechanics, the Basics: Optimising Human Performance, A&C Black Publishers, an imprint of Bloomsbury Publishing plc (p.27); Human Kinetics (p.41, 43 and 60); Pearson Benjamin Cummings (pp.42, 46, 49); Eatwell plate. Crown copyright 2012. Reproduced under the terms of the Open Government Licence (p.72); Mosston and Ashworth's Spectrum of Teaching Styles reprinted with permission of Spectrum Institute for Teaching and Learning (p.127); examples of Dartfish tagging system and image of video analysis reprinted with permission of Dartfish Ltd. (p.140, p.142); Gibbs' reflective cycle reprinted with permission of Oxford Brookes University (p.171).

The publisher would like to thank the following for their kind permission to reproduce their photographs:

(Key: b-bottom; c-centre; l-left; r-right; t-top)

Alamy Images: Johner Images 88, moodboard 37, 144; **Corbis**: Tim Tadder 20; **Getty Image**s: 70, 79, 70, 79, Michael Blann 60t, MLB Photos 60b, The FA 126; **iStockphoto**: Neustockimages 113; **Leeds Metropolitan University**: 172; Photolibrary.com: Doug Allan 38; Rex Features: Karen Fuchs 119; Science Photo Library Ltd: Les and Dave Jacobs, Sean Bagshaw 63; **Shutterstock.com**: auremar 130, CandyBoxPhoto 67, Peter Bernik 108

Cover images: Front: **Corbis**: Dominique Douieb / PhotoAlto

All other images © Pearson Education

Every effort has been made to trace the copyright holders and we apologise in advance for any unintentional omissions. We would be pleased to insert the appropriate acknowledgement in any subsequent edition of this publication.

Foundations in
SPORTS
SCIENCE

Anthony Bush

Max Garrard

Adam Gledhill

Nikki Mackay

Louise Sutton

PEARSON

www.pearsonschoolsandfecolleges.co.uk

Text © Pearson Education Limited 2012

Designed by Brian Melville

Typeset by Brian Melville

Original illustrations © Pearson Education Limited 2012

Illustrated by Pearson Education, Oxford Designers and Illustrators and Brian Melville

Cover design by Brian Melville

Picture research by Elena Wright

Cover photo Corbis: Dominique Douieb/PhotoAlto

The rights of Anthony Bush, Max Garrard, Adam Gledhill, Nikki Mackay and Louise Sutton to be identified as authors of this work have been asserted by them in accordance with the Copyright, Designs and Patents Act 1988.

First published 2012

14 13 12

10 9 8 7 6 5 4 3 2 1

British Library Cataloguing in Publication Data

A catalogue record for this book is available from the British Library

ISBN 978 0 435 04686 6

Copyright notice

Printed in Spain by Grafos

Websites

There are links to relevant websites in this book. In order to ensure that the links are up to date and that the links work we have made the links available on our website at www.pearsonhotlinks.co.uk. Search for this title Foundations in Sports Science or ISBN 9780435046866.

About the authors

Anthony Bush

Dr Anthony Bush is a lecturer in sports studies, education, and coaching in the Department of Education at the University of Bath. He is a former professional badminton player and has over 20 years of coaching experience. His research interests include the development of interpretive-critical research methodologies and engaging a cultural studies sensibility with sports coaching research, an ongoing project that democratises sports coaching research, opening it to critical conversations about social justice, cultural politics, violence and progressive futures.

Max Garrard

Max Garrard is a lecturer in sport and exercise physiology at Leeds Metropolitan University. He has an MSc Sport and Exercise Science and has 10 years of experience teaching and designing courses within Higher Education. He has gained considerable experience of sport and exercise science research in health and performance populations. This includes laboratory and field research, including the challenging environment of high altitude. He has also worked as a personal trainer within the fitness industry. Alongside teaching and research, Max provides sports science support to elite teams and athletes through the Carnegie Centre for Sports Performance and Well Being.

Adam Gledhill

Adam Gledhill has nine years experience teaching sports and exercise sciences and sports therapy courses across Further and Higher Education. He has contributed to the development of a Foundation Degree in Sports Therapy that is currently accredited by the Society of Sports Therapists. Adam has co-authored ten publications within sport or sport and exercise sciences, works as an educational consultant for a national consultancy firm and is currently working towards a PhD in Sport Psychology.

Nikki Mackay

Nikki Mackay has her own Sports Injury Consultancy and Wellbeing clinic working with elite, professional and recreational sports people and clubs. She has recently been appointed as Chief Verifier Sport and Active Leisure for a lead education awarding body. She also works as an educational consultant, freelance lecturer and examiner. Nikki is an assessment associate and writer, and an external examiner for leading educational awarding bodies. She has lectured across a range of programmes and module subjects, including lecturing on teacher training programmes, mentoring and contributing to staff development programmes. Specialising in Sports Therapy, she led the writing and validation of FdSc and BSc Sports Therapy programmes by the University of Northampton.

Louise Sutton

Louise Sutton is a principal lecturer in sport and exercise nutrition at Leeds Metropolitan University. She has delivered on Foundation Degree programmes since their introduction in 2000 and worked with SkillsActive, the Sector Skills Council for Active Leisure, Learning and Wellbeing in the UK, to develop Foundation Degree Frameworks for the Sector. A recipient of the Re-Energise Fitness Professional of the Year award, Louise is known for her commitment and contribution to raising standards in nutrition training and education in the health and fitness industry as well as competitive sport.

Introduction

Who is this book for?

This book is an essential guide for students studying a foundation degree in Sports Science and BTEC Higher Nationals in Sport and Sport and Exercise Sciences.

About foundation degrees

Your foundation degree should enable you to develop the intermediate higher education skills that characterise high-quality graduates needed in the labour market and should integrate academic and work-based learning. It is likely that your foundation degree will have been developed in collaboration with employers and have a focus on the development of work-related skills and knowledge and their direct application to the workplace.

As a foundation degree graduate you should be able to demonstrate the following in your field of study and also in a work context:

- knowledge and critical understanding of the well-established principles
- successful application of the range of knowledge and skills learned throughout your programme
- knowledge of the main methods of enquiry in your subject(s)
- the ability to evaluate critically the appropriateness of different approaches to problem solving
- effective communication of information, arguments and analysis, in a variety of forms, to specialist and non-specialist audiences
- qualities and transferable skills necessary for employment and progression to other qualifications requiring the exercise of personal responsibility and decision making
- the ability to utilise opportunities for lifelong learning, and should you wish to pursue it, a smooth transition route to an honours degree programme.

Your foundation degree will have been developed in line with relevant National Occupational Standards where appropriate.

These Standards recognise established benchmarks of competence. They are developed by employers, academics and other sector experts and define the skills and knowledge required to undertake particular job roles.

As competition for employment opportunities grows, most foundation degrees offer a bridge between learning and earning. Authentic and innovative work-based learning is an integral part of a foundation degree. The work-based learning aspect of your foundation degree should offer you the opportunity of relevant work and training.

In your foundation degree, academic knowledge and understanding should integrate with, and support the development of, vocational skills and competencies. It should enhance and extend your career prospects and foster the development of life-long learning. You should get the opportunity to work on real projects, making a real difference whilst picking up technical and practical skills needed for your chosen career path.

Assessment

Different foundation degrees will assess your work in different ways. The purpose of assessment is to determine your performance in relation to the learning outcomes of your award, level and modules. Assessment methods will include a variety of formal and informal, summative and formative techniques. The assessment strategy for your programme is likely to provide a good mix of competency based assessments, examination and employer feedback that may include:

- case studies
- presentations
- project work
- examinations
- reports
- practicals or simulations
- observations and viva examinations
- peer and self assessment
- personal development plans and evidence portfolios.

You should understand the relationship between learning outcomes and assessment and develop your confidence in tackling different forms of assessment.

About BTEC Higher Nationals

BTEC Higher Nationals are designed to provide a specialist vocational programme, linked to professional body requirements and National Occupational Standards where appropriate. They offer a strong, sector-related emphasis on practical skills development alongside the development of requisite knowledge and understanding. The qualifications provide a thorough grounding in the key concepts and practical skills required in the sector and their national recognition by employers allows direct progression to employment. A key progression path for BTEC HNC and HND learners is to the second or third year of a degree or honours degree programme, depending on the match of the BTEC Higher National units to the degree programme in question.

The BTEC HNC and HND in Sport and in Sport and Exercise Sciences offer progression routes to membership of The Institute of Sport and Recreation Management (ISRM) and The Institute for Sport, Parks and Leisure (ISPAL).

BTEC Higher Nationals in Sport and in Sport and Exercise Sciences have been developed to focus on:

- providing education and training for a range of careers in the sector
- the education and training of those who are employed, or aspire to be employed, in a variety of types of work, such as in performance analysis, nutrition for sport and exercise, sports therapy, sports development, sports coaching, education, research and development
- opportunities for you to gain a nationally-recognised vocationally-specific qualification to enter employment in the sector or progress to higher education qualifications such as a full-time degree in a related area
- an understanding of the roles of those working in the sector, including how their role and that of their department fits within the overall structure of their organisation and within the community
- opportunities for you to focus on the development of the higher level skills in sport, sport and exercise sciences and related areas
- the development of your knowledge, understanding and skills in the field of sport, sport and exercise sciences and related areas

- opportunities for you to develop a range of skills, techniques and attributes essential for successful performance in working life.

Assessment

For BTEC Higher Nationals the purpose of assessment is to ensure that effective learning of the content of each unit has taken place. Evidence of this learning, or the application of the learning, is required for each unit. The assessment of the evidence relates directly to the assessment criteria for each unit, supported by the generic grade descriptors. The process of assessment can aid effective learning by seeking and interpreting evidence to decide the stage that you have reached in your learning, what further learning needs to take place and how best to do this. Therefore, the process of assessment should be part of the effective planning of teaching and learning by providing opportunities for both you and your assessor to obtain information about progress towards learning goals.

The role of the Sector Skills Councils

Sector Skills Councils (SSCs) are independent, employer-led, UK wide organisations that are licensed by government to build skills systems relevant to employment. They have four key goals:

- to reduce skills gaps and shortages
- to improve productivity, business and public service performance
- to increase opportunities for skills development
- to improve learning through National Occupational Standards, apprenticeships and further and higher education.

SSCs make labour market information available to key stakeholders. This information is at the centre of effective careers counselling. SkillsActive is the SSC for Active Leisure, Learning and Wellbeing. This sector covers everything from the grass-roots through to performance sport and they ensure the sector has suitably qualified employees and volunteers to support the delivery of sport and sport related activities. Find out more about SkillsActive at www.skillsactive.com.

How to use this book

This book is divided into chapters that cover the theory you will need to help you through your studies and chapters that cover the practical aspects of studying for a foundation degree or a BTEC Higher National. This book contains many features that will help you use your skills and knowledge in work-related situations and assist you in getting the most from your course.

Features of this book

The appendicular skeleton (Figure 1.5 a–d), page 6 consists of all the bones which attach to the axial skeleton, and can be divided into six regions.

- Each arm consists of a humerus, an ulna and a radius.
- Each hand consists of eight carpals, five metacarpals, five proximal phalanges, four middle phalanges, five distal phalanges and two sesamoids.
- Each pectoral girdle consists of two clavicles and two scapulae.
- The pelvis consists of left and right os coxae, which are formed by the fusion of the illium, ischium and pubis.
- Each leg consists of a femur, tibia, patella and fibula.
- Each foot contains seven tarsals, five metatarsals, five proximal phalanges, four middle phalanges, five distal phalanges and two sesamoid bones.

Functions of the skeletal system

The skeletal system has a number of physiological and mechanical functions.

- **Protection** – The skeletal framework protects the vital tissues and organs in your body: the cranium protects the brain; the thorax protects the heart and lungs; the vertebral column protects the spinal cord; and the pelvis protects the abdominal and reproductive organs.
- **Attachment for skeletal muscles** – The skeleton provides a framework for attachment of the skeletal muscles via tendons as well as the attachment of ligaments. The skeletal system provides a lever system in order to create joint motion and movement.
- **Support** – The skeletal frame provides a structural framework, giving the body a supportive framework for soft tissue, and providing shape.
- **Store of minerals** – Bone stores minerals, such as calcium, phosphate (a stored form of phosphorus) and magnesium, which are essential for growth and bone health. Minerals are released into the bloodstream as the body requires them. The yellow bone marrow stores fat.

- **Source of red blood cell production** – Red bone marrow found within the bone produces red blood cells, white blood cells and platelets.

> **Remember**
>
> Functions of the skeleton can be remembered with the acronym PASSS.
>
> **P**rotection
> **A**ttachment
> **S**upport
> **S**torage
> **S**ource

Male and female skeletal systems differ. A female pelvis is wider and flatter to assist childbirth, with associated widening of the sacrum. The cartilage found at the **pubic symphysis** in a female is broader, allowing a greater spreading of the pelvis during childbirth. The female ribcage is more rounded and smaller than a male ribcage, with the lumbar curve greater and the pelvis anteriorly tilted. The greater hip width results in an increased femur angle from the hip to the knee (increased Q angle). Males generally are taller and have heavier bones. Males have greater muscle bulk, with tendon attachments being more prominent and easier to palpate.

> **Key term**
>
> **Pubic symphysis** – a cartilaginous joint articulating the superior rami of the left and right pubic bones

> **Stop and think**
>
> The function of calcium is to promote healthy bone mass. Calcium also plays a vital role within exercise; an additional supply of calcium is required to ensure levels of calcium ions are adequate for working muscle to elicit the relaxatory response. Ninety nine per cent of calcium is found in bones and 1 per cent in the body's fluids and cells. A diet deficient in calcium can lead to osteopenia in later life. What kind of foods do you think contain calcium?

7

Useful information

Key facts that are crucial to the course or to professional practice are highlighted throughout the text.

Key terms

Technical words and phrases are easy to spot. You can also use the glossary at the back of the book.

Activities

There are different types of activities for you to do throughout the text that will help you to develop your knowledge, skills and understanding.

Top tip

Be sure to record all items as consumed, it is often fluid intake that is under reported most in food records as drinks are often consumed outside of meal times.
* After completion look at your food and activity record and compare it to the UK National Food Guide recommendations

Take it further

As well as the types and amounts of food you eat, your record may give you an idea about how your daily life dictates what, when, where and why you eat. Take another look at your food record and ask yourself the following questions:
* Is there room for improvement, or is your diet actually better than you thought?
* Do you eat regularly or frequently skip meals?
* Are some days better than others and do you eat differently at weekends?
* Is there enough variety in your diet?
* What constraints are there placed on your diet by your lifestyle that may prevent you from making any necessary dietary changes?
* How did activity or exercise influence your intake?

Food composition tables and dietary analysis software

For quantitative assessment of nutritional intake, food composition tables and dietary analysis software can be employed. In the UK the Food Standards Agency maintains a record of food compositional data in a National Nutrient Databank. From time to time this information is published in book and electronic format as McCance and Widdowson's *The Composition of Foods*. Food tables and nutritional analysis computer packages that use such databases are valuable resources in dietary analysis. However there are limitations and common pitfalls to be aware of in their use and application. It is important to note that the composition of a particular food can vary on account of the way in which it has been stored, processed, manufactured and cooked, whilst acknowledging plant or animal genetics and farming practices that will also impact.

There is a range of nutrient analysis software programmes available for dietary analysis. Some of the less sophisticated software, particularly that designed for use by the general public or for use in schools, often contains abbreviated data and as such needs to be used with caution. Where full data is available, and leaving aside the compositional variation of nutrient content of food, there are many opportunities for error to occur in the diet analysis process, such as in the coding of food items, portion sizing and the requirement for food substitution for items not within the database. As such any detailed or complex dietary analysis, particularly that requiring major dietary change, should always be referred to a State Registered Dietitian or Accredited Nutritionist.

Stop and think

What factors would you need to give consideration to in the practical application of dietary assessment techniques in sport?

Take it further

The National Diet and Nutrition Survey (NDNS), designed to be representative of the UK population, is a continuous cross-sectional survey of the food consumption, nutrient intakes and nutritional status of people aged 18 months and older living in private households in the UK. The NDNS is funded by the Food Standards Agency and the Department of Health in England, and is carried out by the National Centre for Social Research, Medical Research Council Human Nutrition Research and the University College London Medical School.

Intakes are compared with government recommendations and comparisons with findings from previous surveys are also made. Take a look at the latest NDNS Report findings on the Food Standards Agency website (to obtain a secure link to their website, visit www.pearsonfe.co.uk/foundationsinsport). What observations do you make about population intake compared to recommendations?

84

Top tip

Suggestions on good practice.

Take it further

Extra activities to develop your skills.

Case studies

Case studies provide snapshots of real workplace issues and show how the skills and knowledge you develop during your course can help you in your career.

Case study (for recommended answers, see www.pearsonfe.co.uk/foundationsinsport)

Jo Lee is a triathlete and has recently had her most victorious triathlon yet. The sprint triathlon consisted of a 400 m swim, 20 km on the bike followed by a 5 km run. Jo achieved an overall time of 1 hour 11 minutes 21 seconds, finishing second in the 25-29 years age group and an overall ranking of thirteenth female. Jo's swim split was impressive - fastest woman with 6 minutes 4 seconds, positioning her seventh fastest overall of all male and female competitors and age groups. Jo had a modest ride on the bike with a split of 41 minutes 12 seconds and a 5 km run in 21 minutes 30 seconds. Jo's training regime requires commitment and dedication, consisting of three swim sessions a week (1 × 2 hours, 2 × 1 hour), four run sessions (4.8-14.4 km per run, with a mixture of speed, interval and endurance), and four bike sessions covering around 12.8 km each session with a longer weekly ride around 32-48 km. In addition to this she does 1 × 1 hour circuits, 1 × 1 hour pilates and one other session such as body balance or core weekly with a fortnightly 1 × 1 hour spin session.

1. Discuss the joint movements involved in cycling.
2. Discuss the muscles responsible for the movements identified in question 1.
3. Discuss the joint movements involved in running.
4. Discuss the types of muscle contraction occurring for movements identified in question 3.

Knowledge checks

At the end of each chapter these questions are there to check your knowledge. You can use them to see how much progress you've made and then check the answers on the companion website at **www.pearsonfe.co.uk/foundationsinsport**

Check your understanding (for answers, see www.pearsonfe.co.uk/foundationsinsport)

1. Describe the axial and appendicular skeleton, making reference to the names, types of bones and their function.
2. Briefly describe the three classifications of joints.
3. Describe the gross structure of a muscle.
4. Describe the micro structure of a muscle.
5. Differentiate between the functions of a ligament and a tendon.
6. Describe lordosis and its effect on the muscular system.
7. Describe kyphosis and explain which sports may predispose an athlete to this condition.
8. Observe a rugby player performing a squat and complete the following table for the up and down phase.

Joint	Action	Muscle	Contraction

Time to reflect

Questions and tasks prompting you to think about how you can apply what you have learnt in the chapter.

Time to reflect

1. Think about a somersault, cartwheel and pivot turn and ascertain what plane of movement the technique takes place in.
2. Practise the movements that are possible at each joint.
3. Choose a technique from a sport you are interested in. Reflect on which joints, movements and muscle are involved.
4. Can you identify all the bones of the body, and discuss the type of bone in relation to its function?
5. Can you identify the action of all the muscles?
6. Can you specify the origin and insertion of all the muscles?
7. Choose a sporting movement, such as a press up. Can you identify the working muscles and their actions? Can you identify the type of muscle contraction taking place?
8. Can you choose 10 muscles and identify their fascicular arrangement?

20

Chapter 1

Functional anatomy

Introduction

A comprehensive understanding of functional anatomy is essential for any good sports scientist. It can make the difference between passing or failing your foundation degree, or excelling within the industry. Sports scientists apply the principles of science with the aim of improving sports performance. Understanding and knowing anatomical terms are fundamental to being able to communicate with other personnel within a multi-disciplinary team, as well as understanding theoretical concepts and principles. Anatomy can be learned through books and the Internet but there is no substitute for first hand learning and application.

Functional anatomy is key to your ability to understand complex sporting movements. It is essential to understand how your players move, the effect of training principles upon the body, the correct sporting technique and the ability to identify muscular imbalances. This chapter will help you to develop your understanding through the practical application of anatomy. It should be re-visited frequently as you progress through the other chapters of the book. In a sports science foundation degree no module should be viewed in isolation. For example, while exploring *Chapter 2: Biomechanics* you can relate joint types and movements to the body's biomechanics.

Learning outcomes

After you have read this chapter you should be able to:

- understand anatomical terminology
- describe key structures and functions of the skeletal system
- explain joint classifications
- describe key structures of the muscular system.

Starting block

Get into pairs and take it in turns to be the model for the activities below.

- Using sticky notes, write down as many names of bones and muscles as possible. Can you place the names of the bones and the muscles on the correct location on your model?

- Using sticky notes, write down as many joint names and

their classification as possible (don't forget joints such as sternoclavicular). Place them correctly on your model.

- Using an eyeliner, draw as many muscles as you can onto the anterior and posterior surfaces of your model (ask for consent).

If you don't have a model, use a body outline on paper, borrow a doll or use an art model.

Anatomical terminology

Anatomical terminology is commonly used within the medical profession in treatment notes and in communication between professionals. It is therefore very important you are able to understand the most common terms used. The anatomical position is the position your athlete assumes when you are documenting your anatomical terms (or the position your model assumes when demonstrating anatomical terms).

Three common anatomical terms used are sagittal, transverse and coronal planes (see Figure 1.1).

- **Sagittal plane** – vertical plane (from head to toe) passing through the navel dividing the body into left and right.

- **Transverse plane** – also known as the horizontal plane, divides the body into superior and inferior body segments.

- **Coronal plane** – also known as the frontal plane, divides the body into dorsal and ventral segments (front and back).

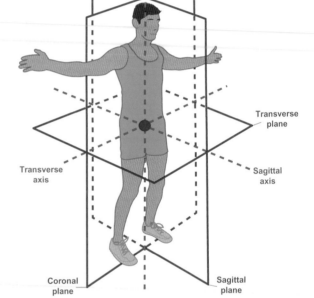

Figure 1.1: Planes

Key term

Supinated – when the forearm is supinated the palm of the hand is facing forward when in the anatomical position

The anatomical position of the athlete is anteriorly viewed with arms by the side with forearms **supinated**. This is the position used for all anatomical references (see Figure 1.2). Table 1.1 (see next page) describes common anatomical terminology used within sports science.

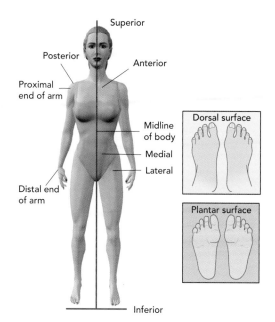

Figure 1.2: Anatomical positions

As a sports scientist you need to understand the movements available at each joint. Table 1.2 describes common movement terminology used in sports science. Movements available at joints are addressed later in the chapter on page 11.

Table 1.1: Anatomical terminology

Terminology	Description
Anterior	Front view, in front or towards the front of the body
Posterior	Rear view, behind or towards the rear of the body
Medial	Towards or at the midline of the body
Lateral	Away from or at the midline of the body
Proximal	Near to or closer to the centre of the body
Distal	Away from or further from the centre of the body
Superior	Above or towards the head of the body
Inferior	Below or away from the head of the body
Superficial	Nearer to the surface
Deep	Away from the surface
Ipsilateral	Same side as the body
Contralateral	Opposite side of the body
Prone	Lying face down
Supine	Lying face up

Table 1.2: Movement terminology

Movement	Description	Picture
Flexion	Reduction of the joint angle	
Extension	Increasing the joint angle	

Table 1.2: Movement terminology (continued)

Movement	Description	Picture
Abduction	Taking away from the midline	
Adduction	Taking towards the midline	
Pronation	Palm turning downwards	
Supination	Palm turning upwards	
Plantar flexion	Pointing the toes away, pushing the sole of the foot away	
Dorsiflexion	Moving the top of the foot towards the body, showing the sole of the foot	
Hyperextension	Increased extension beyond the norm	
Rotation	Movement of a bone (or the trunk) around its own longitudinal axis	
Medial rotation	Turning towards the midline	
Lateral rotation	Turning away from the midline	

Key structures and functions of the skeletal system

The average adult skeleton consists of 206 bones. The precise number varies and with age some bones may become fused. The skeleton can be divided into two components: the **axial skeleton** contains 80 bones and the **appendicular skeleton** contains 126 bones.

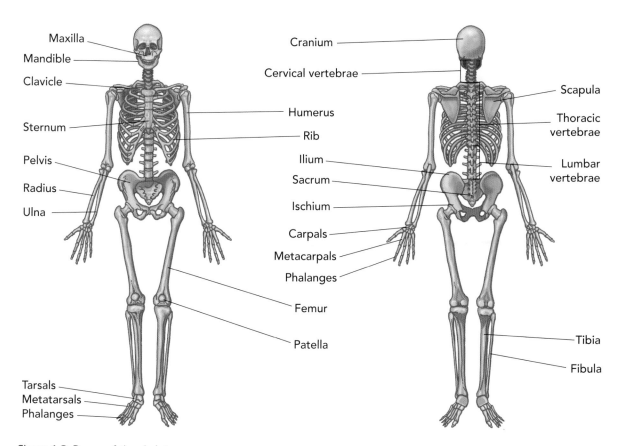

Maxilla
Mandible
Clavicle
Sternum
Pelvis
Radius
Ulna
Tarsals
Metatarsals
Phalanges

Cranium
Cervical vertebrae
Humerus
Rib
Ilium
Sacrum
Ischium
Carpals
Metacarpals
Phalanges
Femur
Patella

Scapula
Thoracic vertebrae
Lumbar vertebrae
Tibia
Fibula

Figure 1.3: Bones of the skeleton

The number of bones can vary in the human body due to anatomical variation, such as an extra lumbar vertebrae, cervical rib, lumbar rib or **sutural bones** in the skull. The appendicular skeleton is not fused, allowing for a much greater range of motion.

The axial skeleton (see Figure 1.4 a–c overleaf) forms the upright axis of the body and consists of the:

• cranium, which consists of the parietal, temporal, frontal, occipital, ethmoid and sphenoid bones

• facial bones, consisting of maxilla, zygomatic, mandible, nasal, palatine, inferior nasal concha, lacrimal and vomer bones

• hyoid bone, which is a U-shaped bone located in the neck

• vertebral column consisting of the cervical, thoracic and lumbar vertebrae, as well as the sacrum and coccyx

• thoracic cage, consisting of the sternum and ribs

• auditory ossicles, consisting of the malleus, incus and stapes found in the inner ear.

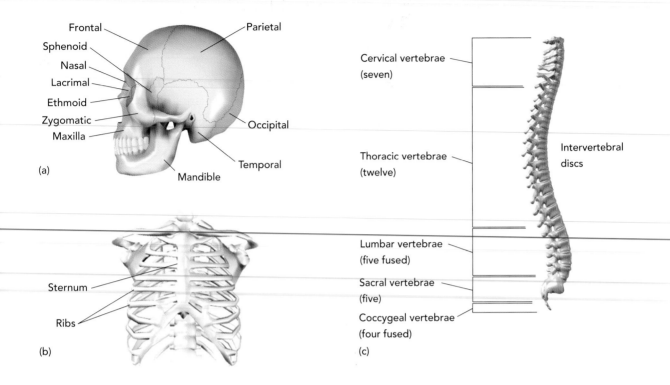

Frontal
Sphenoid
Nasal
Lacrimal
Ethmoid
Zygomatic
Maxilla
Parietal
Occipital
Temporal
Mandible
(a)

Cervical vertebrae
(seven)

Thoracic vertebrae
(twelve)

Lumbar vertebrae
(five fused)

Sacral vertebrae
(five)

Coccygeal vertebrae
(four fused)

Intervertebral
discs

Sternum
Ribs
(b)

(c)

Figure 1.4: Bones of the axial skeleton: a) the cranium, b) the thorax and c) the vertebral column

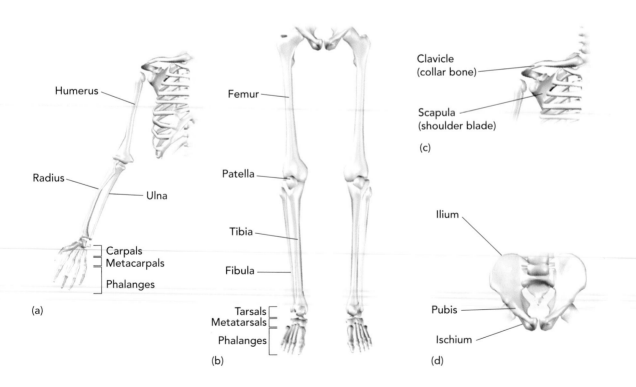

Humerus
Radius
Ulna
Carpals
Metacarpals
Phalanges
(a)

Femur
Patella
Tibia
Fibula
Tarsals
Metatarsals
Phalanges
(b)

Clavicle
(collar bone)
Scapula
(shoulder blade)
(c)

Ilium
Pubis
Ischium
(d)

Figure 1.5: Bones of the appendicular skeleton: a) the upper limbs, b) the lower limbs,
c) the shoulder girdle and d) the pelvis

The appendicular skeleton (Figure 1.5 a–d), page 6 consists of all the bones which attach to the axial skeleton, and can be divided into six regions.

- Each arm consists of a humerus, an ulna and a radius.

- Each hand consists of eight carpals, five metacarpals, five proximal phalanges, four middle phalanges, five distal phalanges and two sesamoids.

- Each pectoral girdle consists of two clavicles and two scapulae.

- The pelvis consists of left and right os coxae, which are formed by the fusion of the illium, ischium and pubis.

- Each leg consists of a femur, tibia, patella and fibula.

- Each foot contains seven tarsals, five metatarsals, five proximal phalanges, four middle phalanges, five distal phalanges and two sesamoid bones.

Functions of the skeletal system

The skeletal system has a number of physiological and mechanical functions.

- **Protection** – The skeletal framework protects the vital tissues and organs in your body: the cranium protects the brain; the thorax protects the heart and lungs; the vertebral column protects the spinal cord; and the pelvis protects the abdominal and reproductive organs.

- **Attachment for skeletal muscles** – The skeleton provides a framework for attachment of the skeletal muscles via tendons as well as the attachment of ligaments. The skeletal system provides a lever system in order to create joint motion and movement.

- **Support** – The skeletal frame provides a structural framework, giving the body a supportive framework for soft tissue, and providing shape.

- **Store of minerals** – Bone stores minerals, such as calcium, phosphate (a stored form of phosphorus) and magnesium, which are essential for growth and bone health. Minerals are released into the bloodstream as the body requires them. The yellow bone marrow stores fat.

- **Source of red blood cell production** – Red bone marrow found within the bone produces red blood cells, white blood cells and platelets.

Remember

Functions of the skeleton can be remembered with the acronym PASSS.

Protection

Attachment

Support

Storage

Source

Male and female skeletal systems differ. A female pelvis is wider and flatter to assist childbirth, with associated widening of the sacrum. The cartilage found at the **pubic symphysis** in a female is broader, allowing a greater spreading of the pelvis during childbirth. The female ribcage is more rounded and smaller than a male ribcage, with the lumbar curve greater and the pelvis anteriorly tilted. The greater hip width results in an increased femur angle from the hip to the knee (increased Q angle). Males generally are taller and have heavier bones. Males have greater muscle bulk, with tendon attachments being more prominent and easier to palpate.

Key term

Pubic symphysis – a cartilaginous joint articulating the superior rami of the left and right pubic bones

Stop and think

The function of calcium is to promote healthy bone mass. Calcium also plays a vital role within exercise; an additional supply of calcium is required to ensure levels of calcium ions are adequate for working muscle to elicit the relaxatory response. Ninety nine per cent of calcium is found in bones and 1 per cent in the body's fluids and cells. A diet deficient in calcium can lead to osteopenia in later life. What kind of foods do you think contain calcium?

Types of bone

Bones are a specific shape and size for a reason.

- **Long bones** (see Figure 1.6) such as the tibia, fibula, humerus and ulna are found in the limbs. They have a long shaft known as the **diaphysis** Each end of the bone is known as the epiphysis.

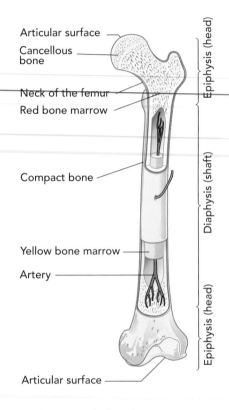

Figure 1.6: Structure of a long bone

Articular surface
Cancellous bone
Neck of the femur
Red bone marrow
Compact bone
Yellow bone marrow
Artery
Articular surface

Epiphysis (head)
Diaphysis (shaft)
Epiphysis (head)

- **Short bones** such as the carpals and tarsals (see Figure 1.5, page 6) are in the wrist and ankles. These are strong, small, light and cube shaped, consisting of cancellous bone (also known as spongy bone) encased by compact bone.

- **Flat bones** include the scapulae (see Figure 1.5), sternum and bones of the cranium. They are thin, flat, have a large surface area and aspects curved in shape to allow for a strong attachment site. Flat bones are particularly strong and their function is to provide protection.

- **Sesamoid bones** such as the patella (see Figure 1.5) are small bones located within a tendon.

- **Irregular bones**, such as the vertebrae (see Figure 1.4) have irregular shapes and do not fit into any of the above categories.

The vertebral column

This is a segmented flexible pillar made up of five regions: the cervical, thoracic, lumbar, sacral and coccyx. Before the developmental years the vertebral column consists of 33 single vertebrae. The cervical, thoracic and lumbar regions comprise a total of 24 single vertebrae. During the developmental years five vertebrae fuse to form the sacrum, and between two and four fuse to form the coccyx.

The second cervical vertebra (C2) to the sacrum (S1) consists of individual **articulations**, held firmly in position by intevertebral discs (comprised of **fibrocartilage**) and ligaments. Due to the natural **lordosis** in the cervical and lumbar areas, the disc tends to be thicker **anteriorly**. Each vertebra consists of various processes (transverse, spinous and superior articular process), an arch and a body which supports the weight. The vertebral foramen is a hole through which the spinal cord passes (see Figure 1.7).

Key terms

Diaphysis – main shaft of the bone

Articulation – the contact of two or more bones at a specific location

Fibrocartilage – this cartilage is very rich in type 1 collagen and is strong and durable. It can be found, for example, in the menisci of the knee and intevertebral disc

Lordosis – exaggerated curvature of the lumbar spine

Anteriorly – towards the front

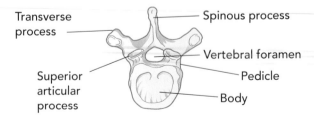

Transverse process
Spinous process
Vertebral foramen
Pedicle
Body
Superior articular process

Figure 1.7: A vertebra

The movements available within each section of the vertebral column differ widely due to the complex anatomical structure. The vertebrae increase in size from the top down and are held together by strong ligaments, allowing minimal movement between individual vertebra, but allowing the vertebral column a considerable amount of flexibility. Generally, the degree of movement permitted reduces from top down. Gross movements of the vertebral column include flexion, extension, lateral flexion and rotation (see Table 1.2, page 3).

Stop and think

- The average vertebral column length is 72–75 cm.
- Intervertebral discs are responsible for 25 per cent of its length.
- The length of the vertebral column is responsible for 40 per cent of the height of the human.
- Age associated decline in height is due to the thinning of the discs.

Your height can vary 2 cm during the day due to **diurnal variations**. Measure yourself at the start and end of each day and compare the results.

Key term

Diurnal variations – fluctuations which occur each day

The five regions of the vertebral column include:

- **Cervical section of the vertebrae** – This is the upper seven vertebrae (C1–C7) forming the cervical curve of the vertebral column in a convex shape. In functional anatomy the **occipital condyles** play an important function in transferring the weight of the head to C1. The first cervical vertebra (C1) is known as the atlas, and the second vertebra (C2) is known as the axis (its function is to rotate the head). The atlanto-occipital joint and atlanto-axial joint do not contain **intervertebral discs** The joint type formed is a pivot joint, allowing movement of the cranium. The cervical vertebrae directly support the weight of the head, and therefore have the most available movement, although stability is compromised. The cervical spine is more vulnerable due to the vertebrae rising above the shoulders.

- **Thoracic section of the vertebrae** – The next 12 vertebrae (T1–T12) form the thoracic curve of the vertebral column in a concave shape. The peak of the thoracic curve is around T6–T8. The true ribs (first seven ribs) articulate directly with the sternum, originating from the thoracic vertebrae to form the rib cage. Ribs eight to ten either 'float' or attach to the **costal cartilage**.

- **Lumbar section of the vertebrae** – The next five vertebrae (L1–L5). The lumbar region bears the largest portion of the body's weight, therefore the vertebrae are larger. L1–L5 are an important site for muscle attachment, in particular for the hip flexor (iliopsoas). L1–L5 forms the lumbar curve of the vertebrae in a convex shape.

- **Sacral** – The sacrum is triangular in shape and articulates with the pelvis. It plays a significant role in absorbing the ground forces from the lower limb, and weight of the body above. The sacrum is formed from five fused vertebrae. The articulation between L5/S1 is known as the lumbosacral disc, while the articulation between the sacrum and coccyx forms the sacrococcygeal joint.

- **Coccyx** – The second fused section of the vertebrae, consisting of approximately two to four vertebrae, forms the remnants of the tail.

The main functions of the vertebral column are to:

- encase and protect the spinal cord from injury
- distribute and absorb impact (the unique curvature and intervertebral discs act as a shock absorber)

Key terms

Occipital condyles – kidney-shaped with convex surfaces. There are two occipital condyles located either side of the foramen magnum. They articulate with the atlas bone

Intervertebral disc – a fibrocartilage disc which lies between each adjacent vertebrae of the spine

Costal cartilage – hyaline cartilage which connects the sternum to the ribs

- provide a surface for the attachment of the muscles, which are responsible for moving the vertebrae, in turn maintaining balance and erectness of the trunk

- provide a surface for the attachment of the muscles of the pelvic girdle and pectoral area

- support the ribcage.

Whiplash injuries are a result of a violent collision propelling the neck into extension then flexion. The initial extension phase can result in posterior damage. In extreme cases superior vertebrae may dislocate, but more commonly cause damage to the restraining ligaments.

Stop and think

Using a variety of different models, observe the vertebrae, paying particular attention to:
- the cervical region (displays a convex curve (curved inwardly))
- the thoracic region (displays a concave curve (curved outwardly))
- the lumbar region (displays a convex curve (curved inwardly)).

Lordosis, kyphosis and scoliosis are acquired and congenital vertebral abnormalities. Over exaggeration of the vertebral curves can hinder movement, affect muscular alignment, cause nerve compression, protruding or ruptured discs and possibly affect sporting performance.

Remember

Poor postural alignment can be caused by factors such as bone abnormalities and disease such as **ankylosing spondylitis**.

Key term

Ankylosing spondylitis – an inflammatory arthritis affecting mainly the joints in the spine or the sacroilium in the pelvis. However, other joints of the body may also be affected as well as tissues, including the heart, eyes, lungs and kidneys

Lordosis

This is caused through an exaggeration of the lumbar curve, resulting in an increased anterior tilt of the pelvis. Hamstrings and abdominal muscles present as lengthened and weak, whilst the opposing muscles, the quadriceps and muscle found in the lower back, present as shortened and strong.

Kyphosis

This is caused through an exaggerated curve in the thoracic vertebrae. The scapulae are protracted, putting the scapulae and clavicles (shoulder girdle) under constant pull of gravity. Muscles responsible for scapular retraction and on the posterior aspect of the thoracic region, such as the trapezius and rhomboids, present as lengthened and weak. The anterior muscles of the thoracic region, such as the pectoralis major and minor, present as shortened and strong.

Stop and think

Observe athletes' posture in a variety of sports. Do they present with a postural condition, e.g. lordosis or kyphosis? Why do they have this condition? Is it due to muscle imbalances, or does their sport predispose them to this condition? Think of a skydiver, and the technique they assume in flight. You will observe most skydivers have lordosis. It would be detrimental to the athlete's performance if you attempted to correct this muscle imbalance.

Scoliosis

This can sometimes be observed when you palpitate the vertebrae; an S or C shape can be felt deviating to the right or left.

- On observation of the spine, if the curve deviates to the left, muscles on the left aspect of the spine have shortened, creating tension on the vertebrae to the left; the muscles on the right adapt by lengthening.

- If the curve deviates to the right, then muscles on the right aspect of the spine have shortened, creating tension on the vertebrae to the right; the muscles to the left adapt by lengthening.

To maintain correct posture the vertebrae should sit in neutral alignment. Many factors affect the neutral position of the vertebrae, for example, poor posture, injury, the sport played, incorrect exercise techniques, pregnancy, excess body composition (obesity), injury and disease. All of these can predispose the athlete to injury. It is important when performing exercise to consider safety at all times by ensuring a 'neutral spine alignment'.

Force transmission – impact forces transmitted through the body

Articular cartilage – (also known as hyaline cartilage) is smooth and covers the surface of bones

Joint classifications

A joint is a junction where two or more bones articulate (meet). It plays a vital role in allowing movement to occur. Joints act as levers, allow movement, transmit and absorb forces. As a sports scientist you need a very good understanding of joints and their movement. The **force transmission**, as a result of sports participation, can be excessive, causing damage and requiring therapeutic intervention. *Chapter 2: Biomechanics* will explore force transmission, biomechanics and associated sports injuries. Joints can be classified into three groups and each category can be further subdivided.

Synarthrosis/fibrous/fixed joints

The bones which articulate at fibrous joints are connected via fibrous connective tissue. They allow very limited movement. The three sub categories are:

- suture(s), for example are found between the cranial bones

- gomphosis (-es), for example a tooth in its socket

- syndesmosis (-es), an example is the inferior tibiofibular joint.

Amphiarthrosis/cartilaginous/slightly moveable joints

The bones which articulate at cartilaginous joints are connected by either **articular (hyaline) cartilage**, forming a primary joint such as the first sternoclavicular joint, or fibrocartilage, forming a secondary joint such as the intervertebral disc, which may contain an internal cavity or nucleus. The movement permitted is greater than at fibrous joints.

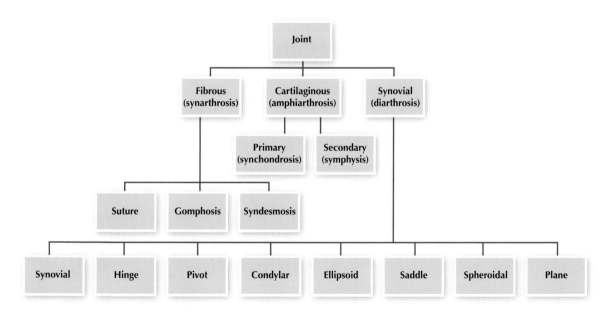

Figure 1.8:Types of joint

Diarthrosis/synovial/freely moveable joints

Synovial joints allow a greater degree of movement than fibrous and cartilaginous. See Figure 1.9 for the structure of a synovial joint. Articular cartilage encases the end of bones that articulate at the joint, allowing freedom of movement and reduction of friction. The joint is surrounded by a strong fibrous capsule, which is lined with a synovial membrane (synovium), providing lubrication and nourishment to the articular cartilage. The **ligaments** attach bone to bone and further strengthen the fibrous capsule. Ligaments are located internal and external to the capsule, and further supported by the surrounding muscle attachments and strong **tendons**. The ligaments' function is to provide joint stability, thus preventing dislocation. If excessive movement occurs ligaments may become damaged.

Key terms

Ligament – a band of tough fibrous tissue connecting bone to bone

Tendon – a band of inelastic tissue connecting a muscle to bone

Bursae are common features. They are fluid-filled sacs preventing friction between the sliding surfaces of structures such as ligaments, tendons and the capsule. Bursae are vulnerable to injury, resulting in a condition known as bursitis. The suffix 'itis' identifies inflammation is present. Bursitis is therefore inflammation of the bursa. Another common inflammatory condition is synovitis, inflammation of the synovial fluid or capsule.

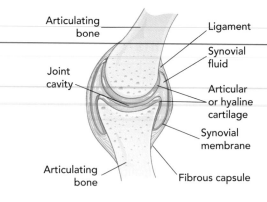

Figure 1.9: Structure of a synovial joint - transverse section of knee joint

Synovial joints can be subdivided into six categories as shown in Table 1.3.

Table 1.3: Sub categories of synovial joints

Joint name	Example	Movement	Figure
Hinge	Humero-ulnar joint	Flexion and extension	1
Pivot	Proximal radio ulnar joints	Rotation	2

Table 1.3: Sub categories of synovial joints (continued)

Joint name	Example	Movement	Figure
Ellipsoid (condyloid)	Metacarpophalangeal	Flexion and extension Abduction and adduction	3 (Scaphoid, Radius, Ulna, Lunate)
Saddle (sellar)	First carpometacarpal joint	Some rotation	4 (Trapezium, Metacarpal of thumb, Radius, Ulna)
Spheroidal (ball and socket)	Coxal joint	Flexion and extension Abduction and adduction Rotation	5 (Acetabulum of hipbone, Head of femur)
Plane (gliding)	Intercarpal joint	Sliding movements	6 (Navicular, Second cuneiform, Third cuneiform)

Stop and think

Devise a table which has four columns labelled: Joint name; Joint type; Movements permitted; Sporting example. Complete the table for every joint.

Key structures of the muscular system

The human body contains three types of muscle tissue:

* **skeletal**, such as gastrocnemius
* **smooth**, which is found in the intestines
* **cardiac**, which comprises the heart.

Skeletal muscle tissue constitutes approximately 30–40 per cent of total human body mass, and is of great interest to sports scientists. You need to understand the function of skeletal muscle in relation to complex sporting movements.

Muscle tissue has two main functions: movement and posture.

* **Production of movement** – muscles are attached to the skeleton via a tendon or broad **aponeurosis**. When a muscle contracts, it exerts a force on the bone and produces movement. Muscles can pull but cannot push, and are positioned across joints in order to produce movement.

Key term

Aponeurosis – a flat, broad tendon

- **Stabilisation of body positions** – body positions are the result of skeletal contraction. Postural muscles contract continually to maintain body positions. The abdominal muscles help to stabilise the spine when standing or sitting, while the erector spinae works to keep the spine erect.

Other functions of the muscular system include:

- **assisting the movement of substances within the body**, such as blood, food, faeces, urine, gases and lymph

- **thermogenesis**, which is when muscle contraction produces a by-product, heat, which helps maintain the normal body temperature of 37°C. Shivering, which is an involuntary contraction, can increase the rate of heat production considerably

- regulation of organ volume, such as the stomach and bladder.

The muscular system contains over 640 named muscles. The main muscles relevant to a sports scientist can be seen in Figure 1.10.

As a sports scientist it is not enough just to learn the name and location of the muscles. You need to understand the action of each muscle. Muscle **origin** and **insertion** knowledge will assist the scientist with analysis of sporting performance. There are many resources which you can use to learn your origins and insertions, and in time you will progress to learn your nerve innervations. Somatic motor neurons directly innervate skeletal muscles, for example the tibial nerve originating from S1 innervates the gastrocnemius responsible for plantar flexion.

Key terms

Thermogenesis – the process of heat production

Origin – the attachment site of a muscle to bone (in a few exceptions muscle). The origin is a fixed location

Insertion – the attachment of a muscle usually via a tendon to bone. The insertion on the bone is moveable as a result of muscle contraction

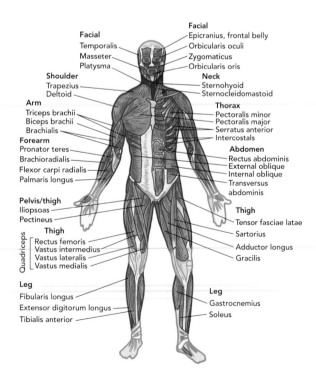
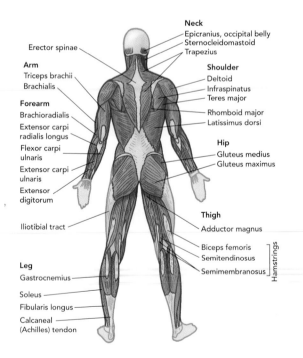

Figure 1.10: Anterior and posterior muscular system

Stop and think

Using a resource such as the Muscle Atlas from the University of Washington's Department of Radiology (see Useful resources, page 21) draw up a table like the one below. Complete a row of the table for each muscle. An example has been completed for you. This will provide a valuable resource for the rest of your sports science career. A similar table can be found on the companion website at www.pearsonfe.co.uk/foundationsinsport, which accompanies this book.

Muscle	Action	Origin	Insertion
Biceps brachii	Supinates forearm, when supine flexes forearm	Short head: tip of coracoid process of scapula Long head: supraglenoid tubercle of scapula	Tuberosity of radius and fascia of forearm via bicipital aponeurosis

Stop and think

The functional part of the muscle name generally represents its function, with the exception of the ankle. For example, a flexor decreases the angle at a joint bringing the anterior surfaces closer together (flexor carpi radialis main function is wrist flexion). Think about the following terms: extensor, adductor, supinator, pronator, levator and sphincter. Can you name a muscle and state its function for each term?

Properties of muscle

Muscle tissue has three main properties that enable the tissue to function optimally:

- **excitability** – it responds to stimuli (excitability is the property of the neuromuscular junction to respond to a stimuli)

- **contractibility** – it can contract forcefully when stimulated, resulting in isometric or isotonic contraction

- **extensibility** – it can stretch without tearing, and can contract forcefully after being stretched

- **elasticity** – after stretching or contracting it can return to its original length.

Gross muscle structure

A skeletal muscle consists of thousands of individual muscle fibres, encased by connective tissue called the **endomysium**. Individual muscle fibres are made up of muscle cells. Muscle fibres are bundled together into fascicles, around 10–100 in any bundle, further encased by connective tissue called the **perimysium**. All the fascicles are collated together and encased by connective tissue called the **epimysium**, which surrounds the whole muscle. The endomysium, perimysium and epimysium all extend from the deep **fascia**.

The endomysium, perimysium and epimysium are continuous connective tissue that may extend beyond the muscle tissue and form the tendon. The tendon is therefore a dense regular connective tissue. The Achilles tendon is a cord of dense connective tissue, which is extended from the gastrocnemius and attaches to the calcaneous. Extension of connective tissue from some muscles can be as a broad, flat layer known as an aponeurosis. The structure of the skeletal muscle is shown in Figure 1.11.

Key terms

Endomysium – connective tissue, encasing individual muscle fibres

Perimysium – connective tissue, encasing fascicles

Epimysium – connective tissue, which encases all the fascicles surrounding the whole muscle

Fascia – fibrous tissue, binding together or separating muscles

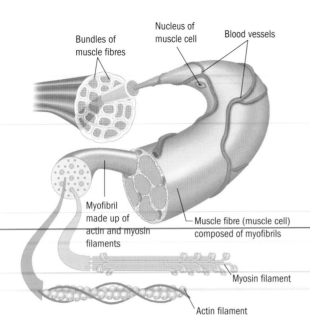

Figure 1.11: Organisation and structure of skeletal muscle

Superficial fascia separates muscle from the skin, provides protection, reduces heat loss and is storage for fat and water. Deep fascia holds similar functioned muscles together, facilitates free movement of muscles, carries blood vessels, lymphatic vessels, nerves and fills any gaps between muscles. Deep fascia also divides muscles into compartments. For example, the lower leg is divided into four compartments by the deep fascia, anterior, lateral, posterior and deep posterior compartments.

The anterior compartment consists of the tibialis anterior, the extensor digitorum longus, and the extensor hallucus longus. Their function is to **dorsiflex** at the ankle. The tibialis anterior also **inverts** the foot.

The lateral compartment comprises the peroneus longus, peroneus brevis and peroneus tertius. Peroneus longus and brevis functions are to **plantarflex** and **evert** the foot, whilst the peroneus tertius dosiflexes and everts the foot.

The posterior compartment comprises the gastrocnemium, soleus and plantaris. Their function is to plantarflex at the ankle. The gastrocnemius is the most superficial of the muscles and has two heads – lateral and medial. The soleus lies under the gastrocnemius and above the plantaris. All three insert into the Achilles tendon onto the calcaneous.

The deep posterior compartment comprises the tibialis posterior, flexor digitorum longus and flexor hallucus longus. Their combined function is to aid plantar flexion. However, flexor hallucis longus also flexes the big toe, flexor digitorium longus flexes the rest of the toes and tibialis posterior inverts the foot. Remember that the posterior and deep posterior compartments all plantarflex at the ankle.

Micro muscle structure

In order to understand muscle contraction, you must understand the micro-structure of a muscle fibre. The cell membrane of the muscle fibre is known as the **sarcolemma**. A muscle fibre consists of long myofibrils (the length of the fibre) between which organelles, such as mitochondria, glycogen granules and **myoglobin** are suspended in the **sarcoplasm.**

Myofibrils are the contractile elements, consisting of thin and thick myofilaments, known respectively as actin and myosin (see Figure 1.11). The myofilaments do not run the length of the myofibril – they are organised into units called sarcomeres. Sarcomere units are repeated along the length of the myofibril, where actin and myosin are present in an overlapping formation.

Sliding filament theory (Tortora and Grabowski, 2000)

The sliding filament model of muscle contraction is a complex process. When a muscle receives a nerve impulse (stimulus) the lengths of actin and myosin (myofilaments) do not change, but are drawn closer together by sliding across each other forming cross bridges. The result is that the sarcomeres shorten due to the contraction of the myofibril. The myofibril becomes shorter and thicker, resulting in muscle contraction.

The relaxation phase is a passive process, where the cross bridges relax, actin and myosin return to their original position, thus the sarcomere and myofilament lengthen to their original position. The muscle relaxes.

The nerve impulse is based on the 'all or nothing law'. Each fibre is capable of either contracting or not contracting – there is no in-between. As the athlete begins to fatigue, it is the strength of the contraction which may decrease.

Characteristics of muscle

The **fascicular arrangement** of a muscle affects the power and range of motion. The cross sectional area of a muscle is the dependent factor for power output; a short fibre can contract as powerfully as a long fibre. A muscle fibre can shorten up to 70 per cent of its resting length upon contraction. Therefore, the greater the length of the fibres, the larger the range of motion produced. The arrangement of fascicles depends on the muscle function, and is generally structured to provide a compromise between power and range of motion. There are five fascicle arrangements of a muscle: parallel, fusiform, circular, triangular and pennate (Figure 1.12).

- **Parallel** The fascicles are arranged parallel to the longitudinal axis of the muscle. The fascicles form a flat tendon at each end.

- **Fusiform** Similar in structure to the parallel arrangement. However, the fascicles taper towards the tendons, resulting in the muscle belly being greater in diameter than the tendon attachments, e. g. biceps brachii. These muscles are limited in power.

- **Circular** The fascicles are in a circular arrangement. Sphincter muscles are circular and enclose an orifice (opening).

- **Triangular** The fascicles are spread over a broad area and taper into a thick tendon, which is central to the muscle belly. The appearance is that of a triangle, e. g. pectoralis major. Triangular arrangement often occurs where restrictive leverage is required.

- **Pennate** The tendon extends nearly the entire length of the muscle, with short fascicles. There are three types of pennate structure.

  - unipennate – the fascicles are arranged on one side, e. g. extensor digitorium longus.

  - bipennate – the tendon is located centrally, with fascicles on each side, e. g rectus femoris muscle.

  - multipennate – there are several tendons, with fascicles attached obliquely, e. g. deltoid muscle.

Due to the short arrangement of fascicles, and the increased number of fibres in a smaller space, these muscles are very powerful.

Key term

Fascicular arrangement – the arrangement of fascicles, which ultimately affects power output and range of movement

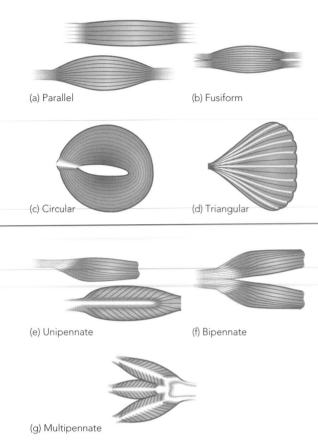

(a) Parallel

(b) Fusiform

(c) Circular

(d) Triangular

(e) Unipennate

(f) Bipennate

(g) Multipennate

Figure 1.12: Fascicle arrangement

Muscle attachments

Several muscles are used to produce effective movement. A high proportion of muscles have two attachments – an origin and insertion. However, there are a variety of muscles, which have more than one origin and/or insertion. When the muscle receives a stimulus it contracts, attempting to bring the origin and insertion closer together. The contraction doesn't always result in muscle shortening. To achieve a wide variety of movements, muscles either work together or in opposition. To enable movement to occur, additional muscles are required to provide support and stabilisation. Skeletal muscles are referred to as **agonists**, **antagonists** and **synergists**.

Agonists are the prime movers producing the main movement, for example during knee extension the prime mover would be the quadriceps group. The hamstring group relax and lengthen allowing the knee to extend, so it is referred to as the antagonist. However, when the hamstrings contract to produce knee flexion they become the agonist,

whilst the antagonist (the quadricep group) relaxes to allow the movement to occur. Movements are rarely isolated, particularly during sport, therefore synergists and fixators play a major role.

Synergists are particularly important if the agonist muscles cross two joints to prevent any unwanted movement at the intermediate joint. For example, the biceps brachii crosses both the shoulder and elbow joint. Its primary action is on the forearm to provide flexion at the elbow. Synergists contracting at the shoulder prevent any unwanted movement. Synergist muscles may assist the agonist muscle in producing movement by altering the direction of pull to allow the most effective movement. During knee flexion the gastrocnemius and popliteus act as the main synergist.

Fixators are muscles which stabilise the origin of the agonist muscle, to allow the agonist to act more efficiently. The origin of the muscle is usually found at the proximal end of the limb, which is stabilised by the fixators, while the movement occurs at the distal end where the muscle inserts.

Key terms

Agonist – the muscle producing the action (movement)

Antagonist – the muscle opposing the action (movement)

Synergist – synergist muscles assist the agonist muscles and provide stabilisation to prevent any unwanted movement

Fixator – provide stabilisation at the proximal end of the limb

Muscles are capable of performing contractile work in a variety of ways. Isotonic contractions result in the muscle creating movement, such as concentric and eccentric contractions. Isometric contraction results in no movement.

- **Concentric contraction** – the muscle shortens as the tension in the muscle increases to overcome the opposing muscle (resistance), resulting in the muscle attachments moving closer together causing movement. The agonist muscle performs concentrically. During the elbow flexion phase of a bicep curl, the biceps and brachialis are the agonist muscles contracting concentrically.

- **Eccentric contraction** – the tension remains the same in the muscle. As the opposing force is greater the muscle lengthens. The antagonist muscle performs eccentrically. During elbow flexion the triceps contract eccentrically. Eccentric contraction is important in slowing down and controlling movement, which would otherwise be rapid due to gravity.

- **Isometric contraction** – the tension within the muscle increases, although the length of the muscle does not alter, thus no movement is created. If the bicep curl is held in mid range the muscles perform isometrically. The muscles do not change in their length, but support the weight.

Key terms

Concentric – muscle contraction generates force, which causes muscle shortening

Eccentric – the muscle lengthens due to the opposing force being greater than the force generated by the muscle

Isometric – force is generated by the muscle without changing length

Case study (for recommended answers, see www.pearsonfe.co.uk/foundationsinsport)

Jo Lee is a triathlete and has recently had her most victorious triathlon yet. The sprint triathlon consisted of a 400 m swim, 20 km on the bike followed by a 5 km run. Jo achieved an overall time of 1 hour 11 minutes 21 seconds, finishing second in the 25–29 years age group and an overall ranking of thirteenth female. Jo's swim split was impressive – fastest woman with 6 minutes 4 seconds, positioning her seventh fastest overall of all male and female competitors and age groups. Jo had a modest ride on the bike with a split of 41 minutes 12 seconds and a 5 km run in 21 minutes 30 seconds. Jo's training regime requires commitment and dedication, consisting of three swim sessions a week (1 × 2 hours, 2 × 1 hour), four run sessions (4.8–14.4 km per run, with a mixture of speed, interval and endurance), and four bike sessions covering around 12.8 km each session with a longer weekly ride around 32–48 km. In addition to this she does 1 × 1 hour circuits, 1 × 1 hour pilates and one other session such as body balance or core weekly with a fortnightly 1 × 1 hour spin session.

1. Discuss the joint movements involved in cycling.
2. Discuss the muscles responsible for the movements identified in question 1.
3. Discuss the joint movements involved in running.
4. Discuss the types of muscle contraction occurring for movements identified in question 3.

Check your understanding (for answers, see www.pearsonfe.co.uk/foundationsinsport)

1. Describe the axial and appendicular skeleton, making reference to the names, types of bones and their function.
2. Briefly describe the three classifications of joints.
3. Describe the gross structure of a muscle.
4. Describe the micro structure of a muscle.
5. Differentiate between the functions of a ligament and a tendon.
6. Describe lordosis and its effect on the muscular system.
7. Describe kyphosis and explain which sports may predispose an athlete to this condition.
8. Observe a rugby player performing a squat and complete the following table for the up and down phase.

Joint	Action	Muscle	Contraction

Time to reflect

1. Think about a somersault, cartwheel and pivot turn and ascertain what plane of movement the technique takes place in.
2. Practise the movements that are possible at each joint.
3. Choose a technique from a sport you are interested in. Reflect on which joints, movements and muscle are involved.
4. Can you identify all the bones of the body, and discuss the type of bone in relation to its function?
5. Can you identify the action of all the muscles?
6. Can you specify the origin and insertion of all the muscles?
7. Choose a sporting movement, such as a press up. Can you identify the working muscles and their actions? Can you identify the type of muscle contraction taking place?
8. Can you choose 10 muscles and identify their fascicular arrangement?

Useful resources

To obtain a secure link to the websites below, see the Websites section on page ii or visit the companion website at www.pearsonfe.co.uk/foundationsinsport

- BBC Science: Human Body and Mind
- Get Body Smart
- IMAIOS
- Instant Anatomy
- University of Washington – Department of Radiology
- Visible Body
- Gray's Anatomy for Students Flash Cards
- Netter's Anatomy Flash Cards

Further reading

Agur, A. and Dalley, A. (2009). *Grants Atlas of Anatomy,* 12th Edition. Philadelphia: Lippincott, Williams & Wilkins.

Behnke, R. (2001). *Kinetic Anatomy*. Champaign, Illinois: Human Kinetics.

Field, D. and Hutchinson, J. (2006). *Anatomy Palpation and Surface Marking*. London: Elsevier

Harris, P. and Ranson, C. (2008). *Atlas of Living and Surface Anatomy for Sports Medicine*. Churchill Livingstone.

Jarmey, C. (2008). *The Concise Book of Muscles*. Chichester: Lotus

Kingston, B. (2005). *Understanding Muscles. A Practical Guide to Muscle Function,* 2nd Edition. Nelson Thornes.

Kingston, B. (2001). *Understanding Joints. A Practical Guide to Their Structure and Function*. Nelson Thornes.

Manocchia, P. (2007). *Anatomy of Exercise*. London: A & C Black.

Palastanga, N., Field, D. and Soames, R. (2006). *Anatomy and Human Movement,* 5th Edition. London: Elsevier.

Seeley, R., Stephens, T. and Tate, P. (2000). *Anatomy and Physiology*. McGraw-Hill.

Standring, S. (2008). *Gray's Anatomy: The Anatomical Basis of Clinical Practice, Expert Consult* (online and print). Churchill-Livingstone.

Tortora, J.T. and Grabowski, S.R. (2000). *Principles of Anatomy and Physiology,* 9th Edition. John Wiley & Sons.

Wirhed, R. (2006). *Athletic Ability and the Anatomy of Motion,* 3rd Edition. Mosby

Chapter 2

Biomechanics

Introduction

Elite level sport is characterised by the need to run faster, jump higher, hit harder and turn faster than your opponent. Have you ever watched sport and wondered how an athlete manages to perform at such a high level, for example how a sprinter manages to set off so quickly or how a football player manages to make a football swerve and dip so quickly? These are questions that can be answered using biomechanics.

Sports biomechanics is the branch of sport and exercise sciences that examines the causes and consequences of human movement; and the interaction of the body with apparatus or equipment through the application of mechanical principles in sporting settings. It is one of the key areas to understand if you want to analyse the performance of both individuals and teams.

Throughout this chapter, you will learn about the fundamentals of biomechanics, including: how movement is described, using consistent terminology; how humans move in sports environments; how it is possible to maximise the distance or speed of sports equipment through air or water. This chapter links closely with *Chapter 8: Performance analysis* as many of the techniques used in performance analysis generate the data that is used to develop the understanding gained through biomechanics.

Learning outcomes

After you have read this chapter you should be able to:

- understand the term biomechanics
- understand movement terminology used in biomechanics
- understand Newton's laws of motion
- understand kinematics and kinetics
- understand projectile motion
- understand fluid dynamics.

Starting block

Have you ever watched two athletes, one that you think has a good technique and one that you think has a bad technique?

- What differences have you observed in their techniques?
- What do you think these differences in technique could be caused by?

Understand the term biomechanics

Biomechanics is the branch of sport and exercise sciences that examines the causes and consequences of human movement; and the interaction of the body with apparatus or equipment through the application of mechanical principles in sporting settings. Biomechanical analysis is also further separated down into two key areas: kinematics and kinetics (see page 26). A fundamental element of biomechanics is being able to describe and quantify movements, using consistent terminology.

Understand movement terminology in sport

Describing relative positions of body parts

When describing the relative positions of the body parts you should use consistent terminology. In Chapter 1 (Figure 1.2 and Table 1.1, page 3), you were introduced to anatomical terminology which should be used when describing relative positions of body parts. The following terms describe the position of body parts in relation to each other.

Planes and axes of movement

Human movements are based on planes and axes.

There are many different movements that occur in the different planes and axes. Figure 2.2 a–c shows movements in relation to their planes and axes.

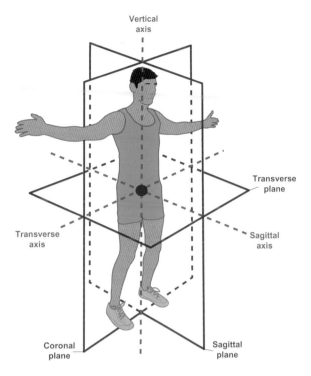

Figure: 2.1: The three axes of rotation

Key terms

Biomechanics – branch of sport and exercise sciences that examines the causes and consequences of human movement; and the interaction of the body with apparatus or equipment through the application of mechanical principles in sporting settings

Sagittal plane – splits the body into imaginary left and right halves

Frontal plane – separates the body into imaginary front to back halves

Transverse plane – splits the body into imaginary top to bottom halves

Axis – straight line around which we rotate when we move

Vertical axis – imaginary line drawn from your head to your toe

Sagittal axis – imaginary line drawn from your back to your front

Frontal axis – imaginary line drawn from left to right

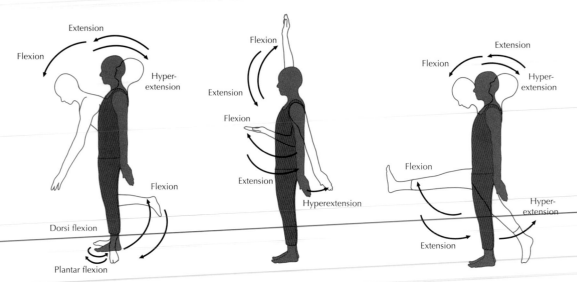

Figure 2.2a: Movements in the sagittal plane about the frontal axis

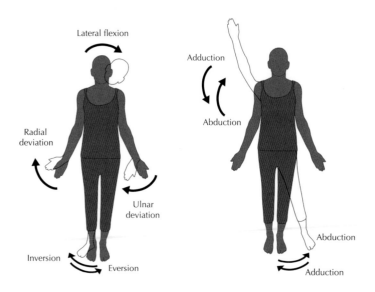

Figure 2.2b: Movements in the frontal plane about the sagittal axis

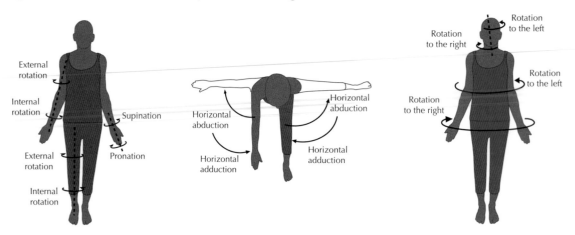

Figure 2.2c: Movements in the transverse plane about the horizontal axis

Stop and think

For each of the sporting actions below, explain the movement using movement terminology related to planes and axes of motion.
- An Olympic diver performing a tuck front somersault.
- A football player performing a Maradona turn.
- A gymnast performing a cartwheel in their floor routine.

Levers

A lever system allows humans to move. Levers have three key elements; the load (the body segment plus any extra weight or equipment), the fulcrum (the joint around which the movement occurs) and the effort (the internal force created by the working muscles). There are three types of lever in the human body: first class, second class and third class levers. In first class levers, the fulcrum is located between the effort and the load (e.g. heading a football). In second class levers, the load is between the effort and the fulcrum (e.g. standing on your tip toes). In third class levers, the effort is between the load and the fulcrum (e.g. conducting a barbell curl). The lever systems are shown in Figure 2.3.

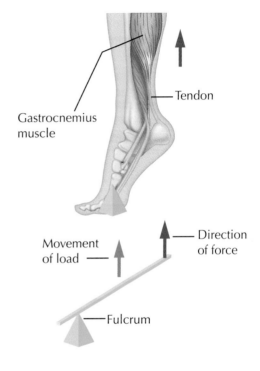

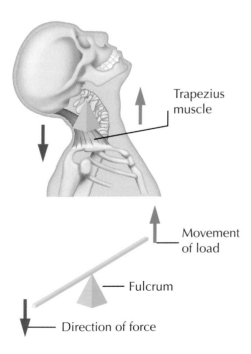

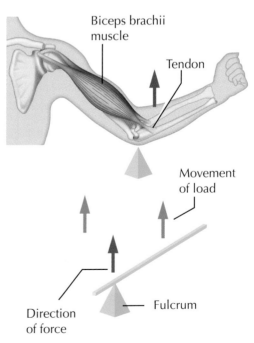

Figure 2.3: Can you think of different sporting movements that use each type of lever?

Understand Newton's laws of motion

Sir Isaac Newton produced laws of motion that are fundamental to the understanding of human movement. These laws can be applied to a sport setting to help sports scientists explain the different factors associated with producing techniques and can be applied in either linear motion or angular motion contexts. The application of these laws in a sports injury context can be seen in Table 2.1.

Table 2.1: Newton's laws of motion and their application to sports injury

Understand kinematic and kinetic principles in movement

Within biomechanics, there are two key terms: **kinematics** and **kinetics**.

Key terms

Inertia – tendency for a body to remain in its state of motion

Kinematics – description of movements without reference to the forces involved

Kinetics – assessment of movement with respect to the forces involved

Law	Description	Application
Newton's first law – the law of **inertia**	A body will remain at rest (or in uniform motion) unless acted upon by a force	*A hard frontal tackle in rugby league*: Prior to the tackle, the player in possession of the ball will be sprinting at a given velocity. When the player is tackled, the outside force will rapidly decelerate or stop the player. For a short time, the player's head will obey Newton's first law as it will keep travelling forwards, flexing the neck. The structures in the neck then prevent any further forward movement by resisting the forward motion thus causing rapid extension into hyper extension. This flexion – hyper– extension pattern is typical of a cervical whiplash injury
Newton's second law – the law of acceleration	A force acting on a body will produce an acceleration that is proportional to that force; as demonstrated through the equation: $force = mass \times acceleration$	*A weightlifter attempting to dead lift 250 kg*: The body structures involved with the technique (e.g. quadriceps, knee joint) must be able to produce sufficient force to move the weight in an upward motion and must be able to resist the load that is placed upon them. If they are not able to produce the necessary force or withstand the load, they will become more susceptible to injury (e.g. muscle strain, ligament strain or cartilage tear)
Newton's third law – the law of action – reaction	For every action there is an equal and opposite reaction	*Ultra endurance athlete training for competition*: The concept of ground reaction forces is important in this scenario. Every time an ultra endurance athlete goes road running, they will be running for long periods of time. As the foot repeatedly strikes the floor, the ground exerts an equal and opposite force on the foot that acts through the lower extremities. Depending on the size, duration, frequency and rate of the force applied (as well as other factors such as footwear), this could result in overuse injuries such as stress fractures. Knowledge of the different factors that have resulted in the injury can help the sports scientist reduce the risk of further injury by introducing interventions to control the risk factors

Stop and think

Can you think of any other sports-based examples of Newton's laws of motion?

Kinematics

Kinematics refers to the description of movements without reference to the forces involved. It uses recordings of different actions to describe the movement with reference to time and space, concentrating on whole body position and rate of movement, individual body segment position, movement pattern and rate of movement, and the actions of different sports implements. Kinematic factors used to describe movement include linear motion, angular motion and measurements of body position. Fundamental to understanding linear and angular motions are two terms: **scalar quantities** and **vector quantities** (see Table 2.2). A scalar quantity has a magnitude (e.g. how big, how fast something is) whereas vector quantities have a magnitude and a direction (e.g. how fast you moved up or down).

Linear and angular motion

Linear motion can occur in a straight line (**rectilinear motion**) or in a curved line (**curvilinear motion**). Some sports, such as the 200 metres in athletics, are part rectilinear and part curvilinear as the athlete needs to run in a straight line for one part and then a curved line for another part. When you examine motion, you will consider factors such as distance, displacement, speed, velocity and acceleration.

Table 2.2: Linear and angular motion factors separated in scalar and vector quantities.

Scalar quantities	Vector quantities
Distance	Displacement
Speed	Velocity
Acceleration	Acceleration in a direction

Distance and displacement

The distance travelled is the sum of all movements regardless of direction, whereas displacement is the straight line distance from point A to point B travelled in a particular direction. For example, if you look at a 200 metre sprint race, the sprinter

in the inside lane will have sprinted a distance of 200 metres from start to finish, but will have only displaced 123.8 metre at an angle of 36° (Blazevich, 2010).

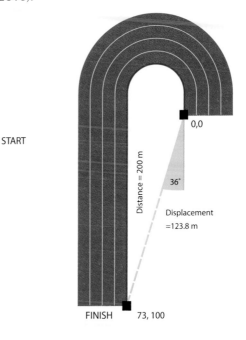

Figure 2.4 Distance and displacement in a 200 metre race (Blazevich, 2010)

Key terms

Scalar quantities – quantity that only has a magnitude (e.g. speed)

Vector quantities – quantity that has a magnitude and a direction (e.g. velocity)

Rectilinear motion – movement in a straight line (e.g. 100 metre sprint race in athletics)

Curvilinear motion – movement in a curved line (e.g. 200 metre sprint race in athletics)

Remember

Sometimes you may have an average velocity of zero because the displacement is zero (for example, in a 400 metre race the distance travelled is 400 m, but the displacement is zero because you started and finished in the same place). Therefore it is important to look at changes in velocity during a particular part of the race.

Speed

Speed is how quickly a body moves and is measured in metres per second (m.s^{-1}). You calculate speed by using the equation:

speed = distance ÷ time

Velocity

Velocity is how quickly a body has moved and in what resultant direction; it is also measured in ms^{-1}. You calculate velocity by using the equation:

velocity = displacement ÷ time

You can use this equation to find the average velocity (the velocity over the full race) or velocity during specific parts of a race (for example the velocity from 150 to 200 m during a 200 metre race).

Acceleration

Acceleration is the rate of change of velocity and is measured in metres per second per second (ms^{-2}). You calculate acceleration by using the equation:

change in velocity ÷ time

To calculate the change in velocity, you use the equation:

final velocity – starting velocity

Acceleration with an increase in velocity is known as positive acceleration whereas a decrease in velocity is known as negative acceleration or deceleration.

Practical applications of speed, velocity and acceleration

Carling, Bloomfield, Nelson and Reilly (2008) examined literature surrounding the relative contributions of speed, velocity and acceleration in elite soccer. They reported that acceleration may be of more importance in elite soccer than speed or velocity because the average sprint distance is 20 metres and lasts for less than four seconds, which suggests that players may not achieve their maximum speed in this time or distance. This information is useful for sports scientists and coaches as they can use it to design more appropriate training programmes for their athletes.

Angular kinematics

Biomechanists use the same quantities to explain angular motion as linear motion; however in this context they become angular displacement, angular velocity and angular acceleration.

Angular displacement

Angular displacement is the rotation of a body around an axis and is usually measured in degrees. If the direction of the rotation is stated, then the term angular displacement is used. Angular displacement is measured in radians (rad) and one radian is equivalent to 57.3° therefore a 360° motion would equate to 6.28 rad.

Angular velocity

Angular velocity is the angle through which a body travels in one second and is measured in radians per second (rads^{-1}). Angular velocity is calculated using the equation:

Angular displacement (radians) ÷ time taken

Angular acceleration

Angular acceleration is the rate of change of angular velocity and is measured in radians per second per

Stop and think

At the IAAF World Championships in Berlin in 2009, Usain Bolt broke the 200 metre world record by running a time of 19.19 seconds (s). We know that the distance travelled was 200 metres and that the time was 19.19 seconds, so can you calculate the speed using that information?

Sometimes you will want to know the velocity or speed at different points during the race to help your performer improve their overall performance. Can you calculate these values using the split times (the times for particular parts of the race) below?

- 0 – 50 m = 5.60 s
- 50 – 100 m = 4.32 s
- 100 – 150 m = 4.52 s
- 150 – 200 m = 4.75 s

Why is it important to have information on a range of factors in sports such as sprinting?

second (rads^{-2}). You calculate angular acceleration by using the equation:

change in angular velocity ÷ time

Practical applications of kinematics

Kinematic data is often gained through using video recording techniques then playing and replaying videos frame by frame to be able to examine key factors in performance. When combined with IT programmes such as *Dartfish®* that can be used to calculate variables, this approach can provide a combination of qualitative and quantitative data that can help improve performance. Typically, the practical applications of kinematics take two forms:

- identifying the cause of any problems with sports techniques
- suggesting ways of solving these problems to improve performance.

For example, a biomechanist could use kinematic data to calculate the linear velocity of centre of gravity and take-off angle of a triple jumper to see how these could be altered to improve performance.

Kinetics

As with kinematics, kinetics also uses recordings of actions but combines these with references to the **forces** involved with that movement.

Force

Force is the mechanical action or effort applied to a body that produces movement. It is measured in **Newtons**. A Newton is the force required to move a mass of 1 kilogram at a rate of 1 ms^{-2}. When understanding human movement, biomechanists use a combination of internal forces and external forces. Internal forces come from within the body to influence movement (e.g. force created by muscles), whereas external forces are the interaction between the body and the environment (e.g. **ground reaction forces** or **friction**). Biomechanists may also refer to centric and eccentric forces. A centric force is one that acts through an object's **centre of gravity**, whereas an eccentric force is one that applies outside the centre of mass.

Practical application of forces

If a football player kicks the football straight through the ball's centre of mass (applying a centric force), the ball will travel in a straight line at a rate that is proportional to the amount of force created. However, if the player kicks the ball outside the centre of gravity (applying an eccentric force), the ball will spin as well as accelerating forwards, making the ball move either to the left or the right. This knowledge can be used to help football players develop specific shooting techniques from dead ball situations, such as penalties or free kicks.

Measurement of force

A kinetic analysis uses data from measurement tools such as **force platforms** and **strain gauges** and synchronises this data to provide a more objective element to the analysis of movement.

Strain gauges

A strain gauge is used to measure force (or more specifically, torque) through either electrical resistance, mechanical or optical principles. Strain gauges work by a force being applied to a cable. When the force is applied, the cable changes in length and cross-sectional area. As the resistance of the cable is dependent upon its length and cross-

---

Key terms

Force – mechanical action or effort applied to a body that produces movement

Newton – force required to move a mass of 1 kg at a rate of 1ms^{-2}

Ground reaction force – equal and opposing force that is exerted by the ground on a body

Friction – resistive force produced when one body moves across another and their surfaces are in contact

Centre of gravity – the point at which gravity acts through a body. This changes every time you move but is at about 55–57 per cent of standing height when in the anatomical position

Force platform – device that measures forces

Strain gauge – device used to measure force or torque in sport settings

sectional area, the voltage output of the cable changes and the voltage change is related to known forces.

Force platforms

Force platforms are either fixed or portable plates that measure external forces acting on the platform, using Newton's third law of motion. When a force is applied to the platform, the electrical charge in the platform changes and an equal but opposite force is calculated by the platform. Force platforms measure three ground reaction force components: a vertical force (usually referred to as Fz), a horizontal anterior-posterior force (usually labelled Fy) and a horizontal medio-lateral force (usually labelled Fx). The data gathered from force platforms can be used to calculate net forces produced. This process is called **inverse dynamics** and is an important element of biomechanics as it allows sports scientists to understand musculoskeletal dynamics that create movements. It thus plays an important role in equipment design, technique enhancement and injury reduction.

Key terms

Inverse dynamics – process of calculating net force from multiple forces

Impulse – product of the size of the force and the duration of the force application

Momentum – product of a body's mass and its velocity

Practical application of measurement of forces

Using force platforms has allowed biomechanists to measure ground reaction forces and design individual elements of sport shoes (such as insoles and outer soles) to help the body manage these ground reaction forces to reduce the risk of injury. They have also been useful in helping to enhance the performance of athletes by, for example, measuring how much downward and backward force is exerted on the ground by an athlete and how far this force will propel them forwards and upwards.

Impulse

Although force is an important concept in sport, it is the size and the duration the force is applied that that will influence sport. The product of force and the duration of application is known as **impulse**.

Practical application of impulse

In a 'World's Strongest Man' competition, there is an event called the truck pull. In order to move the truck by pulling it, the competitor can't just apply a huge amount of force; they must apply that force over an extended period of time to keep the truck moving. Therefore impulse is the key to successful performance in this event.

In order to improve performance in sports, such as sprinting, it is important to be able to determine optimal impulse because this will affect how quickly the sprinter can move. To do this, a biomechanist would calculate the braking impulse (the impulse that slows the sprinter down when the foot contacts the floor), and the propulsive impulse (the impulse that propels the sprinter vertically and horizontally so that they can sprint forwards). When the biomechanist has done this, they will be able to work with other sports scientists, the athlete and the coach to maximise the propulsive impulse and minimise the braking impulse.

Momentum

Momentum is key in sport because it determines how difficult it will be to stop a body from moving. Momentum (p) is the product of a body's mass (m) and its velocity (v), shown through the equation:

$$p = mv$$

There is a link between impulse and momentum because you will have to apply an optimal amount of force over an extended period of time to change the velocity of the body you want to move.

Practical example of momentum

Think about the truck pulling example earlier; we said that to move the truck, you would have to increase the impulse. The mass of the truck remains constant, but as the truck accelerates, the velocity increases, which then increases the truck's momentum.

Pressure

Pressure is vital in sport performance as it affects everything from injury to an athlete's ability to turn quickly. Pressure is the amount of force applied over a given area and the unit of measurement is the Pascal.

 Key term

Pressure – amount of force applied over a given area

Practical application of pressure

Knowledge of pressure has been an important element in sports shoe design. Rugby players have studs on their boots, which allow them to turn more easily at speed. This is because the studded boot applies more pressure to the ground than a normal running shoe would. This is because the surface area of each individual stud compared to the large surface area of the whole sole of a normal running shoe is much smaller. Increasing the pressure through the stud allows it to pierce the surface and sink into the grass, which creates greater traction and allows the rugby player to change direction quickly.

Work, energy and power

Work, energy and power are three separate elements but are often considered together because of their reciprocal influences on each other. The example earlier of the truck pull in the World's strongest man can be applied here again. In order to move the truck, a sufficient amount of force must be applied over a period of time in order to accelerate the truck. If a force is applied over a period of time, then work has been done. The unit of measurement for work is joules, and it is calculated by multiplying the magnitude of the force by the distance covered.

Power is often linked to work because power is the rate at which work is done and is measured in watts. So the competitor who can get the truck moving in the shortest period of time would be said to have the higher levels of power, even if they had the same maximal strength as their opponent. This can be seen through the equation:

$$\text{Power (watts)} = \text{force} \times \text{velocity}$$

Energy is related to work and power because energy is the capacity to do work and is separated into kinetic and potential energy. The law of conservation of energy says that it isn't possible to destroy energy; only that energy can be changed from one form to another.

Kinetic energy (KE) is the energy that is related to a body's motion and is the product of the mass and velocity of a body. A 120 kg American football player, running at 7 ms^{-1} would have much more kinetic energy than a 70 kg marathon runner running at 5 ms^{-1}. A far greater momentum and a greater level of force would be needed to stop the American football player's movement.

Potential energy (PE) is energy that is associated with the position of an object and is the product of the object's mass, acceleration due to gravity and the height of the object as demonstrated through the equation:

$$\text{PE} = mgh$$

There is a relationship between kinetic energy and potential energy that can be explained by examining a shot putt. When the shot is in the putter's hand, it has only PE because it has a mass, but the velocity is 0 ms^{-1}. It does not have any KE. When the putt is released, it suddenly has high amounts of KE to begin with, which gradually decreases up to the putt's peak height. As the KE is decreasing, it is being converted to PE (remember, the law of conservation of energy states that energy will not be destroyed, only converted to another form). At the peak, the putt momentarily becomes stationary. When it no longer has enough KE to fly against the effects of gravity, it then starts its descent. As the velocity of the putt starts to increase again on its downward path, the levels of KE once again increase and the PE decreases.

Angular kinetics

There are a number of key factors that influence angular motion including **moment of inertia**, **radius of gyration**, **angular momentum** and **torque.** Newton's laws of motion also apply in an angular context.

Key terms

Moment of inertia – tendency for a rotating body to remain in its present state of motion

Radius of gyration – relative distribution of mass in relation to the axis of rotation

Angular momentum – product of the moment of inertia and angular velocity

Torque – turning effect created by a force around an axis

- **Newton's first law of motion (inertia)** A rotating body will continue to turn about its axis of rotation with constant momentum unless an external couple or eccentric force is exerted upon it. For example, a figure skater will continue to spin quickly in circles unless they redistribute their mass. This can be achieved by them extending their arms out.

- **Newton's second law of motion (acceleration)** The angular acceleration of a body is proportional to the torque causing it and takes place in the direction in which the torque acts. For example, a gymnast will try to create greater torque whilst preparing for a difficult dismount from the high bar.

- **Newton's third law of motion (action – reaction)** For every torque that is exerted by one body on another, there is an equal and opposite torque exerted by the second body on the first. For example, in the long jump, the legs are brought forwards and upwards to land, which results in the arms being brought forwards and downwards.

Torque

Torque is the turning effect of an applied force and is measured in Newton metres (Nm). It is created when a force is applied at a distance from the axis of rotation of an object. As torque is the product of the size of the force and the distance from the axis, the further away you apply the force, the greater the torque will be. Therefore, the greater the amount of torque the greater the amount of angular acceleration and angular velocity there is.

Moment of inertia and radius of gyration

In angular motion, a body's moment of inertia is directly affected by its radius of gyration. More simply, a body will remain in its state of motion unless the mass of that body or the distribution of that mass around that axis of rotation changes. The relationship between moment of inertia and radius of gyration can be seen through the following equation:

$$i = mk2$$

where i = moment of inertia, m = mass of the body and k = radius of gyration.

Angular momentum

Angular momentum relates to how difficult it is to stop a body from moving once it is in angular motion and is determined by the moment of inertia and angular velocity. If the moment of inertia is decreased, angular velocity can increase, which will maintain angular momentum for longer. This will result in a continuation of a sporting movement. This principle is important in sports such as figure skating, gymnastics and diving where angular motion occurs in the highest scoring performances.

Practical application of angular kinetics

It is more important for coaches and athletes to understand the practical principles of angular motion, more so than the complex mathematics behind the principles. These principles have a variety of applications and can be applied to both sports equipment and the athlete.

When a tennis player wants to return serve quickly with lots of topspin to keep the ball close to the net and increase the ground reaction forces when the ball hits the floor, the player would hold the racquet by the handle and swing the racquet in to hit the ball (thus creating a high amount of torque). The point of contact between the racquet and the ball would also need to be outside the ball's centre of gravity towards the upper surface on the ball (thus using an eccentric force). The increased torque combined with the eccentric force would make the ball travel quickly and spin on a downward motion, thus keeping the flight path low and making it more difficult to return.

When a diver wants to perform a tuck somersault as part of their routine, they must create enough torque to be able to increase their angular acceleration in order to start the spin. Once they have entered the somersault, the diver must then control the movement. This can be done by altering their body position. In order to speed up, they tuck all their body parts close to the axis of rotation (decreased radius of gyration, decreased moment of inertia, increased acceleration, momentum maintained); whereas to enter the pool on the exit of the dive they extend their body (increased radius of gyration, increased moment of inertia, reduced momentum, deceleration).

Remember

It is more important that an athlete and coach understand the principles of angular motion rather than the complex mathematics behind them.

Understanding projectile motion

Projectile motion relates to the motion of an object (such as a javelin or a human being) that has been projected into the air. In most athletic events that involve projectile motion, such as the javelin and the long jump, the most important performance criteria is the distance the object travels before hitting the ground (or the maximum height achieved if thinking about high jump or pole vault). The distance travelled (or height achieved) by the object is dependent upon three major performance criteria:

- angle of release (also known as projection angle)
- velocity of release or take-off
- height of release or take-off.

Judge, Hunter and Gilreath (2008) provide a good example of how biomechanics of projectile motion can be used to benefit the performance of an athlete. They used specific performance analsyis

techniques and training methods to provide support to a hammer thrower. By introducing a training technique that allowed the thrower to increase the velocity of release whilst maintaining the angle of realease, the thrower was able to produce an American record for the hammer throw.

Angle of release

The angle of release is the angle between the projectile's velocity vector and the horizontal at the instant of release or take-off. Different sports require different angles of release. Figure 2.5 shows that theoretically, if the height of release and velocity of release are the same, an angle of release of 45° is the angle that will provide optimal performance. However, evidence from sport suggests that in practice, the optimal angle of release will differ from 45°. Leigh, Liu, Hubbard and Bing (2010) reported in their study of elite discus throwers that the optimal release angle was specific to each thrower and varied from 35° to 44°. The optimal angle of release is also dependent upon the velocity of release and the height of release relative to the ground.

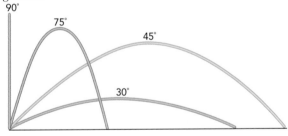

Figure 2.5: What do you think will happen to the projectile if the angle of release is too great or too small?

Velocity of release

The velocity of release is recorded at the instance of release, e.g. when the longer jumper leaves the take-off board or when a javelin thrower releases the javelin. The velocity of release has both vertical and horizontal components. The greater the velocity of release, the longer it will take for the effects of gravity to stop the projectile from rising and make the projectile start falling.

Height of release

The height of release is the distance from the ground (in metres) that the object leaves the thrower. If the angle and velocity of release are the same for two shot putters, the athlete who has a greater height of release will have a longer flight time and, therefore, record a greater range.

It is important to also consider the relative height of release (i.e. the height of release in relation to the landing position of the projectile). If the height of release is higher than the landing level, there is a positive height of release. This usually means that a smaller angle will result in a greater distance achieved. If the height of release is below the landing level, this is known as a negative relative height of release and the optimal angle of release will need to be greater to give the projectile more flight time.

Analysing the shot putt

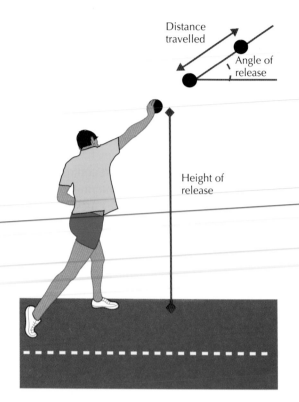

Figure 2.6b: Highlighting two key points from a video: image with example analysis

Figure 2.6a: Highlighting two key points from a video: image without example analysis

Analysis of projectiles can be conducted by hand or by using analysis programmes such as *Dartfish*® (see *Chapter 8: Performance analysis* for details of analysing performance and providing feedback to athletes). Figure 2.6a shows how you can highlight two key points from a video and 2.6b shows how you can then use this to analyse performance. In this example you will see how you can calculate height of release and velocity of release. Assume that the two frames of video are 0.04 seconds apart; that 2 cm on the screen is equal to 1 m (horizontal) and that 1 cm is equivalent to 1 m (vertical) in 'real-life'.

- **Calculating height of release** If the distance between the toe mark and the hand mark is 1.8 cm on screen, you can convert that to 1.8 m in real distance, which means that the height of release is 1.8 m.

- **Calculating velocity of release** If the distance travelled by the shot between frame 1 and frame 2 on screen is 1.2 cm horizontally, you can then scale that to 0.62 m in real distance. As you know that the time taken to travel that distance is

0.04 seconds, you can then calculate the release velocity $0.62 \div 0.04 = 15.5$ ms^{-1}

Stop and think

- How would the height of release change if the distance between the toe mark and the release point was 2.2 cm on the screen? What would this equate to in real terms?

- How would the velocity of release change if the distance travelled between frame 1 and frame 2 on screen was 1 cm?

- How would these results change the required angle of release for optimal flight?

Understand fluid mechanics

So far, all of the projectile motion factors discussed have negated any influence of air resistance. This is where understanding fluid mechanics becomes important. Fluid mechanics is the aspect of biomechanics that explains how a body interacts with the fluid through which it is travelling. Where the fluid the body is travelling through is air, this study is known as **aerodynamics** and where the fluid is water, this is known as **hydrodynamics**. Within these there are two key factors that can influence performance: **drag** and **lift**.

Drag

A drag force is a resistive force that opposes the motion of a body and is created by the fluid that the body is travelling through. This drag resistance is increased if the velocity of the moving air or water increases, for example a sprinter will experience greater drag if they are sprinting into a head wind than if they are sprinting in still conditions. There are a number of different forms of drag, depending on whether the body is travelling through air or water.

The amount of drag created is related to the flow pattern of the opposing fluid at the **boundary layer**. There are two types of fluid flow, **laminar flow** and **turbulent flow**. Laminar flow is the smooth flow of the fluid and provides less resistance to the moving body because of this. Turbulent flow is the rough multi-directional flow of the fluid that

provides greater resistance to the movement of a body. Biomechanists use this knowledge of drag to try to make a body as **streamlined** as possible. Streamlining is the process by which biomechanists alter body shapes and positions to reduce the disturbance to the fluid flow.

Key terms

Aerodynamics – fluid dynamics where the fluid is air

Hydrodynamics – fluid dynamics where the fluid is water

Drag – resistive force that opposes the motion of a body and is created by the fluid that the body is travelling through

Lift – fluid force that acts perpendicular to the relative motion of a body with respect to the fluid it is passing through

Boundary layer – layer of fluid that is adjacent to the surface of the body travelling through it

Laminar flow – smooth flow of fluid over a body

Turbulent flow – disturbed flow of air around a body

Streamlining – altering a body to reduce the disturbance to the fluid flow and drag

Pressure drag

Pressure drag is the opposing force caused by negative pressure, created behind a moving object. This is also sometimes known as profile, wake or form drag. The negative pressure is created by the difference between the high pressure in front of the body and the low pressure behind the body. The different amounts of pressure are caused by the interaction of the boundary layer of fluid around the body, and specifically the amount of separation there is.

Wave drag

Wave drag is the opposing motion caused by the creation of a wave on a water surface. At low speeds, the effects of wave drag are quite low, but at higher speeds they can be quite detrimental to performance.

Surface drag

Surface drag is the opposing force created by the tension in a liquid. This is sometimes referred to as skin friction and in sport is caused by the fluid being in contact with the moving body. As the body is moving in the opposite direction to the flow of fluid, the body pulls the fluid along with it, creating a resistive force from the fluid. The amount of surface drag is also dependent upon the roughness of the surface and the viscosity of the fluid, as these will both determine the type of flow at the boundary layer.

Stop and think

How does understanding the different types of drag benefit the advice a biomechanist could give to a swimmer about their technique and swimwear?

Practical applications of drag

When competing, cyclists ride in a crouched position, use helmets of a particular shape and have skin tight clothing that will not move around. By adopting this position and using those particular types of equipment and attire, the cyclist has a smaller surface area and a smoother surface which results in a more streamlined overall position. As their position is more streamlined, there are fewer disturbances to the air flow, which results in lower resistance to the cycle (less drag) and allows them to cycle faster. Can you explain how this would be different if the cyclist was in an upright position and wearing loose clothing?

Lift

Lift is the fluid force that acts perpendicular to the relative motion of a body with respect to the fluid it is passing through. This concept can be explained by looking at the pressure differences created by different speeds of fluid travelling at either side of a body. The lift force created is determined by the differences in pressure above and below the body. If the resultant pressure is higher below the body than above it, the body will be forced upwards; whereas if the pressure above a body is higher than below it, the body will be forced downwards. The downward force, that is explained through the principles of lift, is sometimes known as downforce. These principles can be used to understand many elements of sport, from how a swimmer stays buoyant to how a Formula 1 car stays on the track whilst cornering at high speeds.

Stop and think

Two approaches that help biomechanists understand the concept of lift are Bernoulli's principle and the magnus effect. Using the recommended reading and websites, investigate these approaches and summarise how they contribute to the understanding of fluid mechanics.

In projectile motion, another factor that directly influences the amount of lift experienced by a body is the **angle of attack**. The angle of attack is the difference between the flight path of the body's centre of gravity and the angle of the body to the ground. By exposing more surface area and increasing the angle of attack (up to an optimal point that varies dependent upon the dimensions of the body), more lift can be created, which will keep the projectile in flight for longer. If the angle of attack is too great, the projectile will stall in flight and achieve a shorter horizontal distance; whereas if the angle of attack is too small, the projectile will start to travel on a downwards path, also resulting in a smaller horizontal distance. The optimal angle of attack also depends upon release velocity (Maier, Wank, Bartonietz and Blickhan, 2000).

Key terms

Angle of attack – difference between the flight path of the body's centre of gravity and the angle of the body to the ground

Remember

The range of factors that will influence the flight of a projectile should be considered on an individual basis because the optimal value for each will vary from athlete to athlete.

Case study (for recommended answers, see www.pearsonfe.co.uk/foundationsinsport)

Monique is a 23-year-old javelin thrower. She has been competing in the javelin event for a number of years but recently has started to notice that her performance does not seem to be getting any better. On discussing the issue with you, she has reported specifically that her throwing distance doesn't seem to be improving at all and she doesn't know what she should change about it. She has spoken to her coach about the problem, but she doesn't feel that he has the specialist knowledge required to be able to help improve her performance because he just seems to be giving her the same advice over and over again.

1. How would you describe the javelin throw, using movement terminology?

2. How would you explain the key projectile factors associated with a javelin throw to Monique?

3. How would you identify which is / are the key area(s) that she needs to alter in order to improve her throwing distance?

4. How could you feed this information back to Monique?

Check your understanding (for answers, see www.pearsonfe.co.uk/foundationsinsport)

1. What is biomechanics?

2. What are the terms used to describe the relative positions of body parts?

3. What are the planes and axes of movement?

4. What is a lever system and what are the different types of lever?

5. What are Newton's laws of motion?

6. What do the terms 'kinematic' and 'kinetic' mean?

7. What are scalar and vector quantities?

8. How is force commonly measured?

9. What are the different factors that will influence the flight of a projectile?

10. What are the two different elements of fluid dynamics?

Time to reflect

1. How can the principles of biomechanics be used in a non-elite setting?

2. What do you think would be some of the challenges facing a sport biomechanist upon entering the work place?

3. Why are the scientific principles that underpin biomechanics an important element of sport performance?

Useful resources

To obtain a secure link to the websites below, see the Websites section on page ii or visit the companion website at www.pearsonfe.co.uk/foundationsinsport

- American Society of Biomechanics

- The British Association of Sport and Exercise Sciences

- International Society of Biomechanics in Sport

- The Physics Classroom

- Top End Sports

Further reading

Bartlett, R. (2007). *Introduction to Sports Biomechanics: Analysing Human Movement Patterns,* 2nd Edition. London: Routledge.

Blazevich, A.J. (2010). *Sports Biomechanics. The Basics: Optimising Human Performance*, 2nd Edition. London: A&C Black.

Carling, C., Bloomfield, J., Nelson, L. and Reilly, T. (2008). The Role of Motion Analysis in Elite Soccer: Contemporary Performance Measurement Techniques and Work-Rate Data. *Sports Medicine*, 38, 839–862.

Hong, Y. and Bartlett, R. (eds.). (2010). *Routledge Handbook of Biomechanics and Human Movement Science*. London: Routledge.

Judge, L.W., Hunter, I., and Gilreath, E. (2008). Using science to improve coaching: A case study of the American record holder in the women's hammer throw. *International Journal of Sport Science and Coaching*, 3, pp. 477– 488.

Leigh, S., Liu, H., Hubbard, M. and Bing, Y. (2010). Individualised optimal release angles in discus throwing. *Journal of Biomechanics, 43, pp. 540– 545.*

Maier, K.D., Wank, V., Bartonietz, K. and Blickhan, R. (2000). Neural network based models of javelin flight: Prediction of flight distances and optimal release parameters. *Sports Engineering*, 3, pp. 57–63.

McGinnis, P.M. (2005). *Biomechanics of Sport and Exercise,* 2nd Edition. Champaign, Illinois: Human Kinetics.

Watkins, J. (2007). *Introduction to Biomechanics of Sport and Exercise.* Oxford: Elsevier Health Sciences.

Chapter 3

Exercise physiology

Introduction

The human body is a complex organism with interacting systems that constantly adapts to the external and internal environment to maintain a stable level of homeostasis. Participating in exercise, places demands on bodily systems. The study of exercise physiology is concerned with the function, responses and adaptation of the human body during various acute (short duration or immediate) and chronic (long duration or long term) exercise situations. It is an applied science that has two main interests: improving exercise performance, and prevention and treatment of chronic disease.

Regular participation in exercise training has dramatic effects on the human body. Exercise physiologists study these effects and apply them to differing situations, such as an Olympic athlete training to reach their maximum performance potential, or somebody training to lose weight and improve their fitness. Exercise physiologists apply their knowledge of the human body to the prevention and treatment of diseases such as diabetes, obesity and arthritis. This chapter takes a systems approach to the functioning of the human body and its responses to exercise. Throughout this chapter you should consider the close interaction between the systems described.

Learning outcomes

After you have read this chapter you should be able to:

- define human homeostasis
- explain energy metabolism within the human body
- demonstrate understanding of the cardiovascular and respiratory systems
- describe how the human body responds to exercise.

You recently took up mountain biking and have been riding in a local forest three times a week. You have noticed that whenever the gradient goes uphill your heart rate increases rapidly, your breathing rate increases and becomes deeper and your quadriceps start to burn from the exertion.

* Why does your heart rate and breathing respond in such a way?

* What is causing your quadriceps to burn when you go uphill but not on the flat?

Human homeostasis

The human body is a complex organism that consists of many systems that interact to enable you to achieve diverse outcomes. For the human body to be able to function in its most efficient and effective manner it must maintain a constant and stable internal environment. An inability to do this can result in injury, disease, or possibly death. Human **homeostasis** is defined as the body's ability to physiologically maintain a relatively stable internal environment when faced with a continually changing external environment. It is this ability that allows most individuals to partake in exercise without serious consequences. Even at rest your body is in a dynamic state of equilibrium, where the internal conditions vary but within relatively narrow limits. Performing exercise contributes additional strain on your internal environment and the body has to work harder to maintain stability.

When you perform exercise you challenge the homeostatic state of your body. A short very high-intensity bout of running will challenge the maintenance of blood acidity (ideally maintained at a pH of 7.35–7.45), whilst a prolonged low to moderate bout of running will challenge the maintenance of core temperature at the desired 37°C. Where you choose to participate in exercise can add to the challenge of homeostasis. Exercise at high altitude, where there is a low partial pressure of oxygen in the atmosphere, will result in de-saturation of arterial oxygen content and add to exercise stress (Sewell et al., 2005). Prolonged exercise in extreme heat will result in greater rates of sweat loss and cause increased dehydration and

reduction in blood plasma volume, thus adding to the exercise stress. In both of these examples, whilst it is inevitable that homeostatic imbalance will occur, a failure to return to 'normal' levels will lead

to severe health consequences.

Exercise in extreme environments places greater stress on the body. To help maintain homeostasis at high altitude mountaineers often supplement oxygen intake with bottled oxygen, especially if they are climbing above 8000 metres, an altitude known as the 'death zone'.

To maintain **homeostasis** of specific **variables**, the body utilises negative-feedback mechanisms. These mechanisms consist of a **control centre**, a **receptor** and an **effector**. An example of a negative feedback mechanism is the regulation of core body temperature. When your body temperature rises, the receptors within the skin and brain sense an increase in temperature and send this information

Homeostasis – the body's state of stable equilibrium between interdependent elements

Variable – the factor or event being regulated

Control centre – determines the set point at which the variable is maintained

Receptor – monitors the environment and detects changes (stimulus) to the variable

Effector – provides the means to respond to the stimulus

to the control centre (brain). The control centre sends the information to the effector, in this case the sweat glands, you begin to sweat, which leads to evaporation from the skin and your body temperature falls. This is just one example; others include the regulation of heart rate, blood pressure, and blood glucose and blood acidity.

Energy and energy systems

The functioning of the human body relies on energy. Energy comes from the carbohydrate, fats and proteins contained within food. However, these nutrients are not directly used for energy; instead the energy they contain is converted into a high-energy compound called **adenosine triphosphate (ATP)**. It is this compound that is used within the cells during energy metabolism. The body stores only a small quantity of ATP, enough for a handful of seconds of exercise, therefore exercising muscles must reform ATP continually. To ensure the body is always able to do this, carbohydrate, in the form of glucose, needs to be ever present in the blood and is also stored as glycogen within muscles and the liver. Fats are stored as triglycerides and can supply large quantities of energy. At rest, energy is equally obtained from carbohydrate and fat stores; as exercise intensity increases, the body relies more heavily on carbohydrate to provide the fuel for reforming ATP.

Adenosine triphosphate consists of one adenosine molecule and three phosphate groups. When the ATP molecule is used for energy, the enzyme **ATPase** causes a reaction and one of the phosphate groups splits away, releasing large amounts of energy. This leaves the compound adenosine diphosphate (ADP) and a free phosphate group. Through chemical reactions a phosphate group is added to ADP reforming ATP. This process is called **phosphorylation**. These reactions can occur without oxygen, called **anaerobic metabolism**, or with oxygen, called **aerobic metabolism**. The three energy systems that generate ATP are:

- the ATP-PCr system
- the glycolytic system
- the oxidative system.

Key terms

Adenosine triphosphate (ATP) – high energy compound used for energy in the human body

ATPase – enzyme that causes the reaction that releases energy from ATP

Phosphorylation – the process of adding a phosphate group to ADP

Anaerobic metabolism – the process of energy production without oxygen

Aerobic metabolism – the process of energy production with oxygen

ATP-PCr system

This is the fastest and simplest of the energy systems, and does not require oxygen; therefore it is classed as anaerobic. Phosphocreatine (PCr) is stored within the cells and is broken down by the enzyme creatine kinase to release a phosphate molecule. This phosphate molecule is simply joined to ADP to reform ATP (Figure 3.1). This process is fast but is not sustainable as the body has limited PCr stores. This system will provide energy for the first 3 to 15 seconds of exercise but any longer will require other energy systems to reform ATP.

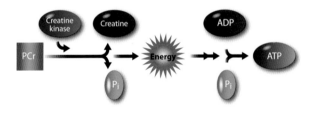

Figure 3.1: Adenosine triphosphate (ATP) can be reformed in a fast anaerobic process by joining a phosphate molecule, donated from phosphocreatine, to adenosine diphosphate (ADP).

Glycolytic system

This system is the process by which glucose is broken down to reform ATP. Glucose circulating within the blood, or glycogen from the muscle or liver stores, is converted to glucose 6-phosphate, which then starts the process of glycolysis. During a series of reactions controlled by specific enzymes within the muscle cells, glucose is broken down to form pyruvic acid. If oxygen is not present, pyruvic acid is converted into lactic acid. In this instance the system is referred to as anaerobic glycolysis (Figure 3.2). If during glycolysis oxygen is present in sufficient quantities, pyruvic acid is the end product and enters the Krebs cycle (discussed in the oxidative system section). Glycolysis does not produce large quantities of ATP but combined with the ATP-PCr system it does enable muscles to generate force even when oxygen is in short supply. The combination of these two systems provides energy predominantly for high intensity exercise. One of the major limitations of anaerobic glycolysis is that lactic acid can accumulate rapidly in the muscle and blood. Lactic acid compromises exercise performance because it affects further glycogen breakdown and impedes muscular contractions. The anaerobic processes of energy production, whilst being able to provide fast energy for high intensity exercise, are not sufficient for generating ATP during long duration exercise. It is during this type of activity that the oxidative system becomes the predominant energy system.

Oxidative system

This system relies on the presence of oxygen and is the most complex of the energy pathways. Since oxygen is required, it is an aerobic process. The oxidative production of ATP occurs within the mitochondria of muscle cells. This system has the capacity to produce large quantities of ATP, therefore it is the predominant pathway used during endurance exercise. One advantage it has over the other systems is that it has the ability to breakdown both carbohydrates and fats. To aid your understanding we will start the discussion with the oxidation of carbohydrate.

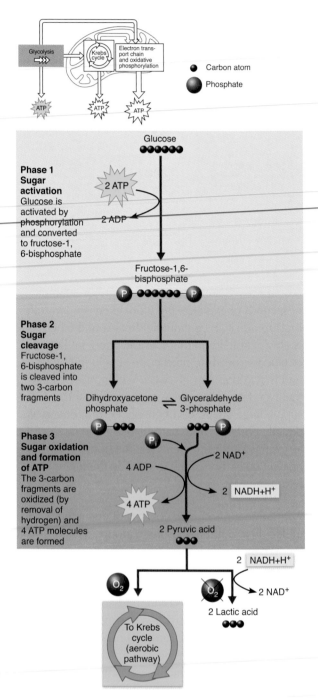

Figure 3.2: Energy production through the process of glycolysis. Note that the end product of pyruvic acid is converted into lactic acid if oxygen is not present.

For complete oxidation of glucose three processes are involved (Figure 3.3):

1. **Aerobic glycolysis** within the oxidative system is the same glycolytic process described previously with the exception that when oxygen is present the end product, pyruvic acid, is converted into acetyl coenzyme A (acetyl CoA).

2. **The Krebs cycle** is a complex series of aerobic chemical reactions that commence when acetyl CoA enters. Providing there is a constant supply of acetyl CoA the Krebs cycle continues to cycle through the chain of reactions. At the end of one cycle ATP has been produced and carbohydrate has been broken down to form carbon dioxide and hydrogen.

3. **The electron transport chain** is the final stage of metabolism of carbohydrate. During glycolysis and the Krebs cycle hydrogen is released. If this were to remain in the system the body would become too acidic. The hydrogen combines with two coenzymes and is carried to the electron transport chain where they are split to form ATP. The hydrogen combines with oxygen to form water and prevent the system becoming too acidic.

Oxidation of fat

The oxidative processes are also capable of breaking down fat and releasing the huge quantities of energy it stores. In a healthy lean adult the body

> ### Key terms
>
> **Glycolysis** – a process used to convert glucose to pyruvic acid
>
> **Krebs cycle** – a series of aerobic reactions that break down acetyl CoA to release energy
>
> **Electron transport chain** – a process that uses hydrogen to form ATP
>
> **Lipolysis** – the process of splitting triglycerides into glycerol and free fatty acids

has enough fat stored for approximately 70 000 calories of energy. In contrast, the same person would have only 2000 calories of energy from carbohydrate stores. The specific fat used for energy is called triglyceride. Triglyceride is broken down into one molecule of glycerol and three molecules of free fatty acids (FFA) in a process called **lipolysis**. The FFA enter the muscle cell and are converted into acetyl CoA. At this point the acetyl CoA enters the Krebs cycle and follows the same process as previously described for carbohydrate metabolism. The complete breakdown of FFA molecules requires larger quantities of oxygen than glucose; therefore use of fat as a fuel source is often only possible during low intensity endurance exercise. The total energy yield from one molecule of fat is 129 molecules of ATP, considerably more than the 39 molecules of ATP from glycogen.

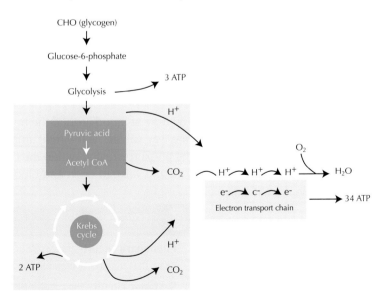

Figure 3.3: An overview of the oxidative system when metabolising carbohydrate.

Energy system use during exercise

Whilst we have described the energy systems separately, it is important that you understand they do not work independently. During any form of exercise, whether it is a 100 metre sprint or a half marathon, each of the energy systems is contributing to the total energy demands. Each system interacts, however one will often be dominant. For example during an all-out 100 metre sprint (approximately 10 seconds) the ATP-PCr system will provide most of the energy, but anaerobic glycolysis and the oxidative system will contribute a small proportion of the energy. Take the other end of the exercise continuum; during a half marathon run (approximately 1 hour 30 minutes) the oxidative system will provide most of the energy with only a small amount coming from the ATP-PCr and anaerobic glycolytic systems. The predominant energy system is determined by the length and intensity of the exercise that is being undertaken.

Stop and think

Tennis matches can last for several hours with rallies lasting anything from one shot to approximately 30 seconds.

Consider which energy systems provide energy for the entire tennis match.

What energy system is responsible for making a serve?

The cardiovascular system

The cardiovascular system includes the heart, blood vessels and blood and plays an important role in maintaining life. The system provides a transport mechanism for all the nutrients required by our bodies, and also provides the means of removing harmful metabolic waste products. Even at rest the demands on the system are great, once exercise commences these demands increase dramatically.

Heart, blood flow and blood

The heart is a muscular pump approximately the size of your clenched fist. Located slightly left centre in the thoracic cavity, it controls the direction and speed of blood flow around the body. It consists

of four chambers (two atria and two ventricles), divided into left and right sides (Figure 3.4). The right atrium acts as a receiving chamber for de-oxygenated blood returning from the body tissues, and the right ventricle sends this blood to the lungs to become oxygen rich. The circuit of the right side is commonly known as the **pulmonary circuit**. The left atrium receives the oxygenated blood from the lungs and the left ventricle pumps this blood out to all the body tissues. The circuit of the left side is commonly known as the **systemic circuit**. During each heartbeat the atria contract to fill the ventricles and the ventricles contract to eject the blood from the heart. Blood leaves the right ventricle via the pulmonary artery and the left ventricle via the aorta.

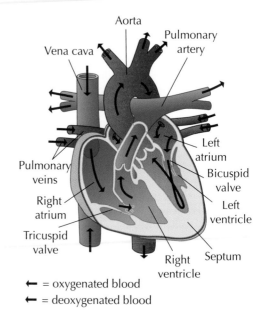

Figure 3.4: The key structures of the heart

The flow of blood around the heart is controlled by one-way valves. As the right atrium fills with blood the pressure created within the chamber forces the tricuspid valve to open and blood flows into the

Key terms

Pulmonary circuit – the circuit of the right side of the heart that transports blood to the lungs

Systemic circuit – the circuit of the left side of the heart that transports blood to the body

right ventricle. As the right ventricle contracts the pulmonary valve is forced open and blood flows into the pulmonary circuit. On return, the blood flows from the left atrium into the left ventricle through the bicuspid valve, and out of the left ventricle through the aortic valve and into the systemic circuit. The purpose of each of these valves is to prevent back flow of blood.

The muscle of the heart is called myocardium. The thickness of the muscle varies throughout the heart but is at its greatest around the chamber of the left ventricle. The greater muscular wall thickness allows for greater force production and is a direct result of increased demands on the left ventricle. Cardiac muscle must have a constant supply of blood rich in nutrients and oxygen. Therefore, as the blood leaves the heart, some of it immediately travels into the coronary arteries that encircle the myocardium.

Blood volume in a healthy man ranges from 5–6 litres, and a woman 4–5 litres. Normally blood contains 55 per cent plasma and 45 per cent formed elements (Wilmore, Costill and Kenney, 2008) (see Table 3.1).

Table 3.1: The composition of whole blood and detailed breakdown of each component

Blood component	Specific composition
Plasma	90% water 7% plasma proteins 3% other (nutrients, enzymes, hormones, gases, antibodies, waste products)
Formed element	99% red blood cells 1% white blood cells and platelets

For exercise physiologists the functions of blood that are of most interest are: transportation, temperature regulation and acid base balance (pH). Blood is the medium that our nutrients, oxygen and metabolic waste products are transported within. Primarily it is the transporter of oxygen that has bound to the haemoglobin within the red blood cells. Additionally, it regulates temperature by picking up heat from the body core and re-distributing

it throughout the body, or sending it to the skin for cooling. It also acts to maintain stable body acidity by reducing the harmful effects of the acid produced during anaerobic metabolism.

Electrical events and cardiac cycle

The heartbeat, or contraction, is initiated by electrical events within the myocardium cells. The electrical activity of the heart allows it to contract without external stimulation at a pre-determined heart rate (HR) of 70–80 beats per minute. To initiate the contraction there is a simple conduction system consisting of: sinoatrial (sa) node, atrioventricular (AV) node, AV bundle (bundle of His) and the Purkinje fibres. The SA node located in the rear wall of the right atrium acts as the pacemaker and generates impulses that travel to the AV node. From here the impulse is conducted to the AV bundle, down the left and right branches into both ventricles. The impulse then travels along the bundles down to the apex of the heart and finally into the ventricular walls via the Purkinje fibres. This electrical activity initiates contraction of the myocardium and blood is ejected from both ventricles.

The cardiac cycle commences when the ventricles contract. This stage is called **systole** and the following relaxation phase is called **diastole**. During systole the pulmonary and aortic valves are forced open and blood flows to the respective circuits. When diastole starts, blood begins to flow back to the heart and the pulmonary and aortic valves close. During systole the volume of the blood ejected out of the left ventricle is termed **stroke volume (SV)**. To understand this measure, you should consider that at the end of diastole, the left ventricle is full of blood; this volume is termed end diastolic

Key terms

Systole – cardiac cycle period when the heart is contracting

Diastole – cardiac cycle period when the heart is relaxing

Stroke volume (SV) – the volume of blood ejected from the left ventricle

volume (EDV). At the end of systole, the ventricle has emptied and the volume of blood remaining is termed end systolic volume (ESV). Stroke volume is simply the difference between EDV and ESV. Stroke volume is used to calculate **cardiac output** (the total volume of blood ejected per minute) by simply multiplying HR and SV. SV at rest in a healthy adult is 60 to 80 ml. A normal resting HR is 70 beats per minute; therefore cardiac output is between 4.2 and 5.6 litres per minute.

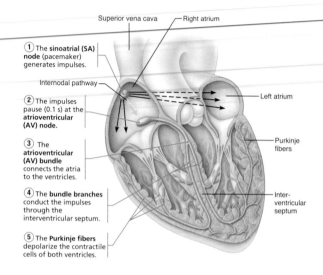

① The **sinoatrial (SA) node** (pacemaker) generates impulses.

② The impulses pause (0.1 s) at the **atrioventricular (AV) node.**

③ The **atrioventricular (AV) bundle** connects the atria to the ventricles.

④ The **bundle branches** conduct the impulses through the interventricular septum.

⑤ The **Purkinje fibers** depolarize the contractile cells of both ventricles.

Superior vena cava — Right atrium

Internodal pathway

Left atrium

Purkinje fibers

Inter-ventricular septum

Figure 3.5: The conduction system of the heart

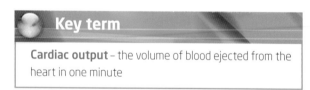

Key term

Cardiac output – the volume of blood ejected from the heart in one minute

Vascular system

Once the blood is ejected from the heart it flows through a series of vessels that transport it to the tissues and back, called the vascular system. Blood flows through the vessels in a specific sequence:

1. arteries
2. arterioles
3. capillaries
4. venules
5. veins.

- **Arteries** carry blood away from the heart under high pressure. Typically they are the largest and most elastic of the vessels.

- **Arterioles** slow blood flow in preparation for it entering the capillaries.

- **Capillaries** are the smallest blood vessel, typically only one cell thick. The microscopic size allows for efficient exchange of gases, nutrients and waste products during metabolism.

- **Venules and veins** carry blood returning to the heart.

It is difficult to quantify the volume of blood within the various body tissues at any given moment because it varies greatly depending on the demands you are placing on the system. At rest the estimated proportion of blood within each of the vessels is:

- 7% throughout heart

- 13% systemic circuit arteries

- 7% systemic circuit arterioles and capillaries

- 64% systemic circuit veins

- 9% pulmonary circuit vessels.

Cardiovascular response to exercise

During exercise great demand is placed on the cardiovascular system, primarily to respond to the increased demand by the exercising muscles for oxygen and nutrients. As an exercise physiologist you need to understand the typical responses to exercise. The measures described below are shown in Table 3.2 on page 51.

Heart rate

Resting heart rate (RHR) averages 60 to 80 beats per minute. Just before exercise commences heart rate usually increases; this is termed anticipatory rise. It is a response to the release of **adrenalin** and **noradrenalin**. On commencing exercise your heart rate increases in direct proportion to the intensity of exercise. It is commonly known that a linear relationship exists between exercise heart rate and exercise intensity (see Figure 3.1 on page 41). Heart rate will continue to rise until the demand for nutrients and oxygen has been met; at this point heart rate will reach a plateau and your body will be in a steady state. If you continue to increase exercise intensity until exhaustion, your heart rate will continue to rise until it approaches its maximum rate (HRmax). HRmax can be calculated by subtracting your age from 220 beats per minute. A reduction in exercise intensity results in a lowering of heart rate in response to a reduced demand for nutrients and oxygen. Increases in heart rate are controlled by the sympathetic nervous system and reductions in heart rate are controlled by the parasympathetic nervous system.

Stroke volume

Stroke volume rises during exercise to allow the heart to function with greater efficiency. There is a progressive increase until stroke volume reaches its maximum, which is thought to occur at an exercise intensity that represents approximately 60 per cent of maximal capacity. In well trained individuals stroke volume can rise to between 160 and 200 ml during maximal exercise. It is believed that the mechanisms responsible for the increases are increased venous return of blood and increased ventricular contractility.

Cardiac output

Since both heart rate and stroke volume increase during exercise, it follows that cardiac output also increases. At rest cardiac output is approximately 5 litres per minute. When you consider the rise in stroke volume during maximal exercise in well-trained individuals it is possible that cardiac output will peak at 40 litres per minute. This peak is dependent on body size and the level of endurance fitness.

Blood flow

Primarily the increase in cardiac output is caused by the greater demand for oxygen in the exercising muscles. For this demand to be met, increasing the rate of flow is insufficient if the flow does not go to the correct locations. Therefore the body is able to redistribute blood to the locations where oxygen is most needed, for instance in the quadriceps of a cyclist riding up a steep hill. Blood is redirected from non-essential areas (such as the liver, kidney and intestines) into the exercising muscles. The change is quite dramatic, with an estimated 80 per cent of cardiac output going to the muscles during exercise compared to only 20 per cent at rest. To

achieve this shift in blood flow blood vessels are able to **vasodilate** and **vasoconstrict**.

Key terms

Adrenalin – is a hormone that increases heart rate and constricts blood vessels

Noradrenalin – is a hormone that acts alongside adrenalin to increase heart rate, blood flow to the muscles and stimulates glucose release

Vasodilation – the process where the blood vessels increase in diameter

Vasoconstriction – the process of narrowing of blood vessel diameter

Blood oxygen content

Cardiac output increases and blood is redistributed during exercise. In essence the body has provided the exercising muscles with the blood containing the oxygen that is required. All that remains is for the muscles to extract the extra oxygen from the blood. At rest arterial blood contains 20 ml of oxygen per 100 ml of blood, and venous blood contains 15 ml of oxygen per 100 ml of blood (Wilmore, Costill and Kenney, 2008). The difference between these two values (5 ml) is termed arterial-venous oxygen difference (a-vO_2 difference). The value represents the quantity of oxygen that the body removes from the blood as it travels through the vascular system. As exercise intensity increases, the quantity of oxygen taken from the blood also increases. It is not uncommon during strenuous exercise for a-vO_2 difference to peak at 16 ml of oxygen per 100 ml of blood.

The respiratory system

It is important that you gain knowledge of the structures and functions of the body that allow the body to remove the oxygen from the atmosphere and transfer it to our tissues – the respiratory system. The four functions of the respiratory system are:

1. pulmonary ventilation

2. pulmonary diffusion

3. transport of blood gases

4. internal respiration.

Pulmonary ventilation

Atmospheric air enters the body through the mouth, nose and nasal cavity before travelling down the pharynx, larynx and trachea. On reaching the trachea the air is within the conducting zone of the respiratory system; it continues down before branching into either the left or right bronchi and into the lungs. The passageways of the bronchi divide and continually reduce in size until reaching the smallest bronchioles. As the air passes through the passageways it is warmed, cleansed of impurities and saturated with water vapour. Once through the smallest bronchioles the air is within the respiratory zone and enters the respiratory bronchioles before passing through the alveolar ducts and into the alveoli. The body has approximately 300 million alveoli making up the majority of the lung volume; each is covered with a network of pulmonary capillaries. These capillaries are responsible for gas exchange between the lungs and the blood.

Air is moved in and out of the lungs because of pressure changes within the thoracic cavity. As you breathe in (inspiration) the volume of the thoracic cavity increases due to the intercostal muscles (between the ribs) contracting and lifting the ribcage. At the same time the diaphragm contracts and flattens. The increase in volume of the thoracic cavity serves to reduce the intrapulmonary pressure within the cavity to below the pressure of the air outside the body, therefore air flows into the lungs. Air will continue to flow into the lungs until the intrapulmonary pressure equals the external air pressure. Expiration is a result of passive relaxation of the muscles and the elasticity of the lung tissue. The relaxation returns the ribs and diaphragm to their resting positions. The thoracic cavity reduces in volume, causing intrapulmonary pressure to rise and forcing air out of the lungs.

Remember

It is important for your appreciation of respiratory function that you understand gases will always flow from a region of high pressure into a region of low pressure.

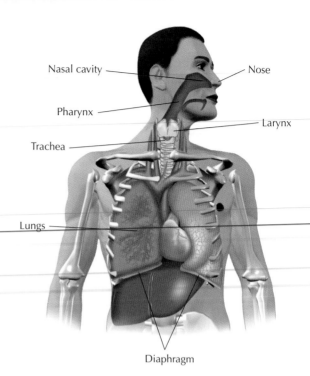

Figure 3.6: The key structures of the respiratory system

Nasal cavity

Nose

Pharynx

Larynx

Trachea

Lungs

Diaphragm

Pulmonary diffusion

This is the process where oxygen is exchanged from the alveolar air into the blood and carbon dioxide is exchanged from the blood into the alveolar air. The most important requirement of pulmonary diffusion is that there is blood (supplied by the pulmonary circuit of the cardiovascular system) within the pulmonary capillaries at the same time that air is within the alveoli. Gas exchange occurs across the respiratory membrane. This membrane is extremely thin to allow for efficient exchange of gases.

Gas flows from high to low pressure. This principle is fundamental in the diffusion of gases across the respiratory membrane. Each gas exerts a pressure in proportion to its concentration in the gas mixture. This pressure is called partial pressure. If there is a difference of partial pressures between two areas there is said to be a pressure gradient. Gas exchange occurs across a pressure gradient from an area of high pressure into an area of low pressure. Within the alveoli air, oxygen exerts a **partial pressure** (PO_2) of 104 mmHg. Within the pulmonary capillaries, because many of the oxygen molecules have been used by the tissues, the PO_2 is 40 mmHg in the blood – 64 mmHg lower than within the alveoli. Due to this **pressure gradient** oxygen will pass across the membrane from the alveoli into the blood. Carbon dioxide exerts a partial pressure (PCO_2) of 45 mmHg within the blood at the pulmonary capillaries. Within the alveoli air, PCO_2 is 40 mmHg. Therefore, moving across the pressure gradient, carbon dioxide molecules are transferred from the blood into the lungs (Figure 3.7).

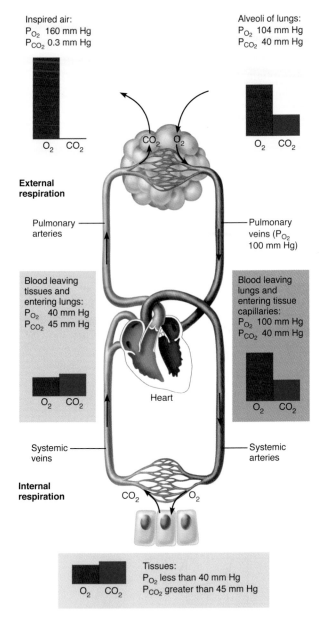

Figure 3.7: Partial pressure of oxygen and carbon dioxide in blood as it is transported around the body. Note the changes that occur within the capillaries at the lungs and muscle as gas exchange occurs.

Key terms

Partial pressure – the pressure a gas exerts on a mixture of gases

Pressure gradient – the difference between the partial pressures of two gases

Transport of blood gases

Oxygen is carried within the blood in two ways – attached to haemoglobin in the red blood cells (98.5 per cent) or dissolved in blood plasma (1.5 per cent). Each haemoglobin molecule has the capacity to carry four molecules of oxygen. Typically adults have between 12 to 18 g of haemoglobin per 100 ml of blood. Each gram of haemoglobin combines with 1.34 ml of oxygen, therefore the oxygen carrying capacity of blood is between 16 and 24 ml per 100 ml of blood when fully saturated. However, the binding of oxygen to haemoglobin depends on the PO_2 in the blood. In normal homeostatic conditions PO_2 is high and allows for approximately 98 per cent haemoglobin saturation. If PO_2 falls, haemoglobin saturation will be reduced. One scenario that alters haemoglobin saturation is a change from normal blood acidity. Carbon dioxide is carried by blood in three ways; dissolved in plasma (7–10 per cent), bound to haemoglobin (20–30 per cent) and as a bicarbonate ion in plasma (60–70 per cent).

Internal respiration

Internal respiration is the gas exchange between the tissues and the blood. Recall that gas exchange takes place within the capillaries of the vascular system. The walls of these capillaries are often only one cell thick, allowing for efficient gaseous exchange. At the capillaries oxygen dissociates from haemoglobin and diffuses out of the red blood cells, passes through the membrane and into the tissues, which require oxygen. This oxygen is then used to produce energy through oxidative energy production. Carbon dioxide is transferred from the tissues into the blood simply because of the partial pressure gradient. During exercise, muscles produce large quantities of carbon dioxide, causing the PCO_2 in the muscle cells to be greater than in the capillary blood. Consequently, carbon dioxide molecules pass out of the muscle into the blood.

Respiratory response to exercise

In most cases performing exercise results in a greater demand for oxygen use within the exercising muscles. At rest a healthy adult will consume around 0.25 litres of oxygen per minute and during high intensity exercise this increases to 3.5 litres per minute. Surprisingly, the main stimulus for respiratory system response to exercise is not a change in oxygen levels but an increase in carbon dioxide production. Respiratory responses are due to a combination of nervous influences and chemical changes within the body. The measures described below are displayed in Table 3.2.

Tidal volume

Tidal volume is the volume of air expired in one breath. At rest a healthy adult would record a tidal volume of approximately 0.5 litres. Tidal volume increases at the onset of exercise and is the first

response of the respiratory system. During maximal exercise it may peak at 2.4 litres.

Breathing frequency

Breathing frequency is the number of breaths taken during one minute. Typically, at rest a healthy adult breathes 12 to 20 times per minute. During exercise the frequency of breathing rises. During maximal exercise highly trained endurance athletes can breathe at a rate of 50 to 60 breaths per minute. The rate of breathing rises in conjunction with increases in tidal volume. Once tidal volume has increased substantially breathing rate takes over as the major mechanism for continued increases in ventilation.

Minute ventilation

Minute ventilation is the volume of air expired in one minute and is calculated by multiplying tidal volume and breathing frequency. As exercise begins, an almost immediate large increase in minute ventilation occurs before a slower rise follows (Figure 3.8). If exercise intensity stays the same,

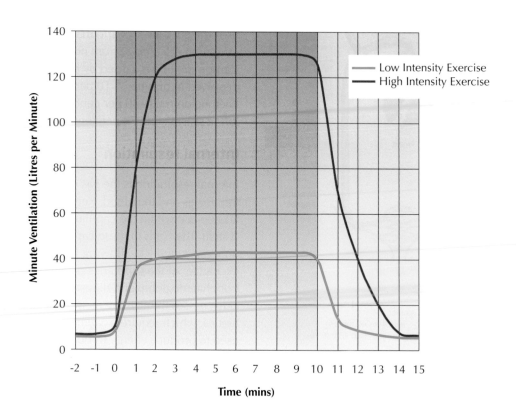

Figure 3.8: Graph representing the typical ventilatory response to exercise at low and high exercise intensities

minute ventilation will reach a steady state within one to two minutes. This steady state represents the point when oxygen supply and demand, and carbon dioxide production and removal, are balanced.
In healthy adults minute ventilation at rest would typically be between 6 to 10 litres per minute. This can increase during high intensity exercise to 150 litres per minute.

Remember

The cardiovascular system and respiratory system work in partnership to provide oxygen and nutrients to your muscles and remove waste products resulting from metabolism. Should one system fail the other becomes worthless.

Table 3.2: Typical cardiovascular and respiratory system values at rest and during maximal exercise

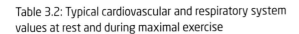

System	Measure	Rest	Maximal exercise
Cardiovascular	Heart rate (beats per minute)	60–80	220 minus age
	Stroke volume (millilitres)	60–80	160–200
	Cardiac output (litres per minute)	3.6–6.4	40
	Arterial-venous oxygen diff. (millilitres)	5	16
Respiratory	Breathing frequency	12–18	50–60
	Tidal volume (litres)	0.5	2.4
	Minute ventilation (litres per minute)	6–10	150

Case study (for recommended answers, see www.pearsonfe.co.uk/foundationsinsport)

Toby Lerone has entered his first marathon and is training to achieve his goal of finishing in a time of 3 hours and 30 minutes. This means he will have to run at a pace of approximately 8 minutes per mile. He believes this is an achievable goal as he has previously run a half marathon in 1 hour 38 minutes 25 seconds. Toby's training plan lasts for 16 weeks and has him running a weekly mileage from 20 miles in week 1, to 50 miles by week 13. Every week he will complete a long steady run, up to 22 miles three weeks before the race day, at a heart rate average of 145 to 150 beats per minute. Consider what happens to Toby's body when he completes his long runs.

1. Discuss the cardiovascular response to running long distances.

2. Discuss the respiratory responses to running long distances.

3. How will Toby's body provide him with energy during the marathon race?

Check your understanding (for answers, see www.pearsonfe.co.uk/foundationsinsport)

1. Give a definition of human homeostasis.

2. How is energy from the food we eat, made available to us for exercise?

3. Briefly describe how the oxidative energy system functions. Consider fat and carbohydrate as fuel sources.

4. What proportion of each energy system do you think provides energy for an elite 800 metre runner during a race?

5. Describe blood flow around the cardiovascular system.

6. Describe the cardiovascular responses that occur during steady state exercise at 80 per cent HRmax.

7. Calculate cardiac output when stroke volume is 115 ml and heart rate is 172 beats per minute.

8. Describe how oxygen is transferred from alveoli air to blood, and blood to muscle tissue.

9. Calculate minute ventilation if breathing frequency is 32 breaths per minute and tidal volume is 1.7 litres.

10. If your minute ventilation was 114.4 litres per minute and your tidal volume was 2.2 litres, how many breaths did you take?

Time to reflect

1. Consider why it is important that the energy systems interact to provide a continual supply of energy.

2. Consider how you could apply your knowledge of the energy systems in the following scenarios.

   • an overweight male wishing to reduce their body mass.

   • an elite female footballer training to improve their physiological performance during pre-season training.

3. You now know that the heart structure contains four chambers and a series of valves. Think about the reasons why the system is structured in such a way. Reflect upon what would happen if there was only one atria and one ventricle. What about if the valves were able to open in both directions?

4. Partial pressure of oxygen is a crucial element of the respiratory system function. At altitude (above 3000 metres) the partial pressure of atmospheric oxygen is reduced. Consider how the function of the respiratory system is affected by exposure to such conditions. How can the body respond to maintain the supply of oxygen to the tissues?

5. The interactions of the cardiovascular and respiratory systems enable the human body to function in an effective manner. Reflecting on this interaction and the responses to exercise, consider how the combined systems function efficiently.

Useful resources

To obtain a secure link to the websites below, see the Websites section on page ii or visit the companion website at www.pearsonfe.co.uk/foundationsinsport

- American College of Sports Medicine
- British Association of Sport and Exercise Science
- British Journal of Sports Medicine
- English Institute of Sport
- Journal of Applied Physiology
- Journal of Sport Sciences
- Medicine in Sport and Exercise Science

Further reading

Abernethy, B., Hanrahan, S.J., Kippers, V., Mackinnon, L.T. and Pandy, M.G. (2005). *The Biophysical Foundations of Human* Movement, 2nd Edition. Champaign,Illinois: Human Kinetics.

Astrand, P.O., Rodahl, K., Dahl, H.A. and Stromme, S.B. (2003). *Textbook of Work Physiology: Physiological Bases of Exercise,* 4th Edition. Champaign,Illinois: Human Kinetics.

Fox, S.I. (2009) *Human Physiology,* 11th Edition. New York: McGraw Hill.

Marieb, E.N. and Hoehn, K. (2010). *Human Anatomy and Physiology,* 8th Edition. San Francisco: Pearson Benjamin Cummings.

Martini, F.H. and Nath, J.L. (2009). *Fundamentals of Anatomy and Physiology,* 8th Edition. Pearson Benjamin Cummings.

McArdle ,W.D., Katch, F.I., and Katch, V.L. (2010). *Exercise Physiology: Nutrition Energy and Human Performance,* 7th Edition. Philadelphia: Lippincott, Williams & Wilkins.

Powers, S.K. and Howley, E.T. (2009). *Exercise Physiology: Theory and Application to Fitness and Performance,* 7th Edition. New York: McGraw Hill.

Sewell, D., Watkins, P., and Griffin, M. (2005). *Sport and Exercise Science: An Introduction*. London: Hodder Arnold.

Stanfield, C.L. (2011). *Principles of Human Physiology,* 4th Edition. Pearson Benjamin Cummings.

Wilmore, J.H., Costill, D.L. and Kenney, W.L. (2008). *Physiology of Sport and Exercise,* 4th Edition. Champaign; Illinois: Human Kinetics.

Chapter 4

Fitness testing and training

Introduction

The human body thrives when stimulated by exercise. It improves its capabilities. When exercise becomes regular with a structured plan it is considered that the individual is participating in fitness training. The extent of the benefits to the human body depends on the amount and intensity of the training. An Olympic champion trains considerably more, and has greater fitness, than somebody training for health and well being. Most people will never compete in the Olympics, but all can improve fitness through correctly structured training plans.

Since fitness is critical for success in sport, sports and exercise scientists need to be able to measure it accurately. It allows them to establish baseline fitness measures, monitor fitness gains and evaluate the effectiveness of any training that is being completed. Fitness testing also serves as a motivating tool for athletes. One of the key roles of sport and exercise scientists is to conduct fitness tests and use the results to identify strengths and weaknesses of athletes in order to devise more effective fitness training plans.

This chapter considers the physiological adaptations to fitness training, before examining how these adaptations can be stimulated, and considering methods for testing common fitness components. You will be challenged to understand the physiology of training adaptation, different methods of fitness training, and common fitness testing techniques.

Learning outcomes

After you have read this chapter you should be able to:

- explain the physiological adaptations that result from fitness training
- understand the principles behind effective fitness training
- describe different methods of fitness training
- describe methods for testing fitness across a range of fitness components.

Starting block

You have been appointed as the sport and exercise scientist at a professional football club. The manager of the team is eager to have the players at peak fitness for the start of the new season in six weeks time. He would like you to design a fitness training plan that improves the players' fitness but still allows him time to develop skill and tactical awareness within the team. Consider:

- how you would approach this task
- what the key components of fitness are that need to be addressed for the players.

Physiological adaptations to fitness training

In *Chapter 3: Exercise physiology* immediate responses to exercise were considered. Regular, structured fitness training that stimulates these responses results in more permanent physiological change, or adaptation. Over a period of time the improvements in fitness are evident in your ability to cope with exercise that may have previously proved difficult. The extent of the adaptations depends on the stimulus applied to each of the body systems. The type, duration and intensity of fitness training all play a role in determining the nature of the adaptation. Table 4.1 on page 58 summarises the key adaptations to fitness training.

Energy system adaptations

Oxidative enzymes

Regular endurance training stimulates cellular adaptations within the muscles; these enhance the **resynthesis** of ATP. There is an increase in the size and quantity of the muscles' mitochondria. Remember from *Chapter 3: Exercise physiology* that oxidative production of ATP occurs within the mitochondria of muscle cells. It depends on the action of oxidative enzymes within the mitochondria. An increase in size and quantity of mitochondria will also result in an increase in the quantity of the oxidative enzymes. A greater quantity will also mean enhanced activity of these enzymes.

Anaerobic enzymes

Regular anaerobic training (such as sprinting and weightlifting) affects the enzymes associated with energy production. In this case the enzymes are those that are directly associated with the ATP-PCr and glycolytic energy systems. Creatine kinase and phosphofructokinase are two enzymes that increase in activity as a result of anaerobic training. Whilst anaerobic enzyme activity increases, it is unclear if this is the major drive for enhanced anaerobic performance (Wilmore, Costill & Kenney, 2008).

Carbohydrate and fat use

An increase in oxidative enzyme activity and **mitochondria** density results in less carbohydrate being used as the fuel source during **submaximal** exercise intensities. Consequently muscle glycogen stores will be spared and lactic acid accumulation reduced. As reliance on muscle glycogen is less following endurance training, the required energy must come from the stored fat. Endurance training enhances the amount of fat (triglyceride) that is stored within muscles (Wilmore, Costill & Kenney, 2008). This additional triglyceride is located close to the mitochondria and is therefore readily available as a fuel source. Couple this with the increase in oxidative enzyme activity and the result is that the endurance trained individual can utilise fats more efficiently, thus helping to spare muscle glycogen. During endurance exercise that lasts for several hours, being able to rely more on stored fat and less on muscle glycogen is advantageous.

Key terms

Resynthesis – the combining of simple compounds or elements to form a more complex one

Mitochondria – a structure in cells where, in the presence of oxygen, food molecules are broken down to form energy

Submaximal – exercise intensity below 100 per cent of maximum heart rate

Cardiovascular system adaptations

Cardiac size

Following regular training the heart's mass and volume increases. Cardiac adaptations are most evident in the left ventricular wall and chamber. Cardiac muscle works harder during exercise and over time this stimulates an increase in muscle fibre size and the contractile elements of the fibres, resulting in an increase in muscle mass. This is termed **cardiac hypertrophy**. Following a period of endurance training left ventricular filling increases as a consequence of increased blood volume, which in turn causes an increase in left ventricular end-diastolic volume (EDV). This helps to reduce heart rate and allows for a longer diastolic filling period. As a consequence of these adaptations the left ventricle chamber size is larger in endurance trained athletes.

Stroke volume

Stroke volume increases following a period of endurance training. At rest and during all intensities of exercise a trained individual has a larger stroke volume than an untrained individual. This increase is due to the left ventricle filling more completely because of increased blood volume and increased time for ventricular filling. In addition to this the increase in muscle mass around the left ventricle causes a more forceful contraction, squeezing more blood out of the heart during **systole**.

Heart rate

Changes in heart rate following training can be summarised into three areas: resting heart rate, submaximal heart rates, and recovery heart rates.

- **Resting heart rate** Decreases significantly following a period of regular endurance exercise. Resting heart rate in elite endurance athletes can be as low as 35–40 beats per minute, roughly half that of untrained individuals. Since stroke volume increases, the heart does not need to beat as frequently to supply the quantity of oxygen to the required locations.

- **Submaximal heart rates** During exercise at submaximal intensities, a trained individual records proportionally lower heart rates than an untrained individual at a specified work rate. This indicates a more efficient heart.

- **Recovery heart rates** Following a period of exercise your heart rate returns to its resting value over a period of several minutes. After regular endurance training the time it takes for your heart to return back to its resting value is reduced.

Cardiac output

Since cardiac output is the product of stroke volume and heart rate, any changes in these values affect cardiac output. As stroke volume increases and heart rate reduces at rest and during submaximal intensities, cardiac output does not alter after endurance training at rest or during a given submaximal intensity. During maximal intensity cardiac output in a trained individual is considerably greater than an untrained individual. This is largely due to an increase in maximal stroke volume as maximal heart rate remains relatively unchanged.

Blood flow

During exercise more blood is distributed to the exercising muscles. As a result of this several adaptations occur.

1. New capillaries develop in the muscles to allow for greater blood perfusion.

2. The existing capillaries within the muscles are able to open up more to allow a greater flow of blood through them.

3. There becomes a more effective redistribution of blood to the active muscles.

Blood volume

Following a period of regular endurance training, blood volume increases. This is termed **hypervolemia**. The increase in blood volume is a consequence of an increase in both plasma volume and the quantity of red blood cells. Plasma volume changes contribute most to hypervolemia.

Key terms

Cardiac hypertrophy – enlargement of the heart due to increases in muscle mass and/or chamber size.

Systole – the contraction of the heart that forces blood out of the ventricles

Hypervolemia – an increase in blood volume.

Respiratory system adaptations

Pulmonary ventilation

Taking part in regular endurance exercise may reduce your breathing rate and minute ventilation at rest and during submaximal exercise. However, during maximal exercise both of these measures will be higher in trained individuals, resulting in increased pulmonary ventilation. Wilmore, Costill and Kenney (2008) state that in untrained individuals pulmonary ventilation during maximal exercise can increase from 100 litres per minute to 150 litres per minute following a period of endurance training. In elite endurance athletes pulmonary ventilation may reach 180-240 litres per minute (Hoffman, 2002).

Pulmonary diffusion

Pulmonary diffusion is unchanged at rest and during submaximal exercise intensities after a period of training. It does however increase during maximal exercise. After regular training, blood flow from within the pulmonary circuit (heart to the lungs) increases, resulting in a greater volume of blood in the capillaries at the alveoli. As ventilation increases, at the same time there is more air within the lungs. Consequently more alveoli are utilised and greater pulmonary diffusion occurs.

Arterial-venous oxygen difference

Following regular endurance training, the arterial-venous oxygen difference increases. This is a result of less oxygen in the venous blood, as arterial blood oxygen content remains unchanged. Essentially the exercising muscles become better at extracting the oxygen from the blood.

Neuromuscular system

Coordination, recruitment and synchronisation

Training induced improvements in muscular strength and function are initiated firstly by neural adaptations. Through specific strength training, better coordination in the activation of desired muscle fibres can be achieved. This means that the actual muscles needed for an activity are fully activated at the exact time that they are required. Training also enables the recruitment of more motor units. The synchronisation of these motor units is improved through training. Improved sychronisation results in more motor units being activated at any one time, resulting in a greater number of muscle fibres contracting simultaneously.

Hypertrophy

Long term strength training causes an increase in muscle size due to changes in the cross-sectional area. This is called hypertrophy and is a result of structural changes in individual muscle fibres. These changes may include: more myofibrils; more actin and myosin filaments; more sarcoplasm; and more connective tissue (Wilmore, Costill and Kenney, 2008).

Metabolic adaptations

Maximal oxygen consumption (VO$_2$max)

Maximal oxygen consumption (VO$_2$max) is defined as the highest rate of oxygen consumption achieved during maximal exercise (Hoffman, 2002). It is often called aerobic capacity and is considered to be one of the best indicators of endurance performance capacity. Later in this chapter you will find out how to measure it. When an untrained individual completes several weeks of regular endurance training their VO$_2$max will increase. An increase of 15 to 20% would be typical in such an individual (Wilmore, Costill and Kenney, 2008). In highly trained endurance athletes VO$_2$max would typically be between 70 and 85 ml kg^{-1}min^{-1}, with males scoring more highly than females. In 2003, Paula Radcliffe set a new female world marathon record of 2 hours 15 minutes 25 seconds. During the same year she recorded a VO$_2$max of 70 ml kg^{-1} min^{-1} (Jones, 2006), an exceptional value for a female athlete.

Key term

Maximal oxygen consumption (VO$_2$max) – the highest rate of oxygen consumption achieved during maximal exercise

Stop and think

A common adaptation to endurance training is an increase in maximal oxygen consumption. This increase is a consequence of multiple smaller adaptations throughout the body.

What are the specific physiological adaptations that cause maximal oxygen consumption to increase?

Lactate threshold

Lactate threshold (LT) is a physiological measurement related to endurance performance. Blood lactate concentrations reflect the balance between the rate of lactate production and removal. During low to moderate exercise intensities, the energy demands are met sufficiently by the oxidative processes (see *Chapter 3: Exercise physiology*), therefore lactate does not accumulate within the blood. As exercise intensity increases a greater reliance on anaerobic processes is required to supply the energy demands. The point at which the body's energy demand exceeds the supply from the aerobic processes and the muscles rely on the anaerobic processes to supply the energy is termed the **lactate threshold**. Lactate threshold is normally graphically represented and expressed as a point at a given work intensity (i.e. running speed). Figure 4.1 shows a typical lactate threshold graph and how it responds to a period of endurance training. Following endurance training you can exercise at a higher intensity before lactate begins to accumulate. This provides an advantage to endurance performance.

Key term

Lactate threshold – the point at which the body's energy demand exceeds the supply from the aerobic processes and the muscles rely on the anaerobic processes to supply the energy

		Training method	Adaptation
Energy systems	Oxidative Enzymes	Endurance	⇧ Activity
	Anaerobic Enzymes	Sprinting and weightlifting	⇧ Activity
	Fuel Use	Endurance	⇧ Fat Use ⇩ Muscle Glycogen Use
Cardiovascular system	Cardiac size	Endurance	⇧ Muscle Mass ⇧ Left Ventricular Volume
	Stroke volume	Endurance	⇧ at rest and all intensities
	Heart rate	Endurance	⇩ at rest ⇩ at submaximal intensities
	Cardiac output	Endurance	⇧ at maximal intensity
	Blood flow	Endurance	⇧ in flow
	Blood volume	Endurance	⇧ in volume
Respiratory system	Pulmonary ventilation	Endurance	⇩ at rest and submaximal intensities ⇧ at maximal intensity
	Pulmonary diffusion	Endurance	⇧ at maximal intensity
	Arterial-venous oxygen difference	Endurance	⇧ in difference
Neuromuscular system	Coordination	Strength	Improved
	Recruitment	Strength	Improved
	Synchronisation	Strength	Improved
	Muscular hypertrophy	Strength	⇧ in fibre size
Metabolic adaptations	Maximal oxygen consumption	Endurance	⇧ in consumption
	Lactate threshold	Endurance	⇧ in threshold intensity

Table 4.1 Summary of key adaptations to fitness training

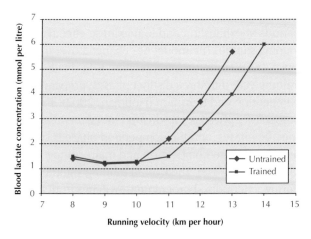

Figure 4.1: Graph representing the change in lactate threshold with running velocity, following a period of endurance training.

Principles of fitness training

The human body has an amazing ability to improve its capabilities when stimulated by correctly applied fitness training. A well designed structured fitness training programme allows athletes to peak for important athletic events, and regular individuals to maintain a level of fitness sufficient for health benefits. For athletic performance, coaches and sport and exercise scientists are constantly striving to find more effective training methods that give their athletes an extra performance advantage. For regular individuals optimal performance is not the goal, but the foundation of training remains similar to those of elite athletes. In all fitness training contexts there are principles which, when applied correctly, assist in achieving performance adaptations. These are the principles of training.

Principles of training

Specificity

Training adaptations are specific to the type of activity performed. Specificity relates to the muscles trained, the energy systems utilised and the intensity of the exercise. In other words specific exercise causes specific adaptations, creating specific training effects (McArdle, Katch and Katch, 2010). When applying this principle to the design of training programmes, activities should be closely associated with the performance goal. For instance,

a cyclist would not spend large amounts of time running. Likewise a marathon runner would not spend large amounts of time cycling. However, there are instances where activities that would appear to not be directly related to the performance activity are beneficial and can be made specific. An example of this is a 100 metre sprinter completing large volumes of strength training. Whilst lifting weights may not be running based, if the muscle groups trained, and the loads and velocities lifted are specific to sprint running, the athlete will achieve beneficial performance adaptations.

Overload

To achieve beneficial adaptations an exercise overload must be applied to the physiological systems. This is a level of exercise above normal. If this is not achieved adaptation will not occur. An appropriate overload for each individual can be achieved by manipulating training frequency, intensity, time and type. These four elements are collectively known as the FITT principles.

Frequency – the number of times the exercise is undertaken per week.

Intensity – how hard the exercise stress is applied.

Time – the duration that the activity is to be performed for.

Type – the mode of exercise to be performed.

Progression

As training progresses, positive adaptations occur within the body systems that alter the relative intensity or volume of training. In order for overload to be maintained the training stimulus needs to be progressed. In simple terms, if the training prescription required completing three sets of 10 press-ups, and this could only just be achieved at the start of the training period, after a period

> **Remember**
>
> Progression must be applied appropriately, as too fast a progression may result in injury or illness.

of time this would become easier due to positive adaptations. Therefore progression is required to maintain the correct training stimulus. It may now be appropriate to complete three sets of 15 press-ups.

Individual differences

The individual differences principle states that participants respond differently to the same training stimulus (Hoffman, 2002). The level of fitness at the start of training is an important consideration, as are the specific goals of the individual. Genetic differences also affect adaptations. In team sports not all positions require the same type or intensity of training. Therefore training adaptations are most likely to be optimised when programmes are designed to meet the individual needs of the participant.

Reversibility

All the positive adaptations achieved through training can be lost should the training stimulus be removed or reduced. If training is completely removed the individual will eventually revert back to their original level of fitness. This is the principle of reversibility and highlights the need for regular training irrespective of the level of performance.

Recovery

This is one of the most important yet most forgotten principles of training. In order for physiological adaptation to occur periods of recovery must be incorporated into a training programme. These should be included within a weekly schedule and throughout the training year. Inadequate recovery increases the risk of injury and illness. Often elite athletes take several weeks' break from serious training at the end of a long competitive season. This allows the body to recuperate from the stress of training and competing and allows the individual to return for the following season physically and mentally refreshed.

Periodisation

In 1965, Matveyev first published evidence of a mode of training that divided the training year into a series of distinct phases. This model has become known as periodisation and is now the favoured model used by coaches and sports scientists in elite

sport. The objective of periodisation is to minimise periods of exhaustion and to maximise effective training stimuli. The model has changed over the years, but a common interpretation is to divide the training year into three distinct phases: preparation, competition and transition (Hoffman, 2002). The preparatory phase is sub-divided into general and specific phases, and the competition phase is sub-divided into pre-competition and main competition phases (Figure 4.2). The overall training stimulus during a periodised programme switches from a high volume–low intensity focus during preparation to a low volume–high intensity emphasis during competition.

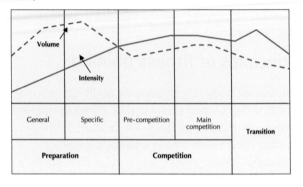

Figure 4.2: Representation of the model of periodisation (adapted from Hoffman, 2002)

- **General preparation** This phase prepares the athlete for intense sport specific training.

- **Specific preparation** This phase builds intensity and makes training more sport specific.

- **Pre-competition** This phase further increases intensity and athletes compete in some minor events to assess the current performance level, focusing the athlete for the main competition.

- **Main competition** This phase allows the athlete to peak for their main competition goal. Training is at its most intense.

- **Transition** This phase allows the athlete to recuperate from a long training and competitive season.

Methods of training

When considering different methods of training you should have a good understanding of the main components of fitness. Each of these components has a different degree of importance depending on the sport or level to be achieved. The main components to consider are:

- **aerobic endurance**
- **anaerobic capacity**
- **speed**
- **strength**
- **power**.

Key terms

Aerobic endurance – the ability of the cardiovascular and respiratory systems to supply the exercising muscles with oxygen over a prolonged period of time

Anaerobic capacity – the ability to sustain very high intensity exercise without the presence of oxygen

Speed – the ability to cover a distance in the shortest possible time

Strength – the ability of a muscle group to exert force to overcome a resistance

Power – the ability to generate muscular strength quickly

Aerobic endurance training

Since aerobic endurance is the ability to sustain long duration exercise it stands to reason that the best method to enhance this fitness component is to complete exercise that is of long duration. This type of training is of great importance to distance runners, cyclists and swimmers. However, it is also an important aspect of games based sports, such as football and rugby. The major physiological adaptations that this form of training aims to improve are maximal oxygen uptake (VO_2max) and lactate threshold. The two most common methods to develop aerobic endurance are long slow distance training and interval training.

Long slow distance (LSD)

Long slow distance (LSD) training usually accounts for the largest volume of any endurance training programme. Typically an LSD training session will last for 60 to 120 minutes at an intensity of 60 to 70 per cent VO_2max. It is common to use heart rate as a simple guide for exercise intensity. An exercising

heart rate of 60 to 80 per cent of maximum heart rate (HRmax) or target heart rate calculated from heart rate reserve (HRR) is normally prescribed for LSD training.

Interval training

Interval training is a form of aerobic endurance training that manipulates the intensity and duration of work periods. They are structured sessions that involve a work period of high intensity followed by a recovery period. The recovery period is often active at considerably lower intensity than the work period but should not exceed the duration of the work period. Several repeats of the desired work period to recovery period are completed. An example of a running interval session would be:

- five repeats of four minutes at 85 per cent HRR (work period) followed by two minutes at 50 per cent HRR (recovery period).

Calculations for heart rate training intensity

Maximum heart rate (HRmax) = 220 – age

Heart rate reserve (HRR) = HRmax – resting heart rate (RHR)

Target heart rate = (HRR x training intensity %) + RHR

For example, prescribing exercise at a target heart rate of 70 per cent for a 20 year old with a resting heart rate of 60 beats per minute would be calculated thus:

HRmax = 200 beats per minute

HRR = 200 beats per minute – 60 beats per minute

HRR = 140 beats per minute

For a target heart rate (THR) of 70 per cent

THR = (HRR x training intensity %) + RHR

THR = (140 beats per minute x 0.7) + 60 beats per minute

THR = 158 beats per minute

Anaerobic capacity training

Adaptations that benefit anaerobic performance are only stimulated during high intensity exercise (more than 90 per cent VO$_2$max). The aim of this type of training is to stress the anaerobic energy systems in a way that facilitates improvements in their efficiency. It is common practice to design training around an interval concept where an intense exercise period is followed by a resting recovery period. As the intensity of such training is high and fatigue may be severe, the exercise periods are short and recovery periods will be relatively long. The exercise duration is determined by the demand of the athlete's event. For example, a 100 metre sprinter will complete repetitions of 10 to 15 seconds, whilst a 400 metre sprinter will complete repetitions of 60 to 80 seconds. A typical training session for each of these athletes may be:

- 100 metre sprinter – 10 repetitions of 100 metres with 3 minute rest periods

- 400 metre sprinter – 6 repetitions of 500 metres with 3 minute rest periods

Development of speed

For many running based sports speed is an important fitness component. Whilst excellent overall speed is important the ability to accelerate quickly is crucial. For a 100 metre sprinter accelerating out of the starting blocks is critical, as is the ability of footballers to quickly change speed when running with the ball. Running speed is determined by stride rate and stride length, therefore the goal of speed training is to increase either, or both, of these two elements. Both of these elements can be enhanced by performing drills that improve coordination and speed of foot movement. Such training includes ladder drills and low hurdles.

Whilst sprinting over specific distances (5–40 metres) improves speed there are other elements of training that also develop speed. There is a relationship between speed, strength and power. If an improvement in strength and power of specific sprinting muscles (quadriceps, hamstrings, glutes and calves) can be achieved sprinting speed will also increase. Consequently effective speed training often involves sprinting with additional resistance. Such training includes parachute runs, tyre pulling and hill sprinting. The key with all speed training is that all repetitions should be short in duration and performed at maximum effort.

Parachute running

Ladder drills

Resistance training for strength

Resistance training can be confusing. There are many different resistance training techniques and methods. All have one thing in common – stressing skeletal muscles to overcome resistances to facilitate adaptation in the individual muscle fibres.

In order for strength to be developed, the resistance must be greater than that which the muscles can comfortably cope with. To achieve this overload it is common to manipulate: exercise selection and order; exercise intensity; length of rest periods; number of repetitions and sets; training frequency. Table 4.2 details a typical general resistance training session. Two commonly used methods for strength training are resistance machines and free weights.

- **Resistance machines** have fixed weights that can be selected depending on the goals of the programme. They are an excellent introduction to resistance training due to their relative safety, but they do limit the exercises that can be performed.

- **Free weights** are an advanced resistance training technique and require special instruction in their use. There is a greater risk of injury when using free weights, such as barbells and dumbbells. Free weights allow a greater selection of exercises to be used and exercises can be tailored to be specific to the movement patterns and speeds of sports. Therefore it is common for elite athletes to incorporate free weight resistance training as part of their programmes.

Plyometric training for power

Plyometric training involves exercises that stretch the muscle and then rapidly contract the same muscle to accelerate the body (Hoffman, 2002). An example is a countermovement jump, where the legs bend (stretching the quadriceps) and then rapidly straighten (quadriceps contracting), propelling the body into the air. Because plyometric exercises are performed with maximum force muscle contractions at high speed, they facilitate the development of power. During the stretch phase of the activity the muscles **contract eccentrically** before powerfully **concentrically contracting**. This process triggers a **stretch reflex** that prevents muscle damage and stimulates maximum force development. Any sports that involve explosive activity, such as high jumping and football, benefit from performing plyometric training.

During plyometric training, the activities usually involve maximal muscle contractions to overcome the athlete's body weight. The intensity is high and there is a greater risk of injury, therefore prior experience of strength training is recommended. For best results the exercises selected should be specific to the athlete's sport. There are many different plyometric exercises and Table 4.3 describes several common ones.

Key terms

Eccentric contraction – muscle is lengthening whilst producing force

Concentric contraction – muscle is shortening whilst producing force

Stretch reflex – an automatic response to a sudden stretching of a muscle

Table 4.2: An example of a typical resistance training session aimed at improving general body strength. Note: 1RM (Repetition Maximum) is the greatest load that an individual can lift for one repetition.

Exercise	Load	No. of repetitions	No. of sets	Rest period between sets
Squats	75% 1RM	8–10	3	90–120 seconds
Leg extensions	75% 1RM	8–10	3	90–120 seconds
Leg curls	75% 1RM	8–10	3	90–120 seconds
Lat pulldowns	75% 1RM	8–10	3	90–120 seconds
Bench press	75% 1RM	8–10	3	90–120 seconds
Shoulder press	75% 1RM	8–10	3	90–120 seconds
Bicep curl	75% 1RM	8–10	3	90–120 seconds
Triceps curl	75% 1RM	8–10	3	90–120 seconds

Table 4.3: Several common plyometric exercises used to develop power (adapted from Hoffman, 2002)

Exercise	Starting position	Action
Standing long jump	Stand with feet shoulder width apart, knees slightly bent	Jump as far forward as possible, utilising a double arm swing and a countermovement with the legs
Squat jump	Stand with feet shoulder width apart, knees slightly bent, hands on hips	Use a countermovement to jump as high as possible without moving hands
Depth jump	Stand on a box 30–60 cm high with toes at the edge of the box and feet shoulder width apart	Step from the box and drop to the ground landing on both feet. As soon as feet make ground contact jump as high as possible. Aim to be in contact with the ground for the shortest possible time
Bounding	Stand with one foot slightly in front of the other with arms at sides	Push off the front leg and drive the knee up and out aiming for maximum height and distance. Use an alternate arm swing for balance and power. Land on the other foot and repeat the action
Medicine ball throw	Stand with feet shoulder width apart, knees slightly bent and a medicine ball overhead	Step forward and throw ball with both arms as far as possible

Fitness testing

Fundamental principles of fitness testing

One of the key roles of sport and exercise scientists is to conduct fitness tests. The results from the tests can be used in different ways. Common uses include:

- identification of strengths and weaknesses in athletic performance
- monitor progress of training to help coaches adapt training programmes
- provide feedback to athletes to aid motivation
- educate coaches and athletes about their respective sport
- predict performance potential to help select individuals for specific sports.

There are numerous tests for each component of fitness and test selection is an important issue. Common fitness tests for key fitness components are shown in Table 4.4. When considering the most appropriate test you need to follow some guiding principles. These principles are:

- relevance – athletes need to see the relevance of the test to their sport
- specificity – tests should assess specific muscle groups, movements and energy systems of the athlete's sport
- validity – tests should measure the fitness component that you are trying to measure. The results obtained should be a true measure of what you are attempting to measure
- reliability – results should be consistent and repeatable. You should be able to carry out the same test method and achieve the same result.

Table 4.4: Common fitness tests for each component of fitness

Fitness component	Fitness test
Aerobic endurance	Maximal graded exercise test Multi-stage fitness test (MSFT)
Anaerobic capacity	Wingate cycle test Repeated 30 metre sprint running test
Speed	10 and 30 metre sprint test
Strength	1 repetition maximum
Power	Vertical jump test

Testing aerobic endurance

Maximal graded exercise test

To accurately measure aerobic endurance it is necessary to conduct a maximal graded exercise test conducted within a sports science laboratory. This test is a **direct method** of assessing VO_2max because it requires expired gas from the participant to be collected and analysed. To achieve the highest possible score the exercise mode should activate the largest total muscle mass. Therefore running on a treadmill or cycling is the preferred choice, although the ergometry selection will depend on the participant being tested. For instance a rower would be tested on a rowing ergometer as this is specific to their discipline.

The test consists of increments of exercise (usually 3 minutes) that progressively increase intensity until the participant has reached volitional exhaustion and cannot continue exercising. At the end of each exercise increment expired air is collected into a Douglas Bag (large airtight heavy duty plastic bag), and used to calculate oxygen consumption.

Participating in a maximal oxygen consumption test

The highest recorded oxygen consumption value, usually at the end of exercise, is called Maximal Oxygen Consumption (VO_2max).

Multi-stage fitness test (MSFT)

The MSFT is an **indirect predictive method** of measuring aerobic endurance (VO_2max). It is indirect because it does not actually require the measurement of expired gases for the calculation of VO_2max. It involves participants running shuttles back and forth over a 20 metre distance to the bleeps of a pre-recorded signal. The objective is for participants to reach the 20 metre line and turn to complete the next shuttle just as the bleep sounds. Participants should not get ahead of the bleeps. As the test progresses the time between bleeps is reduced and participants have to run faster to keep pace. The test ends when the participant fails to reach the 20 metre line on three consecutive occasions; this point should coincide with the participant being physically exhausted. The level and number of shuttles completed is used to predict VO_2max (Table 4.5).

> ### Key terms
>
> **Direct method** – a term used when a test does measure the desired variable
>
> **Indirect predictive method** – a term used when a test does not actually measure the desired variable but measures another variable which is used to predict the desired variable

Table 4.5: Predicted VO_2max scores for the multi-stage fitness test

Level	Shuttle	VO_2 max	Level	Shuttle	VO_2 max	Level	Shuttle	VO_2 max	Level	Shuttle	VO_2 max
4	2	26.8	10	2	47.4	15	2	64.6	19	2	78.3
4	4	27.6	10	4	48.0	15	4	65.1	19	4	78.8
4	6	28.3	10	6	48.7	15	6	65.6	19	6	79.2
4	9	29.5	10	8	49.3	15	8	66.2	19	8	79.7
5	2	30.2	10	11	50.2	15	10	66.7	19	10	80.2
5	4	31.0	11	2	50.8	15	13	67.5	19	12	80.6
5	6	31.8	11	4	51.4	16	2	68.0	19	15	81.3
5	9	32.9	11	6	51.9	16	4	68.5	20	2	81.8
6	2	33.6	11	8	52.5	16	6	69.0	20	4	82.2
6	4	34.3	11	10	53.1	16	8	69.5	20	6	82.6
6	6	35.0	11	12	53.7	16	10	69.9	20	8	83.0
6	8	35.7	12	2	54.3	16	12	70.5	20	10	83.5
6	10	36.4	12	4	54.8	16	14	70.9	20	12	83.9
7	2	37.1	12	6	55.4	17	2	71.4	20	14	84.3
7	4	37.8	12	8	56.0	17	4	71.9	20	16	84.8
7	6	38.5	12	10	56.5	17	6	72.4	21	2	85.2
7	8	39.2	12	12	57.1	17	8	72.9	21	4	85.6
7	10	39.9	13	2	57.6	17	10	73.4	21	6	86.1
8	2	40.5	13	4	58.2	17	12	73.9	21	8	86.5
8	4	41.1	13	6	58.7	17	14	74.4	21	10	86.9
8	6	41.8	13	8	59.3	18	2	74.8	21	12	87.4
8	8	42.4	13	10	59.8	18	4	75.3	21	14	87.8
8	11	43.3	13	13	60.6	18	6	75.8	21	16	88.2
9	2	43.9	14	2	61.1	18	8	76.2			
9	4	44.5	14	4	61.7	18	10	76.7			
9	6	45.2	14	6	62.2	18	12	77.2			
9	8	45.8	14	8	62.7	18	15	77.9			
9	11	46.8	14	10	63.2						
			14	13	64.0						

Testing anaerobic capacity

Wingate test

The Wingate cycle test assesses anaerobic power of the leg muscles using a 30 second all-out supra-maximal sprint on a mechanically braked cycle ergometer. The exercise load is calculated using the participant's body mass (0.075 kg per kg body mass). Following a comprehensive warm-up the participant begins pedalling at maximal velocity. As soon as pedalling starts the load is applied to the flywheel and the participant continues to pedal as fast as they can for 30 seconds. For best results it is important to motivate the participant during the test. This is an extremely stressful test for the participant, with a high risk of fainting or sickness; therefore it should not be conducted unless medical supervision is close by. Computer software is readily available to help control the test and calculate results. At the end of the test peak power output, average power output and fatigue index can be calculated.

- **Peak power output (Watts)** is the highest mechanical power generated during the test. It represents the energy generating capacity of the ATP-PCr energy system (McArdle, Katch and Katch, 2010).

- **Average power output (Watts)** is the mean power generated during the total 30 second period. It represents the energy generating capacity of the anaerobic glycolytic energy system.

- **Fatigue index (%)** is the decline in power output from the peak power output to the final power output at the end of 30 seconds. Fatigue index is calculated as:

Fatigue index (%) = (peak power output – final power output) / peak power output x 100

The objective of the test is to score the highest peak power output and to have a low fatigue index.

Repeated 30 metre sprint running test

This is an excellent test for assessing anaerobic capacity in games based sports. Participants complete seven maximal sprints over a distance of 30 metres with a rest period of 25 seconds between each repetition. Each sprint is timed to the nearest 0.01 second using electronic timing gates. For increased reliability the running surface should be non-slip and environmental conditions must be considered. At the end of the test a graph is plotted to show the time of each of the seven repetitions. It is expected that participants will slow during the test; the lower the drop in speed the better the participant's anaerobic capacity.

Testing speed

10 and 30 metre sprint running test

For many games based sports maximal sprinting speed and fast acceleration are critical for successful performance. Most games based sports do not require maximal sprinting over distances greater than 30 metres, but do require many short sprints under 20 metres. Therefore assessing speed over distances greater than 30 metres is generally not required. For completion of the sprint running test a straight line course of 30 metres is measured. Electronic timing gates are located at 10 metres to measure a split time, and 30 metres to measure total time. The participant starts when they are ready and runs at maximal speed through the two timing gates. Three repetitions are completed with a 3–5 minute recovery period between. For analysis of the results the best recorded 10 metre and 30 metre time is used. The best times do not need to be from the same repetition. The 30 metre time is used to calculate running velocity and the 10 metre time is used to calculate acceleration.

Velocity (metres per second) = distance covered (metres) / time taken (seconds)

Acceleration (metres per second^{-2}) = change in velocity (metres per second) / time taken (seconds)

Testing strength

1 repetition maximum (1RM)

The 1RM strength test can be used to assess strength of any muscle group but it is advised that the chosen exercise should be specific to the muscle activity of the participant's sport. To achieve the most accurate score it is better to use free weights as these enable small increments of weight to be added to the bar after each successful lift.

1. Following a warm-up a comfortable weight is chosen to begin the test.

2. Complete one repetition of the weight and record the weight lifted.

3. Between each lift the participant should rest for 2 minutes.

4. Add 2–5 kilograms of weight to the bar after each successful lift.

5. Continue this process until the participant fails to successfully lift the weight.

6. It is important that correct lifting technique is used for each repetition. If technique fails the lift is deemed to be unsuccessful.

7. The highest weight successfully lifted is considered to be the 1RM.

The 1RM score can be recorded as an absolute score in kilograms, which is then used to calculate training loads, or it can be used to calculate weight lifted relative to body mass by dividing the 1RM score by body mass (kg).

Testing power

Vertical jump test

Jump testing is used to assess lower body muscular power. The test does not directly measure power; instead it predicts muscular power from maximum jump height.

1. Following a warm up the participant stands side on to a wall.

2. Keeping their feet flat on the ground they reach up with their closest hand to touch the wall. This height is marked (chalk on the fingertip works well) and is termed standing reach height.

3. They step away from the wall and using a maximal effort countermovement jump, propel themselves upwards and reach their arms upwards.

4. At the highest point of the jump they should touch the wall and leave a mark.

5. The difference between the standing reach height and the jump height is measured and is recorded.

6. Three attempts are completed with a rest period of 2 to 3 minutes between each; the best score is used for analysis.

Once vertical jump height has been established, peak power and average power can be calculated using established equations from Johnson and Bahamonde (1996).

- Peak power (W) = 78.6 × jump height (cm) + 60.3 × mass (kg) −15.3 × height (cm) − -1308

- Average power (W) = 43.8 × jump height (cm) + 32.7 × mass (kg) −16.8 × height (cm) + 431

Case study (for recommended answers, see www.pearsonfe.co.uk/foundationsinsport)

Harry Bowe was recently appointed as the director of sports science at a second tier rugby league club. The previous season the club achieved some promising results but ended up finishing just outside the promotion places in the league. The club has ambitions to gain promotion in the coming season and has given him responsibility for designing the training and improving the fitness of the players. It was evident last season that the team conceded vital points in the last 10 minutes of several key matches, which ultimately cost them a promotion place.

1. What do you think were the reasons for the team conceding points late in matches?

2. How should Harry apply the model of periodisation to the training year?

3. What fitness testing will Harry conduct?

4. How will the results from the fitness tests be used when designing training programmes?

Check your understanding (for answers, see www.pearsonfe.co.uk/foundationsinsport)

1. What adaptations within the energy systems cause more efficient resynthesis of ATP?

2. Why does endurance training result in a greater utilisation of fat as a fuel source?

3. Briefly describe the mechanisms that result in an increase in cardiac output following a period of endurance training.

4. Why are respiratory system training adaptations most evident at maximal intensity?

5. How do the principles of overload and progression interact to provide effective training stimuli?

6. Describe the differences in the phases of the periodised training year.

7. Calculate a target heart rate of 70–80 per cent for a female cyclist aged 30 years with a resting heart rate of 45 beats per minute.

8. Why is it common practice to test fitness in a group of athletes?

9. During a Wingate test a sprint cyclist scored a peak power output of 1250 W. At the end of the 30 second test their power output was 725 W. Calculate their fatigue index.

10. What is the relative 1RM score for a 95.5 kg male sprinter who successfully lifted 152.5 kg during a squat test?

Time to reflect

1. Consider the adaptations that occur as a result of endurance training within the cardiovascular and respiratory systems. Think about how they contribute to an improvement in endurance performance.

2. Consider your own exercise training and reflect upon whether you apply the principles of training appropriately. Think of some specific examples of your own good practice.

3. As the sports scientist at a professional football club, you have been tasked with designing an individual training programme for a central midfield player who is returning from a long term knee injury. Consider what training methods you would include within the training programme. Think about some specific examples of training sessions.

4. You are currently working with a basketball team and have identified that the players need to improve their fitness. Devise a fitness testing programme that can be administered in an efficient and timely manner. Think about the principles of fitness testing and how best to apply them. How would you report the results to the coach and players?

Useful resources

To obtain a secure link to the websites below, see the Websites section on page ii or visit the companion website at www.pearsonfe.co.uk/foundationsinsport

- American College of Sports Medicine
- British Association of Sport and Exercise Science
- British Journal of Sports Medicine
- English Institute of Sport
- Journal of Applied Physiology
- Journal of Sport Sciences
- Medicine in Sport and Exercise Science

Further reading

Astrand, P.O., Rodahl, K., Dahl, H.A. and Stromme, S.B. (2003). *Textbook of Work Physiology; Physiological Bases of Exercise,* 4th Edition. Champaign, Illinois: Human Kinetics.

Australian Sports Commission (2000). *Physiological Tests for Elite Athletes.* Champaign, Illinois: Human Kinetics.

BASES (2007). *British Association of Sport and Exercise Sciences Physiological Testing Guidelines, Volume 1: Sports Testing.* Leeds: Routledge.

Hoffman, J. (2002). *Physiological Aspects of Sport Training and Performance.* Champaign, Illinois: Human Kinetics.

Johnson, D.L. and Bahamonde, R. (1996). Power Output Estimate in University Athletes. *Journal of Strength and Conditioning Research,* 10(3), pp.161–166.

Jones, A.M. (2006) The physiology of the world record holder for the women's marathon. *International Journal of Sports Science and Coaching,* 1, (2), pp. 101–116.

Marieb, E.N. and Hoehn, K. (2010). *Human Anatomy and Physiology,* 8th Edition. San Francisco: Pearson Benjamin Cummings.

Martini, F.H. and Nath, J.L. (2009). *Fundamentals of Anatomy and Physiology,* 8th Edition. Pearson Benjamin Cummings.

McArdle, W.D., Katch, F.I. and Katch, V.L. (2010). *Exercise Physiology: Nutrition Energy and Human Performance,* 7th Edition. Philadelphia: Lippincott, Williams & Wilkins.

Mujika, I. (2009). *Tapering and Peaking for Optimal Performance.* Champaign, Illinois: Human Kinetics.

Powers, S.K. and Howley, E.T. (2009). *Exercise Physiology; Theory and Application to Fitness and Performance,* 7th Edition. New York: McGraw Hill.

Sewell, D., Watkins, P., and Griffin, M. (2005). *Sport and Exercise Science: An Introduction.* London: Hodder Arnold.

Stanfield, C.L. (2011) *Principles of Human Physiology,* 4th Edition. Pearson Benjamin Cummings

Whyte, G. (2006). *Advances in Sport and Exercise Science Series: The Physiology of Training.* Philadelphia: Churchill Livingstone Elsevier.

Wilmore, J.H., Costill, D.L. and Kenney, W.L. (2008). *Physiology of Sport and Exercise,* 4th Edition. Champaign, Illinois: Human Kinetics.

Winter, E.M. et al. (2007). *Sport & Exercise Physiology Testing Guidelines: Volume 1 Sports Testing.* Leeds: Routledge.

Chapter 5

Nutrition for health and performance

Nutrition is an area in which new discoveries are constantly being made. All physical activity stimulates the body's need for fuel and fluid and sound nutritional practices are important to optimise performance. This is particularly true for those with heavy training and competition loads where poor nutritional planning and preparation might mean the difference between winning and losing or preventing injury and illness.

Good nutritional practices seem simple in theory, but are often difficult to put into day to day practice. Nutritional topics feature almost daily in our newspapers, magazines, TV programmes and advertising, whilst the Internet has become another avenue to promote the latest nutritional supplements and fad diets. Healthy eating and good nutritional practices for sport, along with fitness, rose to prominence in the 1980s. With the continued focus on the role of nutrition in relation to health and exercise performance, accurate advice and information must be available. Often misinterpretation or misleading representation of scientific studies confuses rather than enlightens our understanding of nutrition in practice.

Exercise has a major role to play in disease prevention, and the contribution that diet can have to health and the prevention of disease is equally well recognised. It is important to note that there should be no conflict between eating for health and eating for performance in sport. The foundations of performance nutrition for sport lie in a sound healthy eating approach.

Learning outcomes

After you have read this chapter you should be able to:

After reading this chapter you should have a greater understanding of the relationship between nutrition, health and exercise and be able to describe, understand and begin to analyse the following key principles and concepts in nutrition in the context of sport and exercise:

- the importance of a balanced and varied diet
- dietary reference values, healthy eating principles and the UK National Food Guide
- basic dietary assessment methods
- performance nutrition strategies.

As a **sport and exercise nutrition** professional there are many potential benefits and dangers of providing dietary advice to athletes and coaches. You have been appointed as the performance nutritionist to a professional rugby union team. Consider your role in providing dietary advice to the team. What factors might affect food intake and choice for the players you are working with?

An awareness of these factors when working with athletes and coaches will assist you in formulating and negotiating realistic and achievable dietary goals.

The importance of a balanced and varied diet

Healthy eating is a concept frequently referred to, but there are different ideas about how to put this into practice. For some this might mean calorie counting, for others it is being vegetarian, whilst many probably view it as boring or monotonous and too difficult to achieve on a day to day basis.

Put simply, healthy eating involves choosing the right foods in the right balance to provide all the

Consider the physiological demands of rugby union and how these impact on nutritional requirements of players.

essential nutrients and energy required to maintain optimal health. Healthy eating principles aim to reduce the risk of chronic disease such as coronary heart disease, obesity, type II diabetes and cancer, but following these principles will also benefit performance in sport and exercise.

Typically people will classify foods as good or bad, healthy or unhealthy, with many viewing healthy

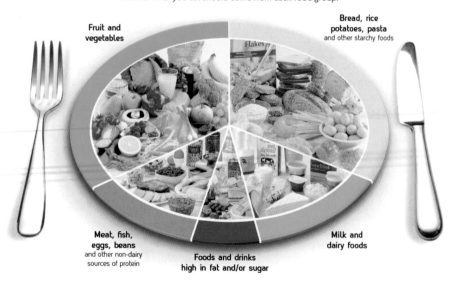

Figure 5.1: The eatwell plate

eating as somewhat of a hardship. The important message is that there are no good or bad foods only good and bad uses of food, and it is better to look at the overall balance of food choices in the **diet** as either healthy or unhealthy.

Key terms

Nutrition – the process by which chemicals from our environment are taken up by the body to provide the energy and nutrients needed to sustain life and maintain health

Sports nutrition – the influence of nutrition on human performance during the preparation for, participation in and the recovery from sport and exercise

Diet – a particular pattern of eating habits or food consumption

The Eatwell Plate, currently promoted by the Food Standards Agency, has been adopted as the UK's National Food Guide. It was devised as a way of helping people to understand and enjoy healthy eating. It attempts to make implementation easier by identifying the types and proportions of food groups required to achieve a healthy, balanced and varied diet. This model applies to most people, including those engaging in regular physical activity and sport. It does not however apply to very young children.

The key messages of this model are to enjoy food and:

- base meals on starchy foods
- eat lots of fruit and vegetables, at least five servings a day
- eat more fish, at least two portions per week, one to include oily fish
- cut down on fat, particularly saturated fat, and sugar
- eat less salt – no more than 6 g a day for adults
- maintain a healthy body weight and get active
- drink plenty of fluids especially water
- avoid skipping breakfast.

Remember

A balanced diet provides the correct amounts of all nutrients without excess or deficiency. When trying to adopt this approach it is best not to view foods as either good or bad, but that we can make good and bad uses of food.

Dietary reference values, healthy eating principles and the UK National Food Guide

In 1987 the Government set up a panel of experts to review the 1979 Recommended Daily Amounts (RDAs) for nutrients and new Dietary Reference Values (DRVs) were established, (Committee on Medical Aspects of Food Policy (DH) (1991). The phrase 'dietary reference value' is a general term applied to any of the following:

Reference Nutrient Intake (RNI): the amount of a nutrient (excluding energy) which is sufficient for almost any individual. (This level of intake is usually above that which most people need, and individuals meeting this value of intake for any nutrient are unlikely to be deficient.) RNI figures are most similar to the old RDA figures and are those that will be most generally used in nutritional assessment to determine adequacy of intake.

Estimated Average Requirement (EAR): is an assessment of the average requirement for food energy or nutrients. Many individuals will require more than the EAR and many will require less. The EAR is the value most used when assessing energy requirements.

Lower Reference Nutrient Intake (LRNI): is the amount of a nutrient thought to be sufficient to meet the needs of a small number of the population who have low requirements. The vast majority of individuals will require much more than the LRNI. If individuals are consistently eating less than the LRNI for any particular nutrient they may be at risk of deficiency of that nutrient.

Safe Intakes (SI): indicate the intake of a nutrient where there is insufficient information to estimate the distribution of requirements within a population. It represents an intake thought to be adequate to meet the needs of most but not too high as to cause undesirable effects on health.

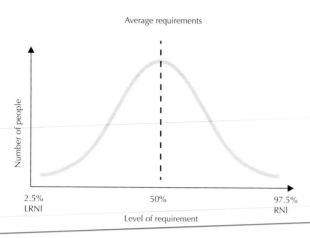

Figure 5.2: Dietary Reference Values

Take it further

To find out more about Dietary Reference Values, take a look at the Department of Health's *Report on Health and Social Subjects 41: Dietary Reference Values for Food Energy and Nutrients for the United Kingdom*, HMSO, 1991.

Macronutrients

Carbohydrate, protein and fat are energy providing nutrients. Required in the diet in relatively large amounts they are referred to as **macronutrients**.

Carbohydrates

Carbohydrates are composed of the chemical elements carbon, hydrogen and oxygen and play a principal role in energy production. One gram of carbohydrate will provide 4 calories of energy. Viewed traditionally, there are two basic types – simple and complex. Simple carbohydrates are formed from single and double sugar units. They are easy to digest and absorb and provide a quick energy source. Complex carbohydrates are composed of many sugar units. These break down more slowly and provide sustained energy for longer periods.

The basic unit of a carbohydrate is the **monosaccharide**, the most common of which in the diet is glucose. Other monosaccharides include fructose and galactose. Monosaccharides are usually found combined together in foods. When two monosaccharides join together they form a

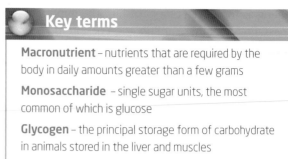

Key terms

Macronutrient – nutrients that are required by the body in daily amounts greater than a few grams

Monosaccharide – single sugar units, the most common of which is glucose

Glycogen – the principal storage form of carbohydrate in animals stored in the liver and muscles

disaccharide. The most common disaccharide in the diet is sucrose, better known as table sugar. Longer chains of monosaccharides, known as polysaccharides, allow large quantities of glucose to be stored in the cells of plants as starch, or in animals as **glycogen**.

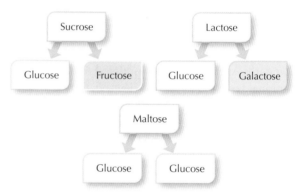

Figure 5.3: Disaccharides and monosaccharides

Carbohydrate is stored in the liver and muscles as glycogen, but only in limited amounts, approximately 375–475 g. During activity glycogen is broken down into glucose to supply the muscles with energy. The intensity and duration of the activity are linked to glycogen availability. When glycogen stores are depleted there is less available energy to continue exercising and fatigue or a drop in intensity will occur. Full glycogen stores at the start of exercise will delay the onset of fatigue.

Current healthy eating recommendations from the Department of Health (1991) suggest carbohydrates should form around 50 per cent of our total daily calories, focusing on the starchy sources to provide the bulk of this. To support sports performance higher levels of intake are required with recommendations between 60–70 per cent of total daily calorie intake dependent on the sport and training load.

Table 5.1: Simple and complex carbohydrates

High carbohydrate foods	
Complex	**Simple**
bread, bagels, flour, crispbreads, crackers, rice cakes, rice, pasta, potatoes, polenta, couscous, noodles, breakfast cereals, pulses, root vegetables	sugar, syrup, jam, marmalade, honey, sugary fizzy drinks and squashes, fruit juice, sweets, fudge, sports drink, energy bars and gels

Below is a simple guide to daily carbohydrate (CHO) requirements based on level of physical activity and training:

Sedentary   3–4 g CHO / kg body weight

Light   < 1hr   4–5 g CHO / kg body weight

Moderate   1–2hrs   6–7 g CHO / kg body weight

Heavy   > 3hrs   8–10 g CHO / kg body weight

Putting it into practice

Someone who is sedentary is likely to have a requirement of 4 g CHO/kg body weight, a recreational gym user working out twice a week 5 g CHO/kg body weight, a footballer training most days of the week 6-7 g CHO/kg body weight and a marathon runner 8-10 g CHO/kg body weight. In exceptional circumstances it has been known for intake to exceed 12 g CHO/kg body weight, such as mountaineers climbing Mount Everest.

Whether eating for health or performance, the best approach to achieving an adequate carbohydrate intake is to eat at regular intervals and ensure that all your meals and snacks are centred around starchy carbohydrate foods. People with high carbohydrate requirements may need to eat more frequent meals and snacks or rely on a greater intake of simple carbohydrates to achieve their requirements. Where greater intakes of simple carbohydrates are necessary to assist in meeting energy and carbohydrate requirements, care should be taken that the over-consumption of sweet foods, often referred to as 'empty calories' because they provide few other nutrients, does not displace more nutrient-dense sources of carbohydrate in the diet.

Glycaemic Index

The **Glycaemic Index** (GI) is a classification system for carbohydrate foods based on the blood glucose response they elicit. As discussed carbohydrate foods are traditionally classified as 'simple' or 'complex' based on their chemical composition, but many foods contain a mixture of complex and simple carbohydrate and do not fit into these traditional categories, such as bananas or cereal bars.

Up to recently it had been assumed that the chemical composition of carbohydrate foods dictates the blood glucose and insulin response when these foods are eaten. Recent research has shown that this simplistic approach is not exact, in that every individual food elicits its own effect on blood glucose separately and unpredictably from its chemical composition.

The GI was devised as an attempt at a more accurate classification system to define carbohydrate foods according to their effect on blood glucose. It is a ranking of foods based upon their effect on blood glucose levels compared to a standard reference food of either glucose or white bread. Development of the GI has shown that it is possible to have both 'simple' and 'complex' carbohydrates that are easily digested and absorbed by the body, and therefore have a high GI. Similarly there are 'simple' and 'complex' carbohydrate foods that are more slowly absorbed and therefore have a low GI. Foods can be grouped into categories of high, moderate or low gylcaemic index.

Key term

Glycaemic Index (GI) – classification system for carbohydrate foods based on the blood glucose response they elicit

Table 5.2: Glycaemic index of common carbohydrate foods

High glycaemic	Moderate glycaemic	Low glycaemic
sucrose	pasta	baked beans
honey	noodles	lentils
bread	porridge oats	soya beans
bagel	plain biscuits	kidney beans
rice	grapes	milk
potato	oranges	yogurt
Weetabix	potato crisps	ice cream
Cornflakes	chocolate	grapefruit
Lucozade	orange juice	apple
fizzy drinks	peanuts	figs
banana	shortbread	plums
raisins	Mars bar	dried apricot
jelly beans	fruit squash	peanuts

Glycaemic index and exercise performance

The specific areas that have been investigated relate to carbohydrate intake before, during and after exercise. It had been proposed that lower GI foods consumed before exercise minimised the decline in blood glucose concentration at the start of exercise and have the potential to increase endurance time. However, recent research has shown no difference in performance when either high or low GI foods were consumed three hours prior to exercise. However, high GI foods in either liquid or solid form taken after exercise in the recovery period will facilitate greater muscle glycogen resynthesis and therefore more effective recovery.

Proteins

Proteins are essential to support life. They are composed of the chemical elements carbon, hydrogen, oxygen and nitrogen. Some also contain minerals such as zinc, sulphur, iron or potassium.

Amino acids represent the simpler units that make up proteins, and it is to these units that they are broken down and digested within the gut. There are 20 known amino acids. Different proteins contain different numbers and combinations of these amino acids. Amino acids are classified as either essential or non-essential depending on whether the body is able to manufacture them or not. There are eight amino acids which the body is unable to make for itself. These are termed **essential amino acids**. By essential it is meant that they are a necessary part

of the diet. The remaining amino acids are termed non-essential and by this it is meant that the body is able to synthesise these, and they are therefore not an essential component of the diet.

The primary function of protein is building and repairing body tissue. It can also be used as a secondary source of energy when carbohydrate and fat supplies are limited, and as such proteins have an energy value of 4 calories per gram. A constant daily supply is required in the diet as the body is unable to store excess protein. However, when protein intake exceeds requirements, the excess amino acids are broken down, the nitrogen element is excreted and the rest of the molecule is used to provide energy immediately or is converted to fat or carbohydrate and stored. Protein foods, like carbohydrate foods, can be classified into two groups, and the value of foods for meeting protein needs is determined by their composition of essential amino acids. Foods containing all essential amino acids are considered to have a high biological value and may be termed first class or complete proteins. These tend to be animal foods, but also include soya. Foods limited in their supply of one or more of the essential amino acids are considered to have a low biological value and may be termed second class or incomplete proteins, these are of vegetable origin.

> **Key term**
>
> **Essential amino acids** – amino acids that must be obtained from the diet and cannot be synthesised by the body

Table 5.3: Protein foods

Protein foods	
High biological value	**Low biological value**
meat, poultry, offal, fish, eggs, milk, cheese, yogurt, soya	cereals, bread, rice, pasta, pulses, peas, beans, lentils, nuts, seeds

When protein foods are eaten they are broken down to the constituent amino acids during **digestion**, **absorbed** and then reformed into the proteins required by your body. Evidence suggests that protein breakdown increases during and immediately after exercise. The longer the duration of exercise the greater the protein breakdown; the more intense the activity the greater the protein breakdown. However, getting enough energy is the body's priority. In general protein intake is related to total energy intake. If someone is eating enough food to satisfy their energy needs, the chances are that their protein needs will be met automatically.

To meet healthy eating and sports performance recommendations, protein intake should fall between 10–15 per cent of total daily calorie intake. A simple guide to daily protein (PRO) requirements based on body weight and level of physical activity and training is shown below:

normal	0.75–1.0 g PRO / kg body weight
endurance activity	1-2–1.4 g PRO / kg body weight
strength activity	1.2–1.7 g PRO / kg body weight
maximum	2 g PRO / kg body weight

Fats

Fats are composed of the chemical elements carbon, hydrogen and oxygen, the same elements as carbohydrates, but they are present in different proportions. The primary function of fat in the diet is to provide an energy source. The basic component is the triglyceride, which consists of a glycerol base and three fatty acids attached. It is to these two substances that triglycerides are broken down when digested and absorbed by the body.

Remember

Dietary proteins vary in nutritional quality. However a mixed diet containing plant and animal sources should be sufficient to meet demands for protein requirements, even for athletes in intense training, providing that energy needs are met.

Table 5.4: Sources and types of fat in the UK diet

Saturated
full fat dairy products, butter, hard margarine, lard, dripping, suet, fatty meat, meat pies, pate, cream, cakes, biscuits, chocolate, coconut and palm oil
Monounsaturated
olive oil, olive oil spreads, rapeseed oil, corn oil, peanuts, peanut butter, peanut oil, avocado, canola oil,
Polyunsaturated
soft margarine, low-fat spreads labelled high in polyunsaturated fats, sunflower oil, safflower oil, groundnut oil, soya oil, oily fish, nuts

Fat acts as the body's back-up storage fuel secondary to carbohydrate in a concentrated form. It is much more energy dense than carbohydrate or protein with one gram of fat yielding 9 calories of energy. Fat also serves to protect vital organs, provides a structural material for cells, acts as an insulator preventing heat loss and as a covering for nerve fibres. Animal fats also convey the fat soluble vitamins A, D, E and K.

There are two essential unsaturated **fatty acids**, linolenic and linoleic acid, that the body requires for good health and just like essential amino acids these must be provided by the diet. Both function as building blocks for other important fatty acids and

Key terms

Digestion – the process by which enzymes in the gut break down larger chemical compounds in foods so that they can be absorbed by the body.

Absorption – the movement of digested food from the stomach and small intestine into body tissues and blood.

Fatty acids – contain chains of carbon atoms to which hydrogen atoms attach. The number of hydrogen atoms relative to the number of carbon atoms determines if a fatty acid is classified as **saturated** or **unsaturated**. Unsaturated fatty acids may be **monounsaturated** or **polyunsaturated**. All fats consumed in our diet are a mixture of these different fatty acid types. Fatty foods containing a majority of saturated fatty acids are generally solid at room temperature, while fats composed of mainly unsaturated fatty acids are usually liquid at room temperature.

play a vital role in the development of every single cell in the body, as well as having a role in the regulation of blood pressure and immune responses.

Healthy eating recommendations encourage eating no more than 30–35 per cent of total daily calories as fat (DH, 1991), and to cut back on intake of saturated fat. For the average male this equates to approximately 90 g per day and the average female 70 g per day total fat based on the estimated average requirement (EAR) for energy. For athletes participating in high training and competition loads it is recommended to eat no more than 20–25 per cent of total dietary calories. In absolute terms this may be similar to that of the sedentary individual eating for health.

Remember

Even though low fat products are common and there is concern over high fat intakes, it is important to remember that fat is an essential body nutrient.

Stop and think

Think back to the starting block activity.
- What are the likely macronutrient requirements of rugby union players? Does position of play influence this?
- How are these likely to change during the course of the season?
- How might macronutrient requirements vary for an endurance athlete such as a race walker or marathon runner?

Stop and think

Critically evaluate the following statements:
- Only people involved in endurance type exercise need to eat a large amount of carbohydrates.
- In order to gain muscle you need to eat more protein foods than usual.

Micronutrients in the diet

In addition to protein, fat and carbohydrate there are more than thirty different vitamins and minerals, necessary to maintain good health; most of these in minute amounts. Failing to achieve adequate intakes of these micronutrients can result in deficiency disorders. However, if a good variety of food is eaten within a balanced diet meeting your need for calories, it is unlikely that the diet will be short of these nutrients.

Vitamins

Vitamins are vital, non caloric, organic substances necessary in very small amounts in order to perform specific metabolic functions within the body and to prevent associated deficiency diseases and disorders. They cannot be produced by the body, with the exception of vitamins D and K, and must therefore be supplied by the diet.

Vitamins are classified into two groups on the basis of their solubility as either fat soluble or water soluble. Vitamins A, D, E and K are fat soluble, and the B group vitamins and vitamin C are water soluble. The body requires differing amounts of each vitamin with specific vitamins having specific functions. Individual vitamin requirements vary and are determined based on age, sex, state of health and levels of physical activity.

A balanced and varied diet providing adequate energy should provide sufficient intakes of all vitamins and minerals for health and performance. Like drugs, vitamins can be harmful if consumed in large amounts excess to the body's requirements. This is especially true for the fat soluble vitamins as they have the potential to be stored in the body. The only time in which large doses may be beneficial is when the body has a severe deficiency or is incapable of absorbing or metabolising the nutrient efficiently.

Remember

Supplementation with high doses of any vitamin should always be medically supervised and not self-prescribed.

Antioxidant vitamins

Beta-carotene, vitamin C and vitamin E are probably the most well known antioxidants, sometimes known as the 'ACE' vitamins. Recent research suggests that antioxidants can help to prevent damage to our bodies from the effects of

free radicals. It is thought that hard exercise may deplete the body's stores of antioxidants and that antioxidants may have an important role to play in the protection of muscles fibres from free radical damage during exercise, and in reducing post-exercise muscle soreness. Eating a wide range of fruits and vegetables and choosing those that are in season will ensure a good intake of vitamins.

Key term

Free radical – an atom or compound with an unpaired electron, thought to cause cellular damage

Remember

Free radicals are atoms or molecules that are generated during normal energy production that contain an unpaired electron. In large numbers free radicals are capable of damaging cell membranes, DNA, oxidising blood cholesterol, and are thought to be responsible for initiating the development of certain cancers and heart disease.

Minerals

Minerals are vital, non caloric, inorganic elements widely distributed in nature that are essential to life. They are classified in terms of their relative amounts within the body, and fall broadly into two categories:

- macro-minerals, those required in relatively large amounts, for example calcium, sodium, potassium, magnesium and phosphorus

- trace elements, those required in much smaller amounts, for example iron, copper, manganese, zinc, iodine, sulphur, cobalt, selenium and chromium.

Remember

Regular, intensive exercise can increase requirements for some vitamins and minerals, especially those involved in energy production. Athletes will need to consume more food to meet energy requirements and will therefore automatically increase their intake of vitamins and minerals.

Stop and think

Think back to the starting block activity.
- What are the likely micronutrient considerations for a high intensity intermittent sport like rugby union?
- Are there any particular athletes that might be more susceptible to micronutrient deficiency in intake?
- What other antioxidant compounds are currently receiving attention in respect of health and performance?

Non-starch polysaccharide (NSP)

NSP forms the major part of plant cell walls and is the principal component of dietary fibre. It resists digestion by the stomach and small intestine. Good sources of dietary fibre include wholemeal grains, wholegrain breakfast cereals, nuts, pulses, fruits and vegetables and potatoes eaten in their skins. NSP aids the transit of food through the digestive system. There are two types of fibre – soluble and insoluble.

Soluble fibre is found in oats, rye, barley, peas, beans, lentils fruits and vegetables, and is important in the control of blood glucose and cholesterol.

Insoluble fibre is found in whole-wheat bread, rice, pasta, wholegrain breakfast cereals, fruits and vegetables, and is important in the prevention of bowel disorders such as constipation and diverticular disease.

Daily adult requirements of NSP are 18 g/day (DH, 1991).

Practical ways to increase fibre intake include:

- eating a wide variety of unrefined foods

- eating potatoes, new and old, in their skins

- eating more pulses, such as peas, beans and lentils

- eating vegetables in their skins (except carrots)

- eating 5+ servings of fruit and vegetables each day

- choosing wholegrain breakfast cereals and breads.

Water

The body cannot survive more than a few days without water and as such water is one of the most important nutrients required by the body. Water acts as the main transport mechanism in the body carrying nutrients, waste products and internal secretions. It also plays a vital role in temperature regulation, particularly during exercise and aids the passage of food through the digestive system. It makes up around 50–60 per cent of total body weight.

During exercise fluid requirements increase according to the type, duration and intensity of exercise and the environmental conditions under which it takes place. Water is lost from the body though a number of routes including urine, faeces and evaporation from skin and expired breath. If water loss is high the body will become dehydrated. A healthy sedentary adult requires between 1.5 to 3 litres of fluid per day, the equivalent of 6–8 cups, but more will be required in hot weather and by those with high training and competition schedules (Thomas and Bishop, 2007). Table 5.5 illustrates the balance between the body's sources of water intake and routes of water loss for a sedentary adult male weighing 70 kg.

Table 5.5: Daily water balance for a sedentary 70 kg adult male

Daily water input		Daily water output	
Source	ml	Source	ml
Fluid	1200	Urine	1250
Food	1000	Faeces	100
Metabolism	350	Skin	850
		Lungs	350
TOTAL	2550	TOTAL	2550

As a rough guide fluid requirements can be predicted based on body weight using the following formula: 30–35 ml per kg body weight or 1 ml per calorie of energy requirement.

Alcohol

Alcohol is a concentrated source of energy providing 7 calories per gram. However, this energy is unavailable to working muscles during exercise as the body can only metabolise it at a fixed rate, so any energy derived from alcohol in excess of requirements will be stored as body fat. Alcohol has long been associated with sport, with consumption often viewed by some to be a vital component of team spirit and camaraderie. Sensible use of alcohol does not impair health or performance; however, consumption post exercise can interfere with recovery, despite the myth that beer is a good source of carbohydrate. The decision to drink alcohol is a personal right; however, in professional sport teams are making more concerted efforts to improve the professional behaviour of players to curb binge drinking. If an injury is sustained alcohol should be avoided as consumption will lengthen recovery due to increased swelling and bleeding to the damaged tissue.

Practical application of hydration strategies in rugby league

Rugby league is thirsty work. Proper hydration is essential for optimum performance, but what to drink and how much? There is no doubt that dehydration will impair performance in rugby league. Fluid losses during training or game play are linked to the player's need to maintain body temperature within very narrow limits. Sweating, the evaporation of water from the surface of the skin, is a powerful cooling mechanism that allows for the loss of heat produced by the working muscles. If this fluid loss is not replaced then the subsequent dehydration can have a negative impact on a range of physiological and skilled performance factors including heart rate, power output, aerobic capacity, concentration, reaction time and coordination.

With the potential for negative impacts on performance to occur at levels of dehydration as little as 1–3 per cent it is vital that players remain as hydrated as possible. The hotter the conditions and the harder they work, the more players sweat and the more they need to drink to minimise dehydration. However, we all sweat at different rates, and there can be great individual differences, but as a rough guide fluid losses may be up to 1 litre per hour during hard endurance-type exercise. A loss as small as 2 per cent of body weight can be enough to begin to affect the ability to perform muscular work. For a 75 kg male this would be the equivalent to only a 1½ litre fluid loss from the body.

Water, often overlooked, is an adequate fluid replacer suitable for most types of exercise. If exercising at higher intensities and for longer duration sports drinks may be useful and fall into three broad categories. Their absorption and use by the body is to a large part dependent upon their carbohydrate concentration. Carbohydrate content is an advantage of sports drinks which can boost energy supply. In addition they include electrolytes such as sodium that are also lost through sweating, but more importantly facilitate absorption and more efficient rehydration.

Hypertonic drinks have a high concentration and contain more carbohydrate, usually greater than 10 g per 100 ml of drink, and are useful for the replenishment of carbohydrate stores in the muscles. These drinks are less quickly absorbed and are not the best choice if fluid replacement is the priority in hot and humid conditions. They are more appropriate for use after training and game play to facilitate recovery.

Isotonic drinks are designed to be in balance with the body's own fluids to provide fast fluid absorption and a boost to carbohydrate supplies. They contain approximately 5–7 g of carbohydrate per 100 ml of drink. This type of sports drink is often favoured before, during and after a game as it fulfils requirements of rapid fluid replacement and an energy supply.

Hypotonic drinks are less concentrated than the body's own fluids and contain approximately 2–3 g carbohydrate per 100 ml of drink. These drinks are designed to be absorbed quickly with the importance on fluid replacement not energy supply.

In hot conditions isotonic and hypotonic drinks are the best choice as they replace fluid losses faster. All the science put aside, although the choice of drink can be related to energy or hydration requirements, an important factor to consider is taste. Simply, a drink that tastes nice is much more likely to be drunk. In addition, when drinks are cool they are more likely to be consumed.

When it comes to how much a player should drink the answer depends upon the individual. Fluid losses are affected by genetics, body size, fitness level, environment, exercise intensity and position of play. Players should be advised to optimise hydration by drinking regularly throughout every day.

Maintaining a high fluid content in the gut also facilitates better absorption and rehydration. Prior to exercise players are encouraged to drink between 200 ml to 600 ml of fluid. During games and training it is important to take every opportunity to drink, which is why water carriers are on the pitch as often as possible during games. In extreme conditions studies have shown that players can lose up to two and a half litres of sweat per hour. It is almost impossible to counter this level of sweat loss during games but players should aim to drink approximately 2 ml of fluid for every kilogram of body weight every 15 minutes during a game or as much as they can tolerate without suffering stomach discomfort.

Stop and think

Think back to the starting block activity.
- What are the likely fluid demands of training and competition in rugby union?
- How might fluid requirements vary for endurance athletes such as race walkers or marathon runners?
- What strategies could you employ to monitor fluid balance and hydration in the team?

Consider the challenges to meeting fluid requirements for Johanna Jackson on the way to winning the Commonwealth Games 20 km walk title in Delhi, India 2010

After games and training it is vital to rehydrate to encourage recovery. A simple measure of how much liquid a player needs to drink to replace the fluid lost is to weigh them before and after a game or training. Each kilogram of body weight lost roughly equates to a 1 litre fluid loss. Rehydration guidelines recommend players will need to drink 150 per cent of any fluid deficit in the 4 to 6 hours post game or training to account for ongoing sweat losses during recovery.

Energy

Energy is obtained from food and used to support basal metabolism (the minimum amount of energy required to sustain the body's vital functions in a waking state) and all activity carried out at work and leisure. Energy is measured in **calories** or **joules**. As both these units are very small they are multiplied by 1000 and referred to as **kilocalories** (the UK system) or **kilojoules** (the metric or international system).

The relative value of fuels for activity differs. Fat and carbohydrate are the main energy fuels for exercising muscles. Protein may be used during prolonged periods of exercise and towards the latter stages of endurance events, particularly if fat and carbohydrate as sources of fuel within the working muscles have become limited. Exercising muscles prefer glucose as a fuel, particularly as the intensity of the activity being undertaken increases. During exercise muscles use energy at a rate that is directly proportional to the intensity of the activity. If this energy is not replaced as it is used up, muscles become unable to maintain their rate of work and the intensity of the activity will be reduced or stopped.

Key terms

Calorie – the energy required to raise 1 g of water by 1°C

Joule – one joule of energy moves a mass of 1 g at a velocity of 1 metre per second. Approximately 4.2 joules = 1 calorie

Kilocalorie – the energy required to raise the temperature of 1 kg of water by 1°C. Equal to 1000 calories and used to convey the energy value of food. Kilocalories are often simply referred to as calories

Kilojoule – a unit of measurement for energy, but like the calorie the joule is not a large unit of energy; therefore kilojoules are used more often

---

Energy balance

Energy balance is achieved when the amount of energy taken in as food and drink (energy input) equals the amount of energy expended (energy output). Weight is neither gained nor lost. There are four major components to energy output: resting metabolic rate (RMR), dietary thermogenesis (DT), physical activity (PA) and adaptive thermogenesis (AT).

- Resting metabolic rate can account for 60–75 per cent of total energy output and represents the largest component of total daily energy expenditure. RMR is closely related to lean body mass and so is influenced by body composition. Muscle tissue is much more metabolically active than fat tissue. Gains in muscle mass will result in increases in RMR. RMR is also influenced by age, sex and genetic background.

- Dietary thermogenesis refers to the energy expended above that of RMR for the processes of digestion, absorption, transport and storage of food. It is influenced by the calorie content and composition of the diet and nutritional status. High energy intakes and a regular eating pattern are thought to help maintain higher rates of dietary thermogenesis, while skipping meals and restrictive dietary practices lead to a reduction in this component of energy output.

- Physical activity represents the most variable component of total energy expenditure. This is the additional energy expended above RMR and DT, and will contribute more to total daily energy expenditure in active individuals. Exactly how much varies according to general lifestyle activity and participation in sport and exercise.

- Adaptive thermogenesis is energy expenditure that occurs as a result of environmental or physiological stresses placed on the body, such as a change in temperature that may require a shivering response or stress that causes anxiety or fidgeting.

Dietary assessment methods

There are five basic methods for assessing the dietary intakes of free-living individuals. Two of these methods utilise records of food consumption made at the time of actual eating, one with actual weight recorded, the other using estimations of weights of food consumed using standard household measures or portion sizes.

The other three methods attempt to assess diet and food consumption in the recent past by asking about food intake the previous day (24 hour recall), over the past few weeks (diet history), or in the recent or distant past (questionnaires). All methods have their relative advantages and disadvantages.

Choice of method

In theory the most accurate method is the weighed food record. All food and beverages consumed are weighed and recorded. This requires robust and convenient scales accurate to +/- 1 g and a demonstration in their use. Any plate waste must also be weighed and subtracted from the original amounts recorded prior to consumption.

If only energy and energy yielding nutrients are to be assessed, a 7-day record is sufficient. Longer periods of observation are required for vitamins, minerals and fibre. The main disadvantage of this procedure is its tedious nature and the degree of co-operation required to undertake it.

The unweighed food record (diet diary) may incorporate the use of models, standard portions, food replicas and household portions. This method is more time consuming for the assessor and requires a high degree of skill at interpreting descriptions. There is also a risk of under and over estimation of portion sizes and the introduction of systematic error.

Remember

Dietary assessments using the unweighed method are likely to be less accurate than the weighed record but are more readily available from subjects.

24-hour recall

24-hour recall is a quick and easy method to use. With this approach the interviewer collects information on what the client usually eats. This relies heavily on memory to recall all food and drink consumed in the previous 24 hours. It is

rarely adequate to provide a quantitative estimate of energy and nutrient intakes, but it can be useful in assessing the qualitative nature of food choices and intake and may reveal obvious or potential dietary imbalances or weaknesses. However, the main value of this method is that it is a useful starting point for further dietary investigation.

Diet history or interview

This is also relatively quick and easy to use. The interviewer collects information on what is usually eaten. This method relies heavily on memory to recall all food and drink consumed in the previous 7 days. It is important to note that recalled intake nearly always underestimates actual intake, whilst there is also the danger of fabrication of intake to impress the interviewer. This method is useful in assessing the qualitative nature of food intake and may be able to reveal obvious or potential dietary imbalances.

Stop and think

To assess your own eating habits, keep a record of all food and drink you consume for at least a three-day period, which should include one weekend day. For a more detailed evaluation, record your intake for a full week. Write down everything you eat and drink. You must be as accurate and honest as possible, and be sure not to modify your usual intake at this stage; otherwise you will not be evaluating your typical diet. You will need to carry your record around with you at all times and record food and drink as it is consumed to avoid forgetting any items. Your record should describe the following.

- The type of food and drink consumed, and how much. Either estimate the portion size using standard household measures, such as slices of bread, pints of fluid, tablespoons of vegetables, etc. or give the weight from food packaging.

- The time that the food and drink was consumed and where you were when you ate or drank it. These points are often useful when assessing external factors that affect dietary intake.

- Any activity or exercise you took part in, including an indication of its duration and intensity, i.e. light, moderate or hard.

Top tip

Be sure to record all items as consumed, it is often fluid intake that is under reported most in food records as drinks are often consumed outside of meal times.

- After completion look at your food and activity record and compare it to the UK National Food Guide recommendations

Take it further

As well as the types and amounts of food you eat, your record may give you an idea about how your daily life dictates what, when, where and why you eat. Take another look at your food record and ask yourself the following questions:

- Is there room for improvement, or is your diet actually better than you thought?
- Do you eat regularly or frequently skip meals?
- Are some days better than others and do you eat differently at weekends?
- Is there enough variety in your diet?
- What constraints are there placed on your diet by your lifestyle that may prevent you from making any necessary dietary changes?
- How did activity or exercise influence your intake?

Food composition tables and dietary analysis software

For quantitative assessment of nutritional intake, food composition tables and dietary analysis software can be employed. In the UK the Food Standards Agency maintains a record of food compositional data in a National Nutrient Databank. From time to time this information is published in book and electronic format as McCance and Widdowson's *The Composition of Foods*. Food tables and nutritional analysis computer packages that use such databases are valuable resources in dietary analysis. However there are limitations and common pitfalls to be aware of in their use and application. It is important to note that the composition of a particular food can vary on account of the way in which it has been stored, processed, manufactured and cooked, whilst acknowledging plant or animal genetics and farming practices that will also impact.

There is a range of nutrient analysis software programmes available for dietary analysis. Some of the less sophisticated software, particularly that designed for use by the general public or for use in schools, often contains abbreviated data and as such needs to be used with caution. Where full data is available, and leaving aside the compositional variation of nutrient content of food, there are many opportunities for error to occur in the diet analysis process, such as in the coding of food items, portion sizing and the requirement for food substitution for items not within the database. As such any detailed or complex dietary analysis, particularly that requiring major dietary change, should always be referred to a State Registered Dietitian or Accredited Nutritionist.

Stop and think

What factors would you need to give consideration to in the practical application of dietary assessment techniques in sport?

Take it further

The National Diet and Nutrition Survey (NDNS), designed to be representative of the UK population, is a continuous cross-sectional survey of the food consumption, nutrient intakes and nutritional status of people aged 18 months and older living in private households in the UK. The NDNS is funded by the Food Standards Agency and the Department of Health in England, and is carried out by the National Centre for Social Research, Medical Research Council Human Nutrition Research and the University College London Medical School.

Intakes are compared with government recommendations and comparisons with findings from previous surveys are also made. Take a look at the latest NDNS Report findings on the Food Standards Agency website (to obtain a secure link to their website, visit www.pearsonfe.co.uk/foundationsinsport). What observations do you make about population intake compared to recommendations?

Nutritional claims and food labelling

As you know food is comprised of the nutrients carbohydrate, protein, fat, vitamins, minerals, NSP and water, and that the amounts of each nutrient vary from food to food. Most foods are categorised based on their macronutrient content, but usually consist of more than one of these nutrients. For example bread, known as a carbohydrate food, consists of a large amount of carbohydrate, a smaller amount of protein and an even smaller amount of fat.

Food labelling regulations

Since the late 1980s all processed foods and non-alcoholic beverages sold in Britain have been required by law to display a list of the ingredients in descending order of weight. Therefore, the first few ingredients listed are in the greatest quantity, whilst additives and preservatives are usually found at the bottom of the list and are present in small quantities.

Some manufacturers provide information on the nutritional value and content of the food. If provided this should be presented in a standard format specified by food labelling regulations to enable the consumer to compare like for like products. Increasingly also included on labels are nutritional claims made by the manufacturer.

Learning to analyse food labels can reveal some interesting truths about the nutritional composition of foods. To be able to make an educated choice about the foods we eat, calculating the number of calories coming from fat, carbohydrate and protein, can be helpful. Remember that healthy eating targets recommend a daily calorie intake composed of:

- 50% carbohydrate
- 30–35% fat
- 15–20% protein.

The nutrition panel on a food label will usually tell you:

- the total number of kcal per 100 g
- the number of g's fat per 100 g
- the number of g's carbohydrate per 100 g
- the number of g's protein per 100 g.

But what you actually need to know is the percentage of calories coming from these three macronutrients.

To analyse the nutritional panel you need to remember:

- 1 g fat provides 9 kcal
- 1 g carbohydrate provides 4 kcal
- 1 g protein provides 4 kcal.

Below is an example using the nutritional information from a can of creamed rice pudding.

Composition per 100 g of rice pudding:

- Energy   90 kcals
- Carbohydrate   15.2 g
- Protein   3.2 g
- Fat   1.6 g

The percentage energy, in calories, from the three macronutrients is calculated as shown:

Percentage energy from carbohydrate:

$$\frac{15.2 \times 4 \times 100}{90} = \mathbf{67.5\%}$$

Percentage energy from protein:

$$\frac{3.4 \times 4 \times 100}{90} = \mathbf{15.1\%}$$

Percentage energy from fat:

$$\frac{\mathbf{1.6 \times 9 \times 100}}{\mathbf{90}} = \mathbf{16\%}$$

These calculations show that creamed rice pudding is a low fat, high carbohydrate food with reasonable protein content.

Table 5.6: Nutritional claims

Claim	What it means....
FAT	
Low fat	Less than 5 g of fat per 100 g of product
Reduced fat	At least 25% less fat than the standard product
Virtually fat free	Less than 0.3 g of fat per 100 g of product
95% fat free	Less than 5 g of fat per 100 g of product
Low in saturates	Less than 3 g of saturated fat per 100 g of product
SUGAR	
Low sugar	Less than 5 g sugar per 100 g of product
Reduced sugar	At least 25% less sugar than the standard product
Sugar free	Contains no sugar (added or natural)
No added sugar	Contains no sugar (added)
CALORIES	
Low calorie	Less than 40 calories per 100 g of product or serving
Reduced calorie	At least 25% fewer calories than the standard product
FIBRE	
High fibre	Contains at least 6 g of fibre per 100 g of product or serving
SODIUM	
Reduced sodium	At least 25% less sodium than the standard product

Performance nutrition strategies

Take it further

Choose three different food labels and analyse them for the percentage energy contributed by carbohydrate, protein and fat and evaluate any nutritional claims they make. Compare two different supermarkets' approaches to the provision of nutritional information on their own label products.

Stop and think

Why is it important for clear and accurate information to be displayed on food labels?

Does food labelling help or hinder the consumer in making healthy food choices?

Good nutrition can make its greatest contribution in aiding recovery between training sessions. For the regular sports performer, performance improvements are the product of the body's adaptation to the demands of training. Sound nutrition has its biggest impact in supporting the sports performer in training consistently and effectively to achieve desired adaptations in response to training. To achieve steady improvements, all sportspeople must ensure that their diet consistently meets the demands placed on their bodies by training and competition.

Nutritional dilemmas of the sports performer

Athletes are required to peak and taper training depending on their performance calendar. Their training and competition programme can vary daily, weekly, monthly and yearly. For many, feelings of lethargy and tiredness are an occupational hazard. Timing of meals around training and competition can become difficult, particularly if training or competing more than once in one day. The expected image of the athlete can create physical, nutritional and emotional problems. Weight management is a key concern for most athletes. In an effort to maintain or lose weight some athletes will experience disordered eating patterns. Unrealistic aims for weight and body image, with unreasonable calorie restriction, will result in inadequate energy and nutrient intakes, compromising performance and resulting in fatigue and an increased risk of injury.

When developing sound eating habits and nutritional strategies to support training and competition, the following issues are important:

- types of food eaten to support training and competition

- timing of meals and snacks around training and competition

- ensuring a balanced diet is achieved in respect of all nutrients

- maintaining a sufficient fluid intake

- the problems of travelling to training and competition venues

- minimising the risk of injury and illness

- promoting long term health and reducing the risk of chronic disease.

The nutritional requirements for different sports and sportspeople will vary according to:

- type of sport and training methods undertaken

- intensity of training or competition

- duration of training or competition

- frequency of training or competition

- training status and fitness level of the sportsperson.

General recommendations for the sports performer

Sports performers should:

- ensure their diet meets the demands placed on the body

- eat sufficient carbohydrate

- plan well and fit eating around training and competition

- recognise rest days are important and use the time to recover from the stresses of training and competition and to eat sensibly making up for hurried meals and replenishing carbohydrate stores

- maintain a high fluid intake

- rehydrate fully before drinking alcohol after training and competing and stay within the recommended guidelines for health.

Food selection

Before training or competition: Essentially many of the principles of preparing for a competition mirror those of the training diet. For competition, the pre-event meal should aim to top up muscle and liver glycogen stores and should therefore be carbohydrate rich, but also low in fat and fibre and contain a moderate amount of protein. It should be remembered that larger meals will take longer to digest and that nerves can result in delayed digestion.

- Competition is not a time to experiment with new foods. The pre-event meal should therefore be composed of familiar foods, and also provide adequate fluids. Solid foods can usually be consumed with comfort up to two hours before an event, but liquid meals or carbohydrate drinks can be consumed up to 30 or 60 minutes before.

- Sports performers engaging in events lasting longer than 90 minutes should be advised, where possible, to taper training in the week leading up to the event, include a rest day, and consume a higher than normal carbohydrate and fluid intake.

During training or competition: During training and competition, fluid loss is a major consideration. During intense training or competition isotonic sports drinks – which assist with fluid replacement but also provide a source of fuel – may be beneficial, especially if training or competition lasts longer than 60 minutes. During endurance or ultra-endurance events lasting longer than four hours, solid foods may be required. In these instances energy bars or gels or sports confectionery might be useful as a more concentrated source of carbohydrate. Regular sports performers should be encouraged to practise their fluid and fuelling regimes in training to ensure that they do not run into any unexpected problems during competition.

Stop and think

Critically evaluate the following statements:
- The best time to start drinking during exercise is when you start to feel thirsty.
- Sports drinks are essential to maintain fluid and electrolyte balance during and after exercise.

After training or competition: What is consumed, how much and how soon after an intense workout or competition can all influence the recovery process. Refuelling should begin as soon as possible.

Sensible choices in terms of food and fluids will allow the sports performer to recover more quickly for the next training session, particularly for those in intense training or those who have multiple daily workouts, or rounds of a competition.

It is important to refuel as soon as possible after each workout or competition. The longer refuelling is delayed the longer it will take to fully refuel. The sports performer may find it easier to have more small, frequent meals and snacks at regularly spaced intervals to help to maximise glycogen synthesis. To refuel efficiently a high carbohydrate diet is required. Post-exercise carbohydrates that are easy to eat and digest are advised. Sports performers should aim to consume a high-carbohydrate (at least 50 g) low-fat snack as soon as possible after training or competition, preferably within the first half hour, when the muscles' capacity to refuel is at its greatest, and ensure that they eat their next meal, which should be rich in carbohydrate, within two hours.

After exercise, the replacement of fluids lost through sweating should also be a priority. Rehydration should start immediately. Drinks containing carbohydrates will also assist with energy and glycogen replacement. These may be particularly useful if the activity has been very intense and resulted in a suppression of appetite and a reluctance to eat solid foods.

Remember

Optimal performance in sport and exercise requires optimal nutrition. Sportspeople should pay careful attention to foods that can enhance, not hinder, their preparation for, participation in and recovery from training and competition. Most sportspeople will obtain all the energy and nutrients they need by eating to appetite and choosing a balanced and varied diet.

Practical application from the recreational runner to marathon enthusiast

So what about the recreational runner training a couple of times a week, who enjoys a drink and is not too keen on a strict diet?

The healthy eating recommendations for the general population will be sufficient to support their level of training. Calorie intakes can be estimated based on 35 calories per kilogram of body weight. They should aim to achieve at least 50 per cent of calorie (energy) intake from carbohydrate, no more than 30–35 per cent from fat, 15–20 per cent from protein and no more than 6 per cent of calories from alcohol. They should aim for 4–5 g of carbohydrate per kilogram of body weight, a protein intake of between 0.8–1.0 g per kilogram, and a fat intake around 70 g per day for women and 90 g a day for men.

To ensure adequate intakes of vitamins and minerals they should opt for unrefined carbohydrate sources and at least five servings from the fruit and vegetable group each day. If exercise is well spaced they have adequate time to replenish muscle glycogen stores. They should have room for the occasional drink, but always ensure they rehydrate before drinking alcohol after exercise.

They have decided to up the mileage. Does this affect their nutritional requirements?

They will require more energy and to ensure that energy stores are maintained it is best to up the percentage of calories consumed from carbohydrate to 60 per cent and drop fat to 25 per cent. They should aim for a carbohydrate intake equivalent to 5–6 g per kilogram of body weight and a protein intake in the region of 1.2–1.4 g per kilogram of body weight, with again a fat intake around 70 g per day for women and 90 g per day for men. They should be encouraged to base all meals around starchy carbohydrate foods, with protein portions around 3–4oz (75–100 g) and at least three servings from the dairy food group each day. Greater intakes of carbohydrate foods will also result in greater intakes of protein.

Increased frequency and duration of training will incur greater fluid losses from the body, so to minimise the effects of fluid losses whilst running they should be encouraged to always start training fully hydrated and drink plenty during and after. For training periods less than 30 minutes it is not usually necessary to drink during exercise, but during prolonged exercise they should be encouraged to start with the maximum amount of fluid they can tolerate in the stomach and aim to consume 150–200 ml every 15–20 minutes.

They are serious now and training frequency and mileage has increased further, so what is the impact on nutritional requirements?

Carbohydrate requirements will increase further to around 7–8 g per kilogram of body weight per day, protein intakes will remain between 1.2–1.4 g per kilogram of body weight, with again a fat intake around 70 g for a female and 90 g for a male.

Hard exercise is thought to deplete the body of antioxidant vitamins, so care should be taken in achieving adequate intakes of fruit and vegetables. Pure fruit juice is a good choice and if consumed after exercise can facilitate fluid and carbohydrate replacement. As training frequency and intensity increases the timing of meals and snacks, as well as the content, become important to facilitating adequate and efficient glycogen refuelling.

Aim to consume a carbohydrate snack as soon as possible after training when glycogen resynthesis is most efficient. Opt for carbohydrates with a high/moderate glycaemic index as these will be absorbed more quickly. Good choices include bananas, dried fruit, a Mars bar or jam sandwiches. During exercise an isotonic sports drink may help to delay fatigue and maintain training intensity by providing a source of carbohydrate and fluid.

So what about those with excessively high mileage, who are training more than once a day?

The general recommendation for those engaging in heavy endurance training is to achieve a carbohydrate intake of 65–70 per cent of calorie intake, equivalent to 8–10 g per kilogram of body weight per day. To achieve this there will need to be a reliance on increased carbohydrate consumed from sugary sources. Protein requirements should not need to exceed 1.7 g per kilogram of body

weight and again fat intake will probably not exceed the values previously stated. Timing of meals and snacks becomes increasingly important to maintaining glycogen stores. Menu planning will require greater attention and it would be useful to carry high carbohydrate snacks at all times especially for use immediately after training.

It is important to minimise the risks of dehydration. As mentioned fluid losses can be up to 1 litre per hour in endurance exercise and this can be higher if exercising in hot humid conditions. As a rough rule of thumb aim to consume 7 ml per kg body weight as a bolus before exercise, or as much as can be tolerated, and the equivalent of 2 ml per kg body weight every 15 minutes or 200–300 ml every 15–20 minutes. Fluid replacement can be speeded by drinking still, less concentrated, cool drinks of a reasonable volume, but higher exercise intensities will slow fluid absorption.

Weight and urine checks would provide a useful way of monitoring fluid status. A weight reduction of 1 kg during a training session is roughly equivalent to a 1 litre fluid loss. These simple nude weight checks before and after exercise can aid in determining fluid requirements post-exercise. Frequent trips to the toilet to pass plentiful quantities of pale-coloured urine are generally seen as an indicator of good hydration, whilst scant quantities of dark-coloured urine indicate poor hydration. After training fluid losses should be replaced one and a half times to ensure adequate rehydration.

Take it further

The position of the American Dietetic Association, Dietitians of Canada, and the American College of Sports Medicine is that physical activity, athletic performance, and recovery from exercise are enhanced by optimal nutrition. These organisations recommend that appropriate selection of food and fluid and timing of intake are required for optimal health and exercise performance. Take a look at their Position Stand on Nutrition and Athletic Performance (2009) available from their website.

Case study (for recommended answers, see www.pearsonfe.co.uk/foundationsinsport)

Vicky is a hockey player and has just been selected as a member of the national squad. She has a high training load. Her weekly programme often contains more than one daily training session with matches or national squad training at the weekends. She lives on her own and has a demanding job as a social worker. Due to the combined demands of work and training she often misses lunch. She usually stays behind for a social drink in the bar after club training twice a week to catch up with her friends. She often gets home late and does not bother to cook a meal but grabs a light snack before going to bed. She often complains of feeling tired and has found that in training and competition she often lacks energy, especially towards the end of the session and has asked you if this could be related to her diet.

Consider the physiological demands of hockey and how they impact on nutritional requirements.

1. What do you think might be the causes of Vicky's lethargy towards the end of training and competition?

2. What nutritional advice do you think is appropriate for Vicky?

3. Prepare a simple menu plan to help her meet her training and competition requirements. How can you facilitate its practical application with Vicky?

4. How would you monitor the expected outcomes of your dietary intervention with Vicky?

Check your understanding (for answers, see www.pearsonfe.co.uk/foundationsinsport)

1. What are dietary reference values and how are these applied in practice?

2. Describe the principles of the Eatwell Plate. How would you apply these in the context of sport and exercise nutrition?

3. In population terms, based on data from the latest National Diet and Nutrition Survey, are the macronutrient intake targets set for health being achieved?

4. What is the glycaemic index?

5. Whether eating for health or performance, what is the best approach to achieving adequate carbohydrate intakes and how might you determine these?

6. Describe the concept of energy balance.

7. What is the significance of antioxidant vitamins in the context of sport and exercise performance?

8. What are the relative advantages and disadvantages of using the diet history or interview technique as a dietary assessment method?

9. What factors require consideration in the development of nutrition strategies to support the sports performer?

10. How could you ensure optimum glycogen availability before, during and after exercise?

Time to reflect

1. Critically reflect on the inter-relationship between nutrition, health, sport and exercise.

2. How would you apply the principles of the Eatwell Plate in the context of sport and exercise nutrition?

3. What are the nutritional dilemmas for the sports performer and how might these be overcome?

4. What is the significance of optimum energy balance for the sports performer?

5. Critically evaluate the role of nutrient supplements and sports foods in the context of health and performance.

Useful resources

To obtain a secure link to the websites below, see the Websites section on page ii or visit the companion website at www.pearsonfe.co.uk/foundationsinsport

- American College of Sports Medicine
- American Dietetic Association
- Australian Institute of Sport
- British Dietetic Association
- British Nutrition Foundation
- Food Standards Agency

Further reading

DOH (1991) *COMA 41 Dietary Reference Values for Food Energy & Nutrients for the United Kingdom* HMSO

Food Standards Agency (2002) *Food Portion Sizes* 3rd Edition, Her Majesty's Stationary Office

Food Standards Agency (2002) *McCance and Widdowson's The Composition of Foods 6th Summary Edition*, Royal Society of Chemistry

British Journal of Nutrition

Journal of the American Dietetic Association

Journal of Human Nutrition & Dietetics

Nutrition Bulletin

Barasi, M. (2003), *Human Nutrition A Health Perspective,* 2nd Edition, Hodder Arnold

Gibney, M.J. et al., (2009). *Introduction to Human Nutrition,* The Nutrition Society Textbook Series. Wiley Blackwell

Jeukendrup, A. and Gleeson, M. (2010). *Sport Nutrition: An Introduction to Energy Production and Performance,* 2nd Edition. Champaigne, Illinois: Human Kinetics.

Lanham-New, S. et al., (2011) *Sport and Exercise Nutrition*, The Nutrition Society Textbook Series, Wiley Blackwell

Thomas, B. and Bishop, B. (2007). *Manual of Dietetic Practice,* 4th Edition. Blackwell Scientific Publications.

Chapter 6

Sport psychology

Introduction

Sport psychology is the study of people and their behaviours in sports contexts. As elite level sport is characterised by a demand to perform at optimal levels, under exceptionally demanding conditions (Jones, Hanton and Connaughton, 2007), athletes and coaches talk about how sporting success can be attributed to how focused and motivated a player is, or how well a team works together. There is now a growing appreciation of the huge impact that psychology has on the performance and wellbeing of an athlete. Sport psychologists work with coaches, athletes and teams to try to help them to reach the highest levels of health and performance, using a wide application of knowledge and a range of different techniques.

In this chapter, you will learn about the work of sport psychologists, approaches to sport psychology and how to become a sport psychologist, the different key psychological factors that can influence performance, and the use of psychological skills training to enhance sport performance and athlete wellbeing.

Learning outcomes

After you have read this chapter you should be able to:

- know the roles of a sport psychologist
- know the different professional associations within sport psychology
- understand the importance of motivation in sport
- understand the influences of arousal, stress and anxiety in sport
- understand coping in sport
- understand methods of enhancing the performance of athletes.

Starting block

Think of the high profile athletes that you have seen who have had a sudden drop in performance or have had problems in their personal lives. What do you think could have been the cause of such problems? How do you think that sport psychologists could help these types of problems once they occur, or even prevent them from occurring altogether?

Know the role of the sport and exercise psychologist

Roles

Sport and exercise psychologists have three roles: research, education and consultancy. These roles can be independent of each other or combined depending on the individual sport psychologist.

Research

Many sport and exercise psychologists are active in research, contributing to the development of the profession by advancing knowledge and developing new strategies for working with athletes. Their work might be disseminated in academic journals such as *Journal of Applied Sport Psychology, The Psychology of Sport and Exercise* or *The Sport Psychologist*.

Education

Sport and exercise psychologists often work in universities teaching on degree programmes, such as Sport and exercise sciences, Sport and exercise psychology or Applied sport and exercise psychology. Their role is to help students to develop subject specific knowledge and skills so that they can work with individuals in a sport and exercise psychology setting.

Consultancy

Sport and exercise psychologists fulfil this role when they help athletes identify strengths and areas for improvement. They use different psychological skills with individuals and teams to try to enhance performance, help people manage lifestyles, help with injury rehabilitation or conduct team building activities.

Combined roles

Sometimes sport psychologists may combine these roles. For example Chris Harwood (a university lecturer and sport psychologist) worked with a professional football academy (consultancy role), disseminated his work in an academic journal (Harwood, 2008) to help guide the professional practice of others (research role), and this article is now used in teaching on courses that have a psychology of sports coaching or applied sport psychology element (education role).

Know the different professional associations within sport psychology

There are different professional associations for sport psychology. Your membership and recognition may be determined by your location or the philosophy behind your sport psychology work. Each professional body has details about how you can be recognised as a sport psychologist in different countries. The main professional bodies for sport and exercise psychology are:

- American Psychological Association
- Asian South Pacific Association of Sport Psychology
- Association for Applied Sport Psychology
- British Association of Sport and Exercise Sciences
- British Psychological Society
- European Federation of Sport Psychology
- Health Professions Council
- International Association of Applied Psychology
- International Society of Sport Psychology
- North American Society for the Psychology of Sport and Physical Activity.

As well as belonging to a professional body for sport psychology, you may have a particular area of interest and want to work with others of a similar interest. These are known as interest groups or specialist networks, for example the International Network of Football Psychologists.

Motivation

Motivation is defined as the direction and intensity of effort and has historically been used as the key construct to explain why we do what we do. There are three types of motivation: intrinsic motivation, extrinsic motivation and amotivation.

Intrinsic

Intrinsic motivation explains when someone participates in sport without the primary motivation being an external mechanism. There are three key elements to intrinsic motivation:

- accomplishments – when athletes wish to increase their level of skill to get a sense of accomplishment
- stimulation – seeking excitement or a 'rush'
- knowledge – being curious about performance, wanting to know more about it and to develop new techniques or skills to benefit performance.

Extrinsic

Extrinsic motivation explains when someone behaves the way they do because of external mechanisms. Common forms of extrinsic motivation are tangible and intangible rewards. Tangible rewards are physical, like money and medals; intangible rewards are non-physical such as praise or encouragement. You need an in-depth knowledge of your athletes to maximise the effectiveness of extrinsic rewards and to ensure that they do not weaken the athlete's intrinsic motivation (Martens, 2004).

Amotivation

Amotivation is where there is an absence of motivation in an athlete and they see no good reason to continue. Athletes feel powerless to achieve any of their desired results and feel no control over what they do. Signs that indicate amotivation are the athlete constantly feeling defeated and exhibiting high levels of despair (Ryan and Deci, 2000).

Key terms

Motivation – direction and intensity of one's effort. Athletes will choose whether to try to achieve a particular task (direction) and how hard they will try (intensity)

Intrinsic motivation – internal factors that drive an athlete, such as fun and satisfaction

Extrinsic motivation – external factors that drive an athlete, such as money and trophies

Amotivation – condition where there is an absence of motivation in an athlete

Theoretical approaches to understanding motivation

How and why athletes are motivated is one of the most important factors in determining involvement and success in sport. There are different theoretical perspectives that attempt to develop an understanding of motivation.

Self-determination theory

The Self-determination theory views the three types of motivation on a continuum from:

Amotivation > Extrinsic motivation > Intrinsic motivation

It suggests that athletes create goals to satisfy three basic needs of competence, relatedness and autonomy. For example, if a young football player feels that they are at a higher standard than other players within their team (higher perceived competence) but are only set goals at the same difficulty as the rest of the team, their motivation may reduce if they easily achieve the goals. However, if the same footballer can contribute to setting harder goals for self-development that are based on their perceived levels of competence (thus satisfying relatedness, autonomy and competence) they may be more motivated to strive towards achieving the goals. For a detailed analysis of the application of self-determination theory in sport, see Hagger and Chatzisarantis (2007).

Achievement goal theory

Another recent perspective on motivation, the Achievement goal theory, suggests task and ego-orientations to explain involvement and understand perceptions of success in sport. Findings from research suggest that athletes with high task involvement are associated with more adaptive motivational behaviours (e.g. training adherence, psychological skills use), whereas those that are more **ego orientated** generally have more maladaptive motivational behaviours. For example, Harwood, Cumming and Fletcher (2004) in their study of 573 elite young athletes, found that higher **task orientated** athletes reported significantly more imagery, goal setting and positive self-talk use than their higher ego orientated counterparts. For a review of the Achievement goal theory in sport, see Duda and Hall (2001).

> ### Key terms
>
> **Ego orientated** – people who judge success on social comparisons, determining whether they are better than other athletes
>
> **Task orientated** – people who judge success based on self improvement and development

Attribution theory

The Attribution theory examines how people explain success or failure (see Table 6.1). It provides an understanding of an athlete's actions and motivation. This theory says that the reasons people give are known as attributions and can fall into the following categories:

- stability – is the reason permanent or unstable
- causality – does it come from an external or an internal factor
- control – is it under your control or not?

Understand the effects of stress, anxiety and arousal in sport

Stress, anxiety and arousal are three concepts that are often viewed together to explain behaviours in sport. The signs and symptoms of these concepts are similar: they each have physical/physiological signs (e.g. increased heart rate, increased sweating rate, increased muscle temperature, pupil dilation, changes in metabolism and digestion) and psychological/perceptual signs (e.g. narrowing of the attentional field, changes in concentration levels, changes in decision making time).

Stress

Lazarus and Folkman (1984) defined stress as: 'a pattern of negative physiological states and psychological responses occurring in situations where people perceive threats to their wellbeing, which they may be unable to meet'. This suggests that you don't have to be playing in a World Cup final or sprinting in the 100 m final in the Olympics to experience the symptoms of stress. For example,

Table 6.1: Example attributions for success and failure in sport

Type of attribution	Success example	Failure example
Stability	'I was more able than my opponent' (stable) 'I was lucky' (unstable)	'I was less able than my opponent' (stable) 'We didn't have that bit of luck we needed today' (unstable)
Causality	'I tried really hard' (internal) 'My opponent was easy to beat' (external)	'I didn't try hard enough' (internal) 'My opponent was impossible to beat' (external)
Control	'I trained really hard for this fight' (under your control) 'He wasn't as fit as I was' (not under your control)	'I didn't train hard enough for this fight' (under your control) 'He was fitter than I was' (not under your control)

a cricket player who is playing their first friendly game after a year-long injury could show the same symptoms of stress as if they were about to go in to bat on strike at eleven, in the last innings of a cricket game, when their team is two runs behind, and the World Cup is at stake. On the face of it, the friendly game would not be as important as the game-saving situation the cricket player faces, so should not elicit emotional responses that are as great. However, it is the importance that the individual attaches to an event that determines how they respond (Lazarus, 2000), so if the player perceives the friendly game as more important, they will elicit a stronger emotional response.

This discussion of stress focuses mainly on the individual athlete and how they may respond to a significant other (e.g. a coach) or a specific event (e.g. a cup final). More recently, the notion of organisational stress (Fletcher and Hanton, 2003) has been suggested. This idea relates to the stress placed on athletes by the whole competitive sport environment and identifies four key sources of organisational stress: environmental sources (e.g. travel, accommodation, being selected for games); personal sources (e.g. injury, expectations); leadership sources (e.g. coaches, coaching philosophy, coaching practice); team sources (e.g. atmosphere, roles, communication, social support).

Anxiety

Anxiety is seen as a predominantly negative emotional state that is either characterised by feelings of nervousness, apprehension or worry. Anxiety is also considered to be **multi-dimensional** as anxiety consists of **state anxiety** and **trait anxiety** that both have **cognitive anxiety** and **somatic anxiety** components (see Figure 6.1). This explanation is known as the Multi-dimensional anxiety theory (Martens, Vealey and Burton, 1990). Although the definition of anxiety relates to it being a negative emotion, research (e.g. Hanton and Jones, 1999a; Hanton and Jones, 1999b) suggests that if an athlete can view the symptoms of anxiety and arousal as excitement rather than fear, performance will generally be facilitated.

Arousal

Definitions of arousal often refer to a state of alertness and anticipation that prepares the body for action. It involves physiological activation (increased heart rate, sweating rate or respiratory rate) and psychological activity (increased

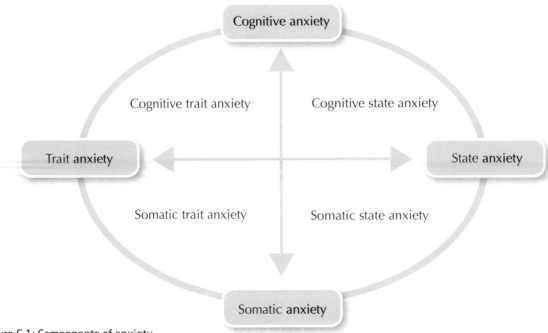

Figure 6.1: Components of anxiety

Key terms

Multi-dimensional – being made up of a number of different dimensions (or factors)

State anxiety – temporary, changeable mood state that is an emotional response to any situation considered threatening

Trait anxiety – aspect of personality and part of an individual's pattern of behaviour. Someone with a high level of trait anxiety is likely to become worried in a variety of situations; even non-threatening situations

Cognitive anxiety – negative thoughts, nervousness or worry experienced in certain situations. Symptoms of cognitive anxiety include concentration problems, fear and bad decision making

Somatic anxiety – relates to the awareness and perception of physiological changes (such as increases in heart rate, sweating and increased body heat) when you play sport

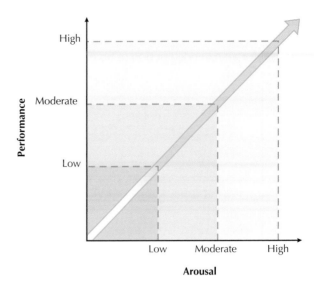

Figure 6.2: The drive theory – why do you think it is difficult to apply this theory to sport?

Inverted U hypothesis

The inverted U hypothesis differs from the drive theory in that it suggests a curvilinear relationship between arousal and performance, rather than the linear relationship suggested in the drive theory. The theory states that at optimal arousal levels, performance levels will be at their highest, but when arousal is either too low or too high, performance levels will be lower. At lower levels of arousal, performance will not be as high as it should be because the athlete is neither physiologically nor psychologically prepared (e.g. heart rate and concentration levels may be too low). As arousal levels increase, so does performance, but only up to an optimal point. At this optimal point of arousal (normally moderate levels), the athlete's performance will be at its highest. After this optimal point performance levels will start to decrease gradually (see Figure 6.3). This theory is more widely accepted than drive theory because most athletes and coaches can report personal experience of under-arousal (boredom), over-arousal (excitement to the point of lack of concentration) and optimum arousal (focus on nothing but sport performance). However, there has been some question over the type of curve demonstrated, specifically regarding whether performance will

attention). Arousal is typically viewed along a continuum, with deep sleep at one extreme, and excitement at the other.

There are a number of theoretical perspectives that have been proposed to attempt to explain the arousal/anxiety performance relationship. It is beyond the scope of this chapter to consider each in detail, but the key explanations are discussed (see Weinberg and Gould, 2007; Williams, 2010 for further discussions of each theory).

Drive theory

The drive theory suggests the relationship between arousal and performance is linear (see Figure 6.2) and that arousal increases will only continue to benefit performance if a skill is well learned. For example, if a professional snooker player experienced the highest levels of arousal, this theory suggests they would never miss a pot whilst arousal continued to increase. Conversely, in instances where the athlete is a novice, increased arousal has a negative effect on performance.

always decrease steadily after optimal arousal and whether an athlete can stay at optimal level of arousal for an extended period of time.

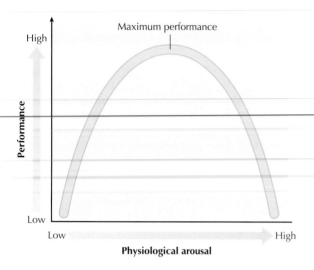

Figure 6.3: The inverted U theory

The catastrophe theory

The catastrophe theory (Fazey and Hardy, 1988) provides an alternative to the inverted U theory in that it suggests that performance is affected by arousal in an inverted U fashion when the athlete is experiencing low levels of cognitive arousal (see Figure 6.4a). It goes on to suggest that if high levels of cognitive anxiety are experienced, the performance decrease will be much more 'catastrophic' (see Figure 6.4b). The suggestions made through the catastrophe theory have been supported in a range of sports. However, more recent research (e.g. Cohen, Pargman and Tenenbaum, 2003) was unable to provide any empirical support for the theory, and research in golf reported that a high level of self-confidence would prevent a catastrophic drop in performance unless both somatic and cognitive and anxiety were at a high level (Hardy, Woodman and Carrington, 2004).

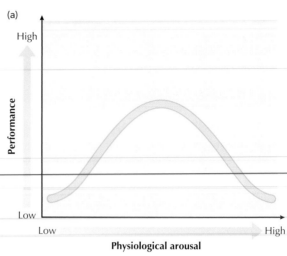

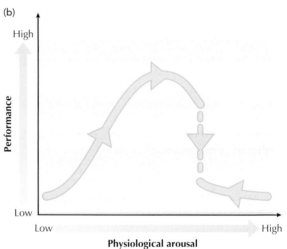

Figures 6.4a and 6.4b: Catastrophe theory, showing relationship between low cognitive anxiety (a) and high cognitive anxiety (b) and performance.

The individual zone of optimal functioning

The individual zone of optimal functioning (see Raglin and Hanin (2000) for a discussion of the IZOF approach in sport) is another alternative to the inverted U theory. It questions the assumption that every athlete's optimal level of arousal will be moderate by suggesting that each athlete has a different optimal level of arousal (in the form of state anxiety), and that highest performance will be maintained whilst the athlete is in their 'zone' (see Figure 6.5).

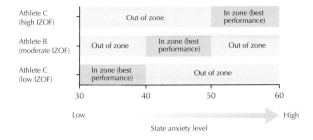

30   40   50   60

Low   High

State anxiety level

Figure 6.5: Individual zone of optimal functioning. How does the IZOF theory differ significantly from others?

Stop and think

Try to think of real-life sporting examples of the occurrence of each of these theories. Which do you find easiest to apply to your chosen sports and why?

Understand coping in sport

Following on from the work on anxiety, stress and arousal, you need to consider the notion of coping. It is widely accepted that athletes need to be able to cope effectively with different stressors (see Nicholls and Polman, 2007, for a detailed review). The more widely held view of coping is the transactional approach. This is where coping is defined as, 'constantly changing cognitive and behavioural efforts to manage specific external and/ or internal demands that are appraised as stressful' (Lazarus and Folkman, 1984, p. 141). Therefore, the transactional approach suggests an athlete's coping style is a process that involves an interaction between internal factors (e.g. self belief, goals) and external factors (e.g. situational demands) and accepts that athletes can develop, select and use a range of coping strategies. There are three main types of coping resource used by athletes.

1. Avoidance coping – where the client doesn't acknowledge there is a problem, e.g. denial, wishful thinking or removes themselves from a stressful situation so that they don't have to deal with it. This is the least effective mechanism of coping but is often used where there is no obvious solution to a problem.

2. Emotion-focused coping (EFC), e.g. imagery, social support – is often used in uncontrollable situations and is used to cope with the emotional response to a stressor.

3. Problem-focused coping (PFC), e.g. goal setting, gathering information – is used to find a solution to a problem and is most effective in controllable situations.

Know how to plan and review a psychological skills training programme

Despite compelling evidence that psychological skills are a key factor in enhancing the performance of athletes (e.g. MacNamara, Button and Collins, 2010), there are few talent development models that systematically encourage the development of psychological skills (Petlichoff, 2004). This section introduces you to different psychological skills that benefit athletes and how to design psychological skills training programmes. In addition to this section, Dosil (2006) and Hemmings and Holder (2009) provide examples of how sport psychology can benefit athletes in specific sports, and Harwood (2008) provides a detailed reflective account of how coaches can help to develop key psychological skills in young athletes.

Methods to enhance motivation

Whilst methods to enhance motivation are present in many sport psychology texts not all techniques to enhance motivation will work with all athletes. For example, sport psychologists talk about the importance of using goal setting with athletes, but not all athletes are the goal setting type or like to feel they have to work towards goals (Karageorghis and Terry, 2011).Therefore, getting to know your athlete is an essential part of developing motivation. Common techniques that are used to enhance motivation include goal setting, performance profiling and the use of rewards.

Goal setting

Goals are important because they influence how athletes change their behaviour and judge their performance. One of the issues with goal setting is that it can be done incorrectly, resulting in ineffective goals, so this section concentrates on different types of goals and the principles of effective goal setting. Using the SMARTS principle (Smith, 1994) is one way to set effective goals. SMARTS stands for:

Specific – goals should show exactly what needs to be done

Measurable – goals should be quantifiable

Action orientated – you should have to do something to achieve the goal

Realistic – goals should be within your reach

Timed – there should be a reasonable time frame

Self-determined – there should be input from the person for whom the goal is intended

Stop and think

Research other commonly used acronyms for goal setting; SCAMP, SMART and SMARTER. What do these mean and how do they differ from the SMARTS acronym above? How do you think this detailed understanding benefits our use of goal setting?

Types of goal

Goals are typically separated into subjective and objective goals. Whilst subjective goals are general statements of intent, objective goals are more useful for sport psychologists. Objective goals are defined as 'attaining a specific standard of proficiency on a task, usually within a specified time' (Locke, Shaw, Saari and Latham, 1981, p. 145). In addition to short and long term goals, there are three types of goals: outcome goals, performance goals and process goals; these are commonly viewed on a continuum (see Figure 6.6). As well as producing individual goals with athletes, team goals have been shown to be strongly associated with team success (Carron, Burke and Shapcott, 2009) and it is important to identify any barriers to goal achievement.

Outcome goals

These focus on the result of your event, like winning a race. This type of goal is often the least effective in enhancing motivation when it is used in isolation as your goal achievement is partly dependent on your opposition. An athlete could run a personal best in a 1500 metre event but still finish last. If the outcome goal is always to win, their motivation could reduce due to constant perceived failure. Spending too much time thinking about this type of goal before or during competition can also increase anxiety and decrease concentration, which reduces motivation. However, this type of goal can improve short term motivation

Performance goals

These focus on an athlete's performance and comparing their current performance to previous performances. They are independent of other athletes, provide a greater sense of control over the goal and can help to avoid negative social comparisons. Having greater control over goal achievement is beneficial for motivating an athlete. An example of a performance goal would be improving pass completion percentage in football to 85 per cent from 78 per cent.

Process Goals	Performance Goals	Outcome Goals
(e.g. improving technique)	(e.g. improve overall performance)	(e.g. win)

Figure 6.6: Continuum of a process - outcome goals

Process goals

These focus on improvements in techniques that will improve overall performance. An example of this type of goal would be a basketball player wanting to improve their jump shot accuracy by making sure they release the ball at the height of the jump. This type of goal is useful for improving motivation as it gives you specific elements of performance to focus on, which facilitate learning and development.

The key to using outcome, performance and process goals successfully is knowing which to use and when. It is hard for an athlete to focus on achieving short term process and performance goals without having a long term outcome to aim for. Reviews (e.g. Burton and Weiss, 2008; Weinberg and Butt, 2005) suggest that using a combination of all three types of goal is better than using any single type of goal when wanting to improve motivation, and that there should be a logical progression from short term to long term goals.

Principles of goal setting

The principles of goal setting (see Gould, 2010 for a detailed account) are important for designing an effective goal setting programme. Key principles from research and practice include:

- set specific goals
- set goals that are difficult but realistic
- set both short term and long term goals
- use a combination of performance, process and outcome goals
- set goals for both practice and competition
- record goals appropriately
- make sure the athlete knows how to achieve the goals
- provide support for achieving goals
- help the athlete to evaluate their goals
- provide appropriate feedback to the athlete.

Performance profiling

Performance profiling is a method of allowing an athlete to reflect on their performance in a manner that is based on their perspective rather than just the perspective of others (e.g. coaches). As the athlete is able to reflect on their specific circumstances, using a performance profile can help shape desirable behaviours and can give the athlete a greater sense of control over what they are doing – thus helping to enhance intrinsic motivation. The performance profile is a good way of identifying strengths and areas for improvements, and can help athletes and support teams to prioritise key areas for improvement. Within this process, the performance profile is an avenue that helps to foster communication between athletes and coaches, so that they have a greater understanding of each other's perspective and often forms the basis of goal setting with athletes. As well as being effective for enhancing motivation on an individual basis, team performance profiling can enhance team motivation through facilitating group goal setting, which can lead to a degree of shared responsibility and shared perceptions (Carron, Burke and Shapcott, 2009). It also has the added benefit of involving the team in a joint activity and facilitating communication within the team (Thelwell, 2009).

Process of performance profiling

Performance profiling is completed as a five stage process.

- **Stage 1** Identify and define key qualities for performance – introduce the idea by asking the athlete what attributes are important for top performance (in non-elite settings, the athlete could be asked to think of an elite performer and write down their qualities). The athlete should record the qualities necessary for performance and their definitions in a table. This helps them and the sport psychologist to develop an understanding of what the terms mean. To avoid misunderstanding ensure the definitions used are produced by the athlete.

- **Stage 2** Profile the current levels – this is an assessment of the athlete's current level of performance. This can be done by the athlete alone, or by the coach and athlete. The key qualities are written in each of the blank spaces around the outside of the circular grid and each quality is given a rating from 0 to 10 by shading the segments up to the estimated level.

- **Stage 3** Interpreting the results – strengths and areas for improvement are identified. Where a coach and athlete have both completed athlete profiles, if there are large differences between estimated levels (a large difference is classed as two points or more), this should lead to a discussion about why the difference is apparent. Often, highlighting the three areas with the lowest scores forms the basis of the psychological skills training programme (PST).

- **Stage 4** Goal setting – goals and strategies to achieve the goals are produced with the athlete. Normally, each of these benchmarks will be at level 10 – any target level below this on the client's behalf suggests that there is some resistance to achieving the ultimate level of performance.

- **Stage 5** Repeat the profiling to monitor progress – performance profiling can be repeated on a number of occasions to assess the athlete's progress. The aim is that the athlete gradually progresses towards the outside of the scale (closer to the rating of 10). If the athlete does not make the desired progress, discussions should take place regarding the progress. Usually, lack of progress means the PST didn't fully account for the athlete's needs (errors in design of programme), you have different views on the importance of a quality (errors in communication and understanding) or the athlete has not put in the effort to achieve the improvements in performance.

Figure 6.7 shows how performance profiling can be used with an athlete and a coach to openly assess the performance of an athlete.

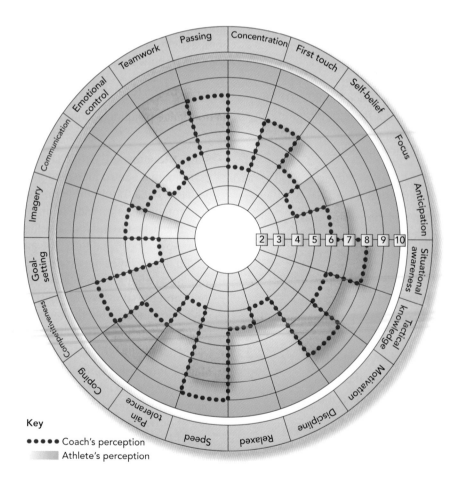

Key

•••• Coach's perception

██ Athlete's perception

Figure 6.7: An example performance profile that compares coach and athlete views on performance. Are there any areas that require discussion between coach and athlete? What do you think are the key areas for improvement?

Rewards

Rewards are small prizes or recognition given to people when they produce a desired behaviour. Rewards come under the headings of tangible and intangible rewards and can influence motivation but only if used correctly. Rewards that are used too frequently with the same individual become under-valued, or if rewards are only given to the very best athletes, the motivational element of the reward is lost on other athletes.

Karageorghis and Terry (2011) demonstrated an example of the effective use of token rewards during their work with an international tennis academy. They used an Olympic medal scenario of gold, silver and bronze medals for the first three people in speed drills, whilst also awarding man or woman of the day awards to people that had performed best on a given day relative to their ability. They offered the acronym 'SCORE' as a useful way of remembering how to effectively use rewards with athletes.

Simplicity – keep the reward system easy to follow and understand to avoid confusion.

Consistency – leaders should be fair and transparent in their use of rewards so that nobody perceives favouritism and everyone believes that they have a fair chance of winning the reward.

Observation – all athletes need to feel that their efforts will be noticed so you should use observation to encourage effort and discourage those who see no reason to try.

Reward – keep the reward in perspective. It is the recognition that comes from the reward, rather than the tangible value of the reward, that makes it effective.

Explanation – clearly explain what you are trying to achieve and why; then explain the reward system. Use clear and accessible language to avoid confusion.

Imagery in sport

Imagery is a topic that is well researched with athletes and is frequently used to try to help enhance the performance of athletes (Morris, Spittle

Remember

Each of the techniques discussed above can help enhance motivation. There is no 'one size fits all' solution for low motivation, so you should use the one (or the combination) that best fits your athlete.

and Watt, 2005). Whilst sport psychology literature (e.g. Hall, 2001) reports research with elite adult athletes, imagery has more recently also been investigated with child and adolescent athletes (e.g. Munroe-Chandler, Hall, Fishburne, O and Hall, 2007) and has a range of benefits in these different populations. The reported benefits of imagery use in sport include: increasing self-confidence and self-efficacy (Munroe-Chandler, Hall, Fishburne, O and Hall, 2007); producing task-specific physiological responses (Wilson, Smith, Burden and Holmes, 2010); increased positive emotions (McCarthy, 2009); injury rehabilitation (Dreidiger, Hall and Callow, 2006); enhancing technique (Hardy and Callow, 1999). Although there are a number of reported benefits of imagery, there is still some confusion over exactly *how* imagery works (see Morris, Spittle and Watt, 2005 and Hale, Seiser, McGuire and Weinrich, 2005 for more detailed accounts of such explanations).

Remember

Whilst there have been many attempts to explain how imagery works, there is not a universally accepted answer.

Types of imagery and their uses

Much of the imagery work in sport has been guided by Paivio's (1985) original framework that suggested imagery had both cognitive and motivational benefits, although recent literature suggests that the motivational function of imagery is potentially overstated (McIntyre and Moran, 2007). Paivio's work has since been advanced so that five common types of imagery are reported: motivational specific, motivational general–mastery, motivational general–arousal, cognitive specific and cognitive general.

- **Motivational specific imagery** Imagine yourself in a highly motivating sport setting such as scoring the winning goal in a football match. This is an example of motivational specific imagery and is aimed at increasing motivation levels in athletes.

- **Motivational general–mastery imagery** Now imagine yourself in a situation where you have to concentrate and think positively, such as at the start of a 100 metre sprint. This is an example of motivational general-mastery imagery and is aimed at helping athletes to remain focused and have confidence in their ability.

- **Motivational general–arousal imagery** This time, imagine yourself breathing deeply just before you take a free throw shot in basketball and how you feel once you have taken the deep breath. This is an example of motivational general–arousal imagery and is aimed at helping you to control arousal and anxiety levels.

- **Cognitive specific imagery** Imagine yourself correctly executing a sport skill of your choice, such as putting a golf ball or potting a snooker ball. This is an example of cognitive specific imagery and is aimed at acquiring, practising and correcting sport skills.

- **Cognitive general imagery** Finally, imagine yourself playing an active part in your team's overall tactics, for example providing an overlapping run for your winger in football so that you can get a cross into the box. This is an example of cognitive general imagery and is aimed at acquiring and practising team strategies or tactics.

Using imagery with athletes

Holmes and Collins (2001) offered the acronym PETTLEP as a method of using imagery with athletes. PETTLEP stands for the following.

Physical – imagery should mirror the physical movements performed in the sport.

Environment – imagery should replicate the competitive setting that the athlete experiences.

Task – imagery should meet the needs of the specific activity and the athlete performing the imagery.

Timing – the timing of imagery should replicate the performance or event requirements.

Learning – the content of the imagery should be adapted in response to learning

Emotion – imagery should also seek to produce the emotional responses experienced through sport.

Perspective – imagery should be performed through the preferred perspective of the athlete, either **internal imagery** or **external imagery**.

Key terms

Internal imagery – imagining an activity from the first- person perspective and concentrating on how the activity feels. This is beneficial as it can generate the same type of muscular activity as physically performing the activity, but to a lesser extent.

External imagery – imagining yourself doing something as though you are watching it on a film so that you can develop an awareness of how the activity looks. This can help athletes to correct errors in performance and develop correct movement patterns.

Methods to regulate arousal in sport

Two of the more commonly used methods to reduce arousal levels are progressive muscular relaxation and self-talk.

Progressive muscular relaxation (PMR)

Muscle tension decreases performance levels due to vastly reduced flexibility and poor co-ordination. PMR (Jacobsen, 1938) is an easy-to-use technique that helps to reduce muscle tension. It raises awareness of levels of muscle tension and, through the relaxation phase, helps the client to distinguish between what is a state of tension and relaxation. The technique involves tensing and relaxing groups of muscles in turn over the whole body. Each muscle group is tensed for five seconds, the tension is then released for five seconds, a deep breath is taken and the process is repeated. This technique can be tailored for use in individual muscle groups.

Self-talk

When performing badly, an athlete can start to have negative thoughts, which can lead to increased levels of anxiety and arousal. Sport psychologists help athletes to learn to talk to themselves more positively during these periods of poor performance. **Positive self-talk** can help the client manage their emotional response to playing badly by increasing their motivation, self-esteem and directing their attention towards specific elements of the performance (Johnson, Hrycaiko, Johnson and Halas, 2004). Figure 6.8 demonstrates the potential impact that changing **negative self-talk** to **positive self-talk** can have on the athlete's responses to poor performance.

Use of music

As well as reducing arousal, sport psychologists may need to help athletes to increase their arousal levels. Music increases and decreases arousal levels, but must be used carefully so it is not detrimental (Karageorghis and Terry, 2011). Anecdotally, music can divert an athlete's focus away from sensations of fatigue, elevates mood state through avoidance of

> ### Key terms
>
> **Positive self-talk** – positive statements used to arouse and direct attention or to motivate people towards achieving goals
>
> **Negative self-talk** – self-critical statements that can distract attention, reduce confidence and self-efficacy levels and make it harder to achieve goals

negative thoughts and increases body temperature, heart rate and breathing rate, which help prepare the body for sport performance.

Acting energised

When athletes have low levels of arousal, acting energised can be a good way to increase arousal (Taylor and Wilson, 2005). These 'energised acts' involve the combination of quick and forceful movements, positive thinking and strong emotional releases. Acting energised heightens concentration levels, can reprioritise goal achievement, increases motivation levels and makes the athlete excited about competing again. In an elite sport setting,

Wicket keeper misses an important catch in cricket

Negative self-talk response:

'I can't believe I dropped that – we'll never get him out now!'

Positive self-talk response:

'Keep your eyes on the ball and you'll catch him next time!'

Athlete responses:

Frustration, anger, despair, hopelessness

Increased muscle tension, increased sweating rate, difficult to concentrate on the next ball

Athlete responses:

Calm, increased confidence in performance, able to concentrate on relevant cues (e.g. bowling type, position of batsman)

More relaxed and comfortable body position, lack of tension

Figure 6.8: Responses to positive and negative self-talk

this type of body language can increase the arousal levels of the crowd (often displayed through cheering on the team more), which can further benefit athletes.

Designing psychological skills training programmes

Psychological skills training programmes are one way of working with athletes to enhance performance. Other approaches (e.g. counselling and psychotherapy approaches) are sometimes outside the scope of expertise of a sport psychologist so may require a referral to another professional. You will need to alter your style of work to meet the needs of different clients, but psychological skills training programmes are generally separated into four distinct phases (see Hemmings and Holder, 2009 for examples of working with different individuals and teams from sport psychology practice):

- needs analysis
- deciding on appropriate techniques
- implementing and monitoring techniques
- evaluation, feedback and identification of future needs.

Needs analysis

A needs analysis involves the sport psychologist trying to answer two important questions.

1. Is intervention needed?
2. Where intervention is needed, am I able to provide that help?

These questions will usually be answered through a range of methods that include using inventories (see Ostrow, 2002 for an expansive list of inventories used in sport psychology and guidelines for use), performance profiling, conducting interviews and observing athletes in training and performance environments. When asking questions during meetings, use a range of open and closed questions and your listening skills, to allow the athlete to provide as much information as possible. Start out using simple questions that don't probe too deeply so that a relationship can be developed before trying to get more detailed/personal information.

Remember

A good listener is somebody who keeps quiet and doesn't interrupt their client. There are two parts to listening:

- content – listening for clues for further probing or questioning
- process – listening for clues about how the consultation is going.

Deciding on programme content

When producing a plan for any PST programme consider how much time should be spent on different aspects of the programme and ensure that there is a suitable evidence base for the techniques you select – you need to know *what* to recommend, and *why* to recommend it. If you are introducing new skills to the PST programme, then distinct training sessions are beneficial but gradually, the aim is to move away from needing distinct sessions to allow the psychological skills to be integrated with normal practice and training. This becomes possible only when athletes are proficient in their new skills, so ensure that there is time to learn them. The content ideally should be decided by the sport psychologist, coach and athlete (and potentially parents/carers) together as this means it has been decided on objectively and takes into account the different perspectives of all involved with the development of the athlete, thus ensuring the content is manageable. Including the athlete in the decision of the daily and weekly content increases their motivation to adhere to the programme, as they will have invested time and effort in its design and will feel more in control.

Remember

You will find that you naturally combine different psychological skills with your client. For example, the athlete may use self-talk to guide themselves through an imagery sequence or the athlete may imagine themselves achieving a goal.

Implementation and monitoring

Once the techniques have been agreed and planned, athletes should be given time to learn the techniques and start to use them in training and competition. The sport psychologist should be available to support the athlete with different techniques.

Evaluation, feedback and identification of future needs

The main ways of reviewing a PST programme are repeating initial inventories to compare pre-intervention results to post-intervention results, interviews (group or individual), consultant evaluation forms and monitoring sport performance (including collecting objective performance data). Detailed feedback is key to reviewing your work with clients.

Interviews

Interviews are a good way of getting more in-depth information from your athletes regarding the effectiveness of the PST programme. Use semi-structured interviews which allow you to probe different areas. Figure 6.9 shows a sample interview guide that could be used in either group or individual settings. It allows you to get qualitative feedback from clients.

Figure 6.9: Why do you think this type of interview will be beneficial when evaluating your work?

Interview Guide

Sport psychology consultant evaluation session

Nature of interview (please circle):   Individual   Group

1   **Working with the consultant**

   a How useful did you find the individual sessions with the consultant?

   b How useful did you find the team sessions with the consultant?

   c Did you prefer the formal or informal meetings?

   d How approachable did you find the consultant?

2   **Techniques used during the programme**

   a Which techniques did you think worked best?

   b Did the programme take into account your personal circumstances?

   c Do you feel you were given enough time to develop the skills through-out the programme?

3   **Future recommendations**

   a Do you think that anything else should be included in the programme?

   b Do you think that anything needs to be taken out of the programme?

   c What do you see as the major strengths of the programme?

   d What do you see as the major limitations of the programme?

- **Consultant evaluation forms** One way of getting feedback is with a consultant evaluation form (see Figure 6.10). This is a questionnaire that the athlete fills in to provide you with qualitative and quantitative feedback on three areas:

- characteristics of the consultant
- effectiveness of the consultant
- suggestions for improvement of future consultancy work.

Consultation evaluation form

Client's name ....

Consultant's name ....

1 Characteristics of consultant

For each of the following statements, please provide a rating from 1-5, with 1 being the lowest rating and 5 being the highest.

Statement	Rating
a The consultant could provide me with information on skills training that applied directly to my sport.	
b The consultant produced a programme that was geared to my individual needs.	
c The consultant was flexible and was happy to work around me.	
d The consultant was positive.	
e The consultant made me feel comfortable.	
f I understood exactly what the consultant expected of me.	

2 Effectiveness of the consultant

Please circle the number that you feel best describes how effective you feel the consultant was in helping overall sporting performance.

a Overall individual performance		
Limited performance		*Helped performance*
-5 -4 -3 -2 -1 0 1 2 3 4 5		
b Overall team performance		
Limited performance		*Helped performance*
-5 -4 -3 -2 -1 0 1 2 3 4 5		

3 Recommendations for improvement

Please use the space below to provide any recommendations you feel will increase the quality of service provided by the consultant. Please continue on the back of this form if necessary.

Figure 6.10: Example consultant evaluation form. Why do you think it is important to reflect on your applied work?

Observing sport performance

Observing performance helps assess the effectiveness of your psychological skills training programme because it allows you to collect objective data relating to performance (e.g. is there an increase in the number of successful passes?) and subjectively observe the athlete (e.g. do they appear generally more calm when playing?). When you observe performance, look for:

- changes in physiological factors
- changes in body language
- differences in the skill level of the athlete
- differences in interactions with team mates, officials or coaching staff.

Identification of future needs

At the end of your PST programme, discuss with your client their strengths, areas for improvement and help them to identify their future needs. These will be particularly useful if you can help your client place them in order of priority. The future needs are methods of PST that your client could use to help further develop their strengths and areas for improvement.

Case study (for recommended answers, see www.pearsonfe.co.uk/foundationsinsport)

Laura is a 21-year-old sprinter who is struggling with her sprint start. She keeps looking around on the start line and thinking 'I can't beat these' and as a result starts to sweat, her heart rate increases and she struggles to concentrate on the starting gun. She has also begun to worry more because she feels her technique is starting to suffer. She always feels really tense but she can't figure out why or where her technique needs to be improved. Laura has now become more distanced from her coach because she feels the advice that her coach is providing is not helping her performance and she has begun to feel as though she may never be able to improve.

1. Is there a problem here, and if so what are the key signs of problems for you?

2. Is this a situation that a sport psychologist could help with?

3. Who else would need to be involved with supporting this athlete?

4. What techniques would you recommend Laura uses and why?

Check your understanding (for answers, see www.pearsonfe.co.uk/foundationsinsport)

1. What are the three main roles of a sport psychologist?

2. What are the main types of motivation?

3. What are the main types of anxiety?

4. What are the different theories of arousal?

5. What are the different types of coping in sport?

6. What are the techniques commonly used to enhance motivation?

7. What does the acronym 'SCORE' stand for and to what topic does it relate?

8. What are the different types of imagery?

9. What does the acronym 'PETTLEP' stand for?

10. What are the different perspectives of imagery?

11. What are some of the methods of regulating arousal that are commonly used with athletes?

12. What are the general stages of designing psychological skills training programmes?

Time to reflect

1. What barriers do you think a sport psychologist could face when working within professional sport?

2. Why do you think it is important for sport psychologists to have specific training pathways?

3. Can you think of any practical sporting examples where you think sport psychology could have been used to enhance performance?

4. Why is it important to evaluate your applied work in sport psychology?

Useful resources

To obtain a secure link to the websites below, see the Websites section on page ii or visit the companion website at www.pearsonfe.co.uk/foundationsinsport

- American Psychological Association
- Asian South Pacific Association of Sport Psychology
- British Association of Sport and Exercise Sciences
- British Psychological Society
- European Federation of Sport Psychology
- Health Professions Council
- International Association of Applied Psychology
- International Society of Sport Psychology
- North American Society for the Psychology of Sport and Physical Activity

Further reading

Burton, D. and Weiss, C. (2008). The Fundamental Goal Concept: The Path to Performance and Process Success. In T. Horn (ed.). *Advances in Sport Psychology* (3rd Edition. pp. 339–375). Champaign, Illinois: Human Kinetics.

Carron, A.V., Burke, S.M. and Shapcott, K.M. (2009). Enhancing Team Effectiveness. In B. Brewer (ed.). *Handbook of Sports Medicine: Sport Psychology* (pp. 64–74). West Sussex: Wiley-Blackwell.

Cohen, A., Pargman, D. and Tenenbaum, G. (2003). Critical Elaboration and Empirical Investigation of the Cusp Catastrophe Model: A Lesson for Practitioners. *Journal of Applied Sport Psychology*, **15**, pp. 144–159.

Cox, R.H. (2007). *Sport Psychology: Concepts and Applications*, 6th Edition. Boston: McGraw Hill.

Dosil, J. (ed.) (2006). *The Sport Psychologist's Handbook: A Guide to Sport Specific Performance Enhancement*. West Sussex: Wiley-Blackwell.

Dreidiger, M., Hall, C. and Callow, N. (2006). Imagery use by Injured Athletes: A Qualitative Study. *Journal of Sports Sciences*, **24**, pp. 261–271.

Duda, J.L. and Hall, H. (2001). Achievement Goal Theory in Sport: Recent Extensions and Future Directions. In R.N. Singer, H.A. Hausenblas, and C.M. Janelle (eds.), *Handbook of Sport Psychology* (pp. 417–443). New York: Wiley.

Fazey, J. and Hardy, L. (1988). *The Inverted U Hypothesis: A Catastrophe for Sport Psychology?* British Association of Sport and Exercise Sciences Monograph No. 1. Leeds: The National Coaching Foundation.

Fletcher, D. and Hanton, S. (2003). Sources of Organisational Stress in Elite Sport Performers. *The Sport Psychologist*, **17**, pp. 175–195.

Gould, D. (2010). Goal Setting for Peak Performance. In J.M. Williams (eds.), *Applied Sport Psychology: Personal Growth to Peak Performance* (6th Edition., pp. 201–220). Boston: McGraw-Hill.

Hagger, M., and Chatzisarantis, N. (2007). *Intrinsic Motivation and Self-Determination in Exercise and Sport*. Champaign, Illinois: Human Kinetics.

Hale, B.D., Seiser, L., McGuire, E.J. and Weinrich, E. (2005). In J. Taylor., and G. Wilson (eds.), *Applying Sport Psychology: Four Perspectives*, pp. 117–135. Champaign, Illinois: Human Kinetics.

Hall, C.R. (2001). Imagery in Sport and Exercise. In R.N. Singer, H.A. Hausenblas and C.M. Janelle (eds.), *Handbook of Sport Psychology*, 2nd Edition, pp. 529–549. New York: Wiley.

Hanton, S. and Jones, G. (1999a). The Acquisition and Development of Cognitive Skills and Strategies: I. Making the Butterflies Fly in Formation. *The Sport Psychologist*, **13**, pp. 1–21.

Hanton, S. and Jones, G. (1999b). The Effects of Multimodal Intervention Program on Performers. II. Making the Butterflies Fly in Formation. *The Sport Psychologist*, **13**, pp. 22–41.

Hardy, L. and Callow, N. (1999). Efficacy of External and Internal Visual Imagery Perspectives for the Enhancement of Performance of Tasks in Which Form is Important. *Journal of Sport and Exercise Psychology*, **21**, pp. 95–112.

Hardy, L., Woodman, T. and Carrington (2004). Is Self–Confidence a Bias Factor in Higher–Order Catastrophe Models? *Journal of Sport and Exercise Psychology*, **26**, pp. 359–368.

Harwood, C. (2008). Developmental Coaching in a Professional Football Academy: The 5C Coaching Efficacy Program. *The Sport Psychologist*, **22**, pp. 109–133.

Harwood, C.G., Cumming, J. and Fletcher, D. (2004). Motivational Profiles and Psychological Skills Use within Elite Youth Sport. *Journal of Applied Sport Psychology*, **16**, pp. 318–332.

Hemmings, B. and Holder, T. (eds.) (2009). *Applied Sport Psychology: A Case–Based Approach*. West Sussex: Wiley-Blackwell.

Holmes, P.S., and Collins, D.J. (2001). The PETTLEP Approach to Motor Imagery: A Functional Equivalence Model for Sport Psychologists. *Journal of Applied Sport Psychology*, **13**, pp. 60–83.

Jacobsen, E. (1938). *Progressive Relaxation*. Chicago: University of Chicago Press.

Johnson, J.J.M., Hrycaiko, D.W., Johnson, G.V. and Halas, J.M. (2004). Self–Talk and Female Youth Soccer Performance. *The Sport Psychologist*, **18**, pp. 44–59.

Jones, G., Hanton, S. and Connaughton, D. (2007). A Framework for Mental Toughness in the World's Best Performers. *The Sport Psychologist*, **21**, pp. 243–264.

Karageorghis, C.I. and Terry, P.C. (2011). *Inside Sport Psychology*. Champaign, Illinois: Human Kinetics.

Lazarus, R.S. (2000). How Emotions Influence Performance in Competitive Sports. *The Sport Psychologist*, **14**, pp. 229–252.

Lazarus, R.S., and Folkman, S. (1984). *Stress, Appraisal and Coping in Sport*. New York: Springer.

Locke, E.A. , Shaw, K.N., Saari, L.M., and Latham, G.P. (1981). Goal Setting and Task Performance. *Psychological Bulletin*, **90**, pp. 125–152.

MacNamara, A., Button, A., and Collins, D. (2010). The Role of Psychological Characteristics in Facilitating the Pathway to Elite Performance Part 1: Indentifying Mental Skills and Behaviours. *The Sport Psychologist*, **24**, pp. 52–73.

Martens, R. (2004). *Successful Sports Coaching*. Champaign, Illinois: Human Kinetics.

Martens, R., Vealey, R.S. and Burton, D. (eds.). (1990). *Competitive Anxiety in Sport*. Champaign, Illinois: Human Kinetics.

McCarthy, P.J. (2009). Putting Imagery to Good Effect: A Case Study Among Youth Swimmers. *Sport and Exercise Psychology Review*, **5**, pp. 27–38.

McIntyre, T. and Moran, A. (2007). A Qualitative Investigation of Meta-Imagery Processes and Imagery Direction Among Elite Athletes. *Journal of Imagery Research in Sport and Physical Activity*, **2**, pp. 1–20.

Moran, A.P. (2004). *Sport and Exercise Psychology: A Critical Introduction*. London: Routledge.

Morris, T., Spittle, M. and Watt, A.P. (2005). *Imagery in Sport*. Champaign, Illinois: Human Kinetics.

Munroe-Chandler, K.J., Hall, C., Fishburne, G., O, J. and Hall, N.D. (2007). The Content of Young Athletes' Imagery Use: A Developmental Perspective. *International Journal of Sport and Exercise Psychology*, **5**, pp. 158–174.

Nicholls, A. and Polman, R.C.J. (2007). Coping in Sport: A Systematic Review. *Journal of Sports Sciences*, **25**, pp. 11–31.

Ostrow, A.C. (2002). *Directory of Psychological Tests in the Sport and Exercise Sciences* (2nd Edition). Morgantown, WV: Fitness Information Technology.

Paivio, A. (1985). Cognitive and Motivational Functions of Imagery in Human Performance. *Canadian Journal of Applied Sports Sciences*, **10**, pp. 22–28.

Petlichoff, L.M. (2004). Self-regulation Skills in Children and Adolescents. In M.R. Weiss (ed.), *Developmental Sport and Exercise Psychology: A Lifespan Perspective* pp. 273–292. Morgantown, WV: Fitness Information Technology.

Raglin, J.S. and Hanin, Y.L. (2000). Competitive anxiety. In Y.L. Hanin (ed.), *Emotions in Sport*, pp. 93–112. Champaign, Illinois: Human Kinetics.

Ryan, R.M. and Deci, E.L. (2000). Self-Determination Theory and the Facilitation of Intrinsic Motivation, Social Development and Subjective Wellbeing. *American Psychologist*, **55**, pp. 68–78.

Smith , H.W. (1994). *The 10 Natural Laws of Successful Time and Life Management: Proven Strategies for Increased Productivity and Inner Peace.* New York: Warner.

Taylor, J. and Wilson, G. (eds.) (2005). *Applying Sport Psychology: Four Perspectives*. Champaign, Illinois: Human Kinetics.

Thelwell, R. (2009). Team Goal Setting in Professional Football. In B. Hemmings, and T. Holder (eds.), *Applied Sport Psychology: A Case-Based Approach*, pp. 161–180. West Sussex: Wiley Blackwell.

Weinberg, R.S. and Butt, J. (2005). Goal Setting in Sport and Exercise Domains: The Theory and Practice of Effective Goal Setting. In D. Hackfort, J. Duda and R. Lidor (eds.), *Handbook of Research in Applied Sport Psychology*, pp. 129–146. Morgantown, WV: Fitness Information Technology.

Weinberg, R.S. and Gould, D. (2007). *Foundations of Sport and Exercise Psychology,* 4th Edition. Champaign, Illinois: Human Kinetics.

Williams, J.M. (ed.) (2010). *Applied Sport Psychology: Personal Growth to Peak Performance,* 6th Edition. Boston: McGraw Hill.

Wilson, C., Smith, D., Burden, A. and Holmes, P. (2010). Participant Generated Imagery Scripts Produce Greater EMG Activity and Imagery ability. *European Journal of Sport Science*, **10**, pp. 417–425.

Chapter 7

Coaching science

Introduction

Sports coaches work with children and adults from grass-roots right through to performance sport. In addition to improving an individual or team's performance, sports coaches are increasingly part of the wider social agenda of healthy living and physical activity. It is estimated that in excess of six million people receive sports coaching in the UK (Department for Culture, Media and Sport, 2002). Approximately 80 per cent of the 1.2 million people involved in the practice of sports coaching contribute their time on a voluntary basis (Skills Active, 2011). However, paid employment as a sports coach represents a significant part of the active leisure, learning and wellbeing sector workforce (in the UK there are 240 000 paid sports coaches).

In the profession of sports coaching there is a strong link between knowledge and competence. You would expect your coach to be knowledgeable and the assumption is that the more knowledgeable the coach, the more effective they will be at meeting your needs. Predominantly it is sports sciences that form the mass of knowledge from which sports coaches select and apply information in a particular coaching context.

Learning outcomes

After you have read this chapter you should be able to:

- understand what sport is

- understand what sports coaching is

- appreciate the areas of sports science impacting on coaching

- explain what is meant by 'coach as teacher'

- understand what coaching science is

- explain the main theories of learning in relation to coaching

- understand learning styles, coaching styles and multiple intelligences

- understand the process of communication and the communication channels used by coaches

- critically appraise your coaching performance.

Starting block

Drawing on experiences that you have had in sport, think about the times when you have had difficulty in understanding what your coach has wanted you to do. Share these with other members of your group and look for similarities and differences in your experiences.

Before unpicking what coaching science is, it is important to explain the context in which it sits. The concepts of sport, coaching and sports science will be explained here.

What is sport?

Sport is often defined in terms of team sports (for example, hockey, netball, football, rugby and volleyball) or individual sports (for example, tennis, badminton, golf, athletics and fencing). The definition is usually refined by adding that sport is normally associated with being physical, requiring skill, involving competition with clearly identifiable winners and losers, and that sport is played or performed according to a set of rules. This definition of sport can lead to intense discussions about whether or not a particular activity is a sport or not. For example, is it sport where a winner or loser is decided by a panel of judges (ballroom dancing, ski jumping, ice skating, weight lifting)? Is it a sport when physical exertion is minimal, but psychological exertion and skill execution is tested to the maximum (archery, pistol shooting, snooker, fishing, darts)? What about sports that have a large degree of physical activity, but are undertaken by large numbers of participants mostly without competition goals (skateboarding, freerunning (parkour), freestyle BMX, surfing, walking, hang gliding)?

In universally adopting a narrow definition of sport, it limits our understanding of what sports coaching is by restricting it to working with participants in a selection of predominantly games based activities that meet a set of rigid criteria. This chapter is underpinned by an understanding of sport to incorporate any physical activity that is undertaken for any reason (including competition and other purposes such as enjoyment, social activity, weight management, friendships and developing self-esteem). Activities that are brought under the banner of a broader physical definition of sport, to sit alongside 'sports' include **exercise**, **health-related activities**, **exergaming**, dance and **activities of daily living**.

Key terms

Exercise – activity that maintains or enhances physical fitness

Health-related activities – activity aimed at improving the health and well-being of an individual

Exergaming – the term used for video games that also incorporate physical activity

Activities of daily living – the things that you normally do in daily living at home or at work

A broader understanding of sport includes any physical activity undertaken for any reason. Do you think that a coach is only important when the aim of an activity is performance improvement?

What is sports coaching?

Sports coaching involves a coach establishing and maintaining **facilitative** relationships within a positive **coaching environment** conducive to meeting the participants' goals for taking part in physical activity. Sports coaches, whether working with elite athletes striving to achieve competition goals, children participating for fun, or the elderly maintaining health levels, are guided by a flexible **coaching philosophy** that directly influences their coaching behaviour.

Facilitative – to assist in making things easier or less difficult

Coaching environment – the physical space in which sports coaching activities take place

Coaching philosophy – the guiding principles that shape a coach's behaviour in the coaching environment

Coaching philosophy

From a coach's perspective, the term coaching philosophy is often used to describe the guiding principles that shape a coach's behaviour in the coaching environment. These guiding principles can be internal to the coach, based on a set of deeply held beliefs, or can be externally imposed expectations from participants and employers or organisations. These guiding principles can collectively be referred to as the ethics of coaching. Morals, values and virtues all combine to provide the sports coach with a framework against which reflection and choices are made. It is these choices in a particular context that will shape the coaching philosophy.

A written record of a coach's philosophy is referred to as a philosophy statement. The following list of questions might be helpful in developing your coaching philosophy statement.

- How important is winning?
- Are you interested in the holistic development of your athletes?
- How important is playing by the rules?
- Are you comfortable with ceding control and power to your athletes?
- Do you want to encourage a coaching environment where athletes feel comfortable questioning you?
- Do you care if your athletes enjoy the session?
- Do you foster an environment that embraces respect for others?
- How would you deal with a 'pushy parent' in your coaching environment?

Here is an excerpt from an example coaching philosophy statement. It has been presented as a list with the most important aspects for this coach at the top. The statement could also easily be presented as a piece of continuous text. This is a coach working with a group of 20 county squad players of an individual sport. The players' abilities range from a competitive social standard through to national level and they are aged between 15 and 17 years old. There are equal numbers of male and female athletes in the group.

1. The sessions should be fun and the player should want to come back to the next session.
2. The coaching environment should be a safe space to be in.
3. All players will be treated as knowledgeable and creative beings, who are able to think for themselves.
4. Players will demonstrate respect for all other individuals in the coaching environment.
5. Players will demonstrate high levels of motivation at all times.
6. Parents are welcome to observe the sessions but can in no way interfere with the players during the session.

In striving to provide a positive coaching environment it is essential that there are no mismatches between a coach's philosophy and the expectations of the individual or team that the coach is working with. Any mismatch would result in conflict or tension in the coaching environment. This could mean that coaches decide to adapt their privately held values and beliefs in order to ensure that conflict is removed, minimised, or at least managed in the coach–athlete relationship. This means that sports coaches can present a very different public face in comparison to their privately held values and beliefs. There will be situations where compromise on certain core values and beliefs might not be an option for a sports coach, and in these cases, it is probably best for the coach to seek out another coaching opportunity that is consistent with their coaching philosophy.

There are approximately 240 000 sports coaches in some form of employment (Skills Active, 2011), and therefore an added layer of complexity for sports coaches to negotiate, in addition to the expectations of the individuals and teams that they are working with, are their employers' expectations. For example, coaches working for a professional club will need to locate winning as a priority, whereas coaches working for a school would need to ensure that the holistic development of the child is central. It is a delicate balancing act for coaches in being flexible and adaptive in relation to the context presented to them, whilst remaining faithful to their deeply embedded set of values.

To avoid potential conflict between the coaches, participants, parents and, where applicable, the employers, the coach should attempt to establish a mutual direction that will guide what takes place in the coaching environment. This would mean presenting the public version of their coaching philosophy, and then asking those with a vested interest in the coaching a series of questions. For example:

- What is the main reason for you participating in this sport?
- What do you want to achieve individually and collectively this season?
- What is it that you most enjoy about this sport?
- What activities do you really enjoy in a coaching session?
- What activities do you particularly dislike doing in a coaching session?
- How are we going to ensure that your experience is satisfying?
- What do we need to do if you become dissatisfied with your experience?

Stop and think

Select and read a sports coach's autobiography and note both internal and external factors that guided the way that they coached. Produce a philosophy statement for the coach.

Remember

The use of the term 'coach–athlete' relationship is problematic in describing the bond that sports coaches establish and maintain because using the term '**athlete**' directly ascribes the notion that there is a performance aspect to the relationship. Using the term 'coach–**participant**' relationship is more consistent with contemporary thinking on the realities of coaching sport.

Key terms

Athlete – a person who competes in organised sporting events

Participant – a person who takes part or becomes involved in an activity

Different approaches to sports coaching

Different approaches to sports coaching are determined by the degree to which the coach controls the coaching environment, or, from the perspective of the participant, the level of dependency on the coach. You can think of the approaches as being situated on a spectrum from complete control by the coach at one end to complete independence of the athlete at the other. The coaching philosophy of the coach and their motivations for coaching, participant variables (for example, age and reasons for participation), and external influences (for example, parent and employer expectations) will all impact on the coaching approach. Table 7.1 (overleaf) summarises the three main approaches to sports coaching.

Table 7.1: Approaches to sports coaching

Approach	Authoritarian	Power sharing	Humanistic
Who is in control?	Coach	Joint	Athlete
Dependence on coach	Coach dependence	Athlete/coach interdependence	Athlete independence
Characteristics	No decision-making responsibility	Shared decision-making	Self-responsibility
Strengths	Safety and security Teaching skills	Sense of control	Personal autonomy Holistic focus
Weaknesses	Participant has no control	Confusion about who is responsible	Reduction in coach accountability

Stop and think

Using the information provided in Table 7.1, discuss with a partner how you think the following will influence the approach used by a coach:

- age of participants
- performance level of participants
- participants' reasons for participation (fun, health, competition)
- employers' expectations.

Remember

Sport is any form of physical activity that is undertaken for any reason (including competition but expanded to include a myriad of other purposes, such as enjoyment, social activity, weight management, friendships and developing self-esteem). Activities that are brought under the banner of a broader physical definition of sport, to sit alongside 'sports', include exercise, health related activities, exergaming, dance and activities of daily living.

What makes a good coach?

Formulate in your mind what you think are the qualities of a good coach. Table 7.2 presents the typical responses of athletes, participants and sports students in response to being asked what they think makes a good coach.

Stop and think

Individually, rank the twenty characteristics identified in Table 7.2 in order of importance to you, with the most important ranked at one. Compare and contrast your ranked list with other members of your group.

Table 7.2: Qualities and characteristics of a good coach

Patient	Flexible	Interested in other things in my life	Good listener
A good player	Experienced	Good communicator	Creative
Not just a dictator	Uses different approaches	Knows what I like	Caring
Sense of humour	Makes me feel good about myself	Punctual	Knowledgeable
Motivator	Good time manager	Appears to enjoy coaching us	Friendly

What motivates somebody to become a sports coach?

The table below (Table 7.3) presents these as intrinsic (internal) or extrinsic (external) reasons that individuals might have for becoming a coach.

Table 7.3: Intrinsic and extrinsic reasons for becoming a sports coach

Intrinsic	Extrinsic
Focus on internal rewards	Focus on external rewards
Coach for the love of the sport	Money
Personal satisfaction	Equipment
Enjoyment	Coaching awards
Fun	Trophies

Sports coaches who are motivated by extrinsic reasons tend to be referred to as coach-centred, whereas those primarily motivated by intrinsic reasons, athlete-centred. A sports coach's motivations or reasons for coaching will have a strong influence on the coaching behaviour that they exhibit.

Areas of sports science impacting on coaching

The academic **discipline** of **sports science** is comprised of many **sub-disciplines**. Many of these will have a direct impact on the practice of sports coaching. These are:

- anatomy
- physiology
- biomechanics
- growth and development
- statistics
- tests and measurements
- motor learning
- psychology
- sports medicine
- nutrition
- sociology
- pedagogy.

Even within the same sport, different coaching situations require a sports coach to draw upon different sub-discipline areas of sports science knowledge. For example, an athletics coach working with a group of adolescent high-jump

Remember

In the UK, the term sport(s) science(s) is used as an umbrella term for academic programmes that focus on the application of scientific principles and techniques with the aim of improving sporting performance. In the US, the term kinesiology is used, and in Australia, human movement studies.

athletes will need to draw extensively on the areas of growth and development, motor learning and biomechanics; whereas an athletics coach working with elite female distance runners would need to be proficient in the science areas of physiology, tests and measurements, and nutrition.

Although primarily working within a specific sport, other factors such as the age and gender of participants and the focus of the coaching session need the sports coach to draw upon different areas

Stop and think

Working in pairs, rank in order of importance the top five sub-discipline areas of scientific knowledge that impact on the following different coaching situations:

- a rugby coach working with a team to develop their kicking accuracy
- a tennis coach working with a player who keeps making service errors in a tie-break
- a volleyball coach of a junior team that has a very high incidence of injuries
- a netball coach who is concerned with the motivation levels of her team
- a modern pentathlon coach who is concerned about weight loss in a group of his elite female athletes.

Key terms

Discipline – a branch of learning or scholarly activity that is taught and researched at university level

Sport(s) science(s) – umbrella term for academic programmes that focus on the application of scientific principles and techniques with the aim of improving sporting performance

Sub-discipline – a field of specialised study within the discipline of sports sciences

of sports science knowledge. The sub-disciplinary areas of scientific knowledge required by practising sports coaches are fluid and constantly evolving in order to meet the demands of each different coaching situation that is presented.

Remember

It is helpful for you to remember that coaching sport is highly **contextual**. The sub-discipline areas of scientific knowledge that you as a coach need to draw upon will be directly influenced by a range of externally imposed factors (such as the age, gender and expertise of participants). Therefore, for a sports coach to be fully effective in different contexts, they must be knowledgeable in a wide range of scientific areas.

The coach as teacher

Coaching sport is a social activity, with the complexities of a coach-participant relationship at its core. For this reason how to coach is a crucial and often overlooked element of being an effective practitioner. For many years the professions of teaching and coaching were presented as being different. However, sports coaches have become more aware of the need to totally develop the individuals that they are working with in line with established practice in a school setting. This is referred to as **holistic** coaching practice, and has blurred the distinction made between the professions of teaching and coaching. Academics and leading coaching figures believe that good coaches act like good teachers. This position is reinforced by Sir Clive Woodward (England Rugby Union 2003 World Cup winning coach) who argues that 'the best coaches are good teachers' (Cain, 2004, p.19). Similarly, Graham Taylor (former coach of the England Football team) believed that he possessed the qualities to become a teacher or a coach, and if he had known in advance that his professional football playing career would be relatively short lived, he says that he would have remained in school to become a teacher. Graham Taylor affirms this by saying that 'coaching really is a form of teaching, so I guess, in a way, I've ended up in the same place!' (Jones et al., 2004, p.21).

Therefore coaching sport is about much more than improving the mechanistic performance of participants through training and skill development, and as such, you should consider establishing an environment conducive to participant learning wherever and whenever you coach. To establish and maintain an effective **learning** environment, **pedagogy** becomes central in coaching sport effectively.

Remember

You must maintain a positive relationship with the participants with whom you are working and thus create a positive coaching climate. A positive coaching climate will create an atmosphere that is favourable to you, creating an effective learning environment. This atmosphere, in a sports coaching context, is referred to as the **motivational climate**.

What is 'coaching science'?

Coaching science relates directly to 'how to coach' or the 'pedagogy of coaching' (PoC). This is a crucial sub-discipline of sports science that is often overlooked. If participants are to get the best out of the physical activity that they are engaged in, then someone has to be responsible for bringing together the sub-discipline areas of sports science in meaningful and helpful ways for the participants (Armour, 2011). This complex undertaking is the task faced by coaches in creating positive learning experiences for participants in the coaching environment. Each of these learning experiences can be termed a **pedagogical encounter**.

Key terms

Holistic – dealing with the whole of someone and not just a part

Learning – the activity of obtaining knowledge

Pedagogy – the principles and practices designed to enhance learning in an individual

Motivational climate – situational induced psychological environment that influences achievement strategies of participants

Pedagogical encounter – learning experience that takes place in the coaching environment

Does the fastest man on the planet need help learning from a coach?

Each learning experience is influenced by a number of factors. These complex factors, grouped together, can be presented as being three dimensions underpinning the pedagogy of coaching (see Figure 7.1). The three dimensions are explained below.

Context

The selection of what knowledge to be coached is always contextual. Whether the coaching is taking place in a school setting, professional club, private club or community centre, or the reasons for participation, will influence what knowledge is appropriate to be coached.

Learners and learning

Participants will have diverse needs in relation to how they prefer to learn. An appreciation of learning theories is central to this dimension. In addition to how participants learn, learners will be affected by multiple factors that will impact upon learning (for example, disaffection, health levels, (dis)ability, gender, sexuality, age, class, ethnicity, interest).

Coaches and coaching

Coaches will draw upon a range of pedagogical tools in order to maximise learning. The pedagogy of coaching can be described as multi-dimensional and multilayered (Kirk et al., 2006). To be effective, coaches must be able to establish a coaching environment conducive to enhancing participant learning by creating high quality learning experiences. This chapter focuses on the dimensions of the learners and also that of the coaches.

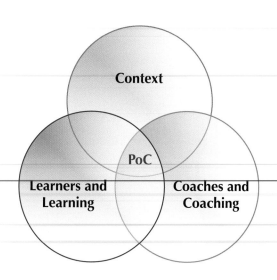

Figure 7.1: The three dimensions of the pedagogy of coaching (PoC)

Learners and learning

Theories of learning

> ### Stop and think
>
> Think of situations (sporting or academic) where you feel that your learning needs have been ignored. What could the teacher or coach have done to improve your learning in those situations?

Learning is a complex concept and can be defined as the act, activity or process of acquiring knowledge or skill. There are four main theories of learning that have evolved over the last century: behaviourism, cognitivism, constructivism and social theories of learning. Table 7.4 summarises these four main theories. Understanding your range of learning theories increases your chances of understanding the participants in a learning experience.

Learning styles and multiple intelligences

Many theories attempt to explain how participants learn. Learning style is the term given to describe a person's preferred way of learning. It highlights the manner and conditions in which a person receives, deals with and gains understanding of the things they are trying to learn. Learning preferences for participants have been presented as hear-learners, see-learners or do-learners. Fleming and Bonwell (2001) developed a questionnaire based on how our senses influence learning preferences. Focusing on three senses (seeing (visual), hearing (aural) and touching (kinaesthetic)), they named their tool a VARK:

- Visual
- Aural
- Read/write
- Kinaesthetic.

A coach who understands these different preferences for receiving and processing information can attempt to be more diverse in the ways that information is presented to their participants. A coach can ensure that by using premeditated *cue* words (in italics below), an activity (such as questioning a participant to extend knowledge) can be explicitly designed to engage learners with different preferences. Using coaching a high serve in badminton as an example, the following is an illustration of the use of cue words in questioning:

- **Visual**: *Watch* my demonstration of the high serve. Tell me what are the three most important things in relation to generating power in the shot?
- **Aural**: *Listen* to the sound of the impact on the shuttle on your strings as you strike it. Why does the sound differ when you slice the shuttlecock to the right of your target?
- **Read/write**: *Read* this article on serving with accuracy. How can you incorporate some of these things in to your service action?
- **Kinaesthetic**: *Feel* the transfer of weight from your back foot through to your front foot during the service action. What can you do differently to increase the transfer of weight?

However, only defining a participant's learning style by these perceptual strengths is limited. The concept of a participant possessing multiple intelligences is a more suitable starting point for coaches to begin to think about the way in which their participants can receive information in the most effective way. Gardner (1993) identified eight intelligences (see Table 7.5) that are independent of each other;

Table 7.4: Theories of learning (adapted from Chambers, 2011)

Theory	Behaviourism	Cognitivism	Constructivism	Social theories of learning
Main theorists	Pavlov Skinner Thorndike Watson	Ausubel Bruner Gagne Koffka Lewin	Dewey Piaget Rogoff Vygotsky	Bandura Engestrom Eraut Lave and Wenger
How does learning happen?	Behaviour changed due to external stimulus	Internal mental processes	Constructing meaning from what we already know	Observation and interaction with others
Purpose of learning	Produces behaviour change in a desired direction	Develops reason, intuition and perception	Constructing new knowledge linked to existing knowledge	Models new roles and behaviour
Implications for coaches	Coach is viewed as transmitter of knowledge Participant viewed as a passive recipient of coach's knowledge Coach controls coaching environment	Coach prepares information and transmits it to learners Participant viewed as information processor Coach controls the information–input process Participants receive, store and act on information	Coach builds upon participants' prior learning Participant actively constructs new understandings Coach facilitates learner agency	Participants develop shared practice with all learners Learning takes place between all members of the group Coach orchestrates social interaction
Coaching strategies	Rote learning Learning drills Clear objectives Learning by doing Repetition Positive reinforcement Activity important	Empower internal mental processes Tasks broken down into steps Start with most simple steps Work towards more complex steps	Task oriented Hands-on Self-directed Activities oriented towards design and discovery Coaching environment is active, energetic and noisy	Individual and group work Use mentors to guide newcomers Establish a community of practice

although described as independent, they are interrelated. Development or progress in one of the intelligences often leads to the whole constellation of intelligences being improved.

Table 7.5: Multiple intelligences (adapted from Gardner, 1993)

Intelligence	Learner characteristic: what does it involve?
Verbal/linguistic	Reading, writing and speaking
Logical/mathematical	Number and computing skills
Visual/spatial	Visual perception, mental images and orientation of body
Bodily/kinaesthetic	Physical co-ordination and dexterity
Musical/rhythmic	Understanding and expressing through music and rhythmic movements
Interpersonal	Communication, understanding and working collaboratively with others
Intrapersonal	Controlling one's inner world of emotions and thoughts
Naturalistic	Understanding the natural world of plants and animals

Possessing an awareness of the existence of multiple intelligences, a coach should ensure that opportunity for practice is given for bodily/kinaesthetic learners, opportunity for discussion for verbal/linguistic learners, setting movement practices to music for musical/rhythmic learners, or creating opportunity for independent work for intrapersonal learners. Coaches working on a one-to-one basis with a participant or with a small group of participants could use one of the multiple intelligence questionnaires (for example Gardner (1993) or the Birmingham Grid for Learning) to provide background information about their participant's intelligence profiles. It is not feasible in a large group situation for a coach to match all activities to all participants' intelligences; however, coaches should be creative and develop a range of activities that stimulate as many of the intelligences as possible.

Fully understanding a person's learning style is even more complex than this. In addition to perceptual strengths and intelligences, other factors also influence a person's learning preferences. These are:

- biological rhythms (time of day)
- sociological (whole group or individual)
- psychological (attention span, concentration, confidence, motivation)
- environment (noise level, temperature, weather)
- physical (fitness levels).

When working with your participants you will need to remember that some will not learn very well in the morning, but perform very well in the afternoon. Some work well in groups or bright, noisy environments; others do their best work on their own in quite places with subdued lighting. Some participants need short, precise information; others need time to ask questions and reflect. Some participants need and want to be told what to do and excel with highly structured, coach directed instructional methods; others do far better when working on their own initiative in informal, unstructured coaching environments.

Using Honey and Mumford's (2001) four factor framework for learning styles provides a very useful scaffold for coaches to build a working understanding of the complex issue of how their participants learn. Honey and Mumford (2001) use the terms activist, pragmatist, reflector and theorist to classify the different learning styles (see Table 7.6). The table presents, for each learning style, how the participant prefers to learn, their dislikes, behaviour clues to look for, relevant skills that they possess and coaching strategies to fully engage learners of this type.

Table 7.6: Learning styles and coaching (adapted from Robinson, 2010)

Style	Activist	Pragmatist	Reflector	Theorist
Prefers to learn	By doing Variety teamwork Role play	By trying Demonstrations Experimenting	By discussion Time to consider response	Facts Structured presentations Mental stimulation
Dislikes	Lengthy presentations Working alone Following instructions	Abstract theories Irrelevant discussions	Facts without meanings Tight deadlines	Irrelevant facts Emotional decisions
Behaviour clues	Competitive First of group to answer Attention wanders	Energetic Impatient Ideas into action	Watches from sidelines Thinks before speaking	Organised Deep thinker Challenges ideas
Skills	Evaluating Chairing	Predicting Exploring Problem solving	Questions Visualises Draws conclusions	Analytical Organised Prioritises
Coaching strategies	Demonstrations Visual aids Feedback Discussion	Demonstrations Repeated practice Feedback	Requires verbal articulation of skill Opportunities to talk Use video	Provide information to analyse Set problems Ask questions

Stop and think

Using Table 7.6 as a guide, for a sport and skill of your choice explain how you would engage an activist, pragmatist, reflector and theorist fully in your session.

Key terms

Style – the way in which the coaching is performed

Method – the style of coaching adopted by the coach

Strategy – the actions taken by the coach in response to identified priorities for coaching

Coaches and coaching

Coaching style, coaching method or coaching strategy?

There is debate over the use of the terms coaching **style**, coaching **method** or coaching **strategy** in the coaching literature. For the purpose of this chapter, a coaching style is independent of the personal characteristics of the coach, and as such can be described as an instructional method. A coaching strategy identifies the priorities for coaching and is therefore directly related to the participants, the coach and the coaching environment. As part of a coaching strategy, a coach will use a range of coaching styles or instructional methods.

What is a coaching style?

As important as *what* you are coaching is deciding on *how* you are going to coach in a particular session. Coaching styles should not be viewed as something implemented by a coach, but as

a component of a strategy aimed at maximising learning. The work of Mosston and Ashworth (2008) in the field of education provides an invaluable framework for classifying the variety of styles that a coach has at their disposal to maximise learning. Referred to as Mosston and Ashworth's spectrum of teaching styles (the spectrum), it presents a continuum categorised by the level of control and decisions made by the teacher or learner. Table 7.7 presents the ten teaching styles (A–J), documenting the name of the style, its key characteristics and when to use it in the coaching environment.

The spectrum can be categorised into two distinct clusters of styles, one associated with reproduction (reproduce, repeat or recall motor skills and known information) (styles A–E) and the other with production (discover new information, solve problems and foster independence) (styles F–J). These two clusters are divided by what is termed the discovery threshold. Figure 7.2 presents the spectrum in diagrammatic form. **Practice** coaching behaviour is synonymous with the styles to the left of the discovery threshold and **Discovery** coaching behaviour is located to the right.

Key terms

Practice – coach controls the learning environment

Discovery – participant controls the learning environment

Table 7.7: The spectrum from a coaching perspective

Letter	Name	Key characteristics	When to use it
A	Command	Coach takes decisions Participants follow instructions	Conformity Activity Safe learning
B	Practice	Coach takes most decisions Participants make some decisions Participants work at own pace	Sustained practice to refine skills Development of new skills
C	Reciprocal	Participants work in pairs Pupils receive feedback from partner	Develop co-operative behaviour Develop observational and analytical skills Practising and refining skills
D	Self-check	Participants assess own learning against given criteria Tasks set conducive to assessment	Evaluate own performance Sustained independent practice Adapting and refining skills
E	Inclusion	Allows for individual practice at appropriate level Assumes self-motivation of participants Awareness by participants of limitations needed	When working with a wide ability range Progression at own pace Responsibility for own learning Adapting and refining skills
F	Guided discovery	Coach leads participants to discover predetermined learning target Questioning used by coach	Understanding of work undertaken (e.g. tactics, game plays, etc.) Participant involvement in learning wanted
G	Problem-solving	Coach presents problem Participants find many alternate solutions	Development of planning and evaluation skills Compositional skills Developing creativity
H	Individual programme	Coach decides general area to work on Participant takes decisions about what and how to do it Coach as facilitator	Develop decision making capability
I	Learner initiated	Participant takes initiative about content and learning process Coach acts as advisor when approached by participant	Develop reflective capabilities
J	Self teach	Participant takes full responsibility for learning	Develop independence from coach (personal autonomy)

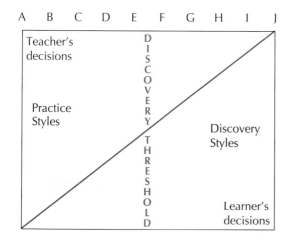

Figure 7.2: Mosston and Ashworth's spectrum of teaching styles

It is a useful skill for coaches to be able to observe another coach in action and identify the range of styles that are deployed and to understand why that style was used. The following proforma is a useful tool for recording such observations.

Figure 7.3: Proforma for recording observations of coaching styles

Style	Task(s)	Why was this style used?
Command		
Practice		
Reciprocal		
Self-check		
Inclusion		
Guided discovery		
Problem-solving		
Individual programme		
Learner initiated		
Self teach		

(this table is available to download at www.pearsonfe.co.uk/foundationsinsport)

Sometimes using the full spectrum of teaching styles developed by Mosston and Ashworth (2008) can be a cumbersome framework to engage with. Therefore the simplified framework developed by Kirk et al. (1996) for coaching styles is a valuable summary of the most frequently used styles in the coaching environment. Kirk et al. (1996) adapted a number of Mosston and Ashworth's (2008) styles as follows:

- **direct** – as Mosston and Ashworth's (2008) command style (style a)

- **task** – as Mosston and Ashworth's (2008) practice style (style b)

- **reciprocal** – as Mosston and Ashworth's (2008) reciprocal style (style c)

- **guided discovery** – as Mosston and Ashworth's (2008) guided discovery style (style f)

- **problem-solving** – as Mosston and Ashworth's (2008) problem solving style (style g).

Remember

The styles are positioned on a continuum. Therefore it is likely that the characteristics associated with a particular style are not necessarily exclusive to that style. Those styles positioned next to each other will share a number of the same characteristics.

The selection of a particular coaching style is dependent on a range of factors: intended learning outcomes; the coaching context and environment; a range of learner characteristics such as ability; reasons for participation; learning preferences. There would be little point in a coach wanting to develop decision making or problem-solving capabilities in their participants and then lead a coaching session using styles from the reproduction cluster. Alternatively, novice participants wishing to develop a new skill would not benefit from a coach predominantly using styles from the production cluster. Ultimately, the most effective coaches are able to switch, adapt and blend a range of styles seamlessly to match the range of factors influencing the learning experience.

The process of communication

Once a coach decides on a particular approach or strategy to adopt in the coaching environment, information should be communicated as effectively as possible to the participants. Effective communication is dependent upon a number of different processes or stages:

- **selection** – selecting the information to communicate

- **coding** – putting the information into an agreeable form(s)

- **transmission** – sending it

- **reception** – another person receiving the information

- **decoding** – recognition of the information

- **interpretation** – making meaning of the information.

Traditionally scholars have presented the process of communication as a one way transmission of information from the coach to the participant. Often in reality, a learning experience involves the transmission of information both ways, from coach to participant and from participant to coach. Effective communication occurs when this complicated series of stages flows without any ambiguity, misinterpretations or mistakes. It places an emphasis on the coach and participant using multiple codes (verbal and visual). For example, this could mean ensuring that the form of language (for verbal codes) is appropriate for the participants

in the coaching environment. When coaching children the form of language will need to be very different from the language used when working with elite athletes. The codes selected by the coach/participant are commonly referred to as the communication channels.

Communication channels

How many words do you need to coach effectively?

Fabio Capello claimed, as manager of England's football team, that a grasp of only '100 words' was sufficient to communicate with the players (*The Telegraph*, 2011). As being able to communicate effectively is a crucial component of coaching practice, this statement highlights that verbal communication might only be one component of many communication channels available to a coach. Broadly speaking, communication channels can be divided into two types:

- verbal (spoken)
- non-verbal (body language, facial expressions, gaze, posture and gestures).

The verbal channel can be further subdivided into the following:

- what is spoken
- how it is spoken (paraverbal).

The paraverbal communication channel is composed of how we modify what we say by patterns of speech (pauses, pace, intonation, volume, speed, pitch and hesitations). Put simply, the paraverbal communication channel consists of elements of speech that go beyond vocabulary and grammar. Importantly for coaching, it is crucial to consider the impact on your participants of how you say something and to take care that what you are saying is not misinterpreted. For example, is what you are saying a question, statement or a command to do something? Are you talking with irony, sarcasm or cynicism? Do you want to emphasise a particular point or draw a contrast between two things? Are you talking in a monotone voice that is demotivating for your participants?

Often communication channels are not used independently of one another. In coaching, a demonstration (by either the coach or a skilled participant) is seen as a crucial element of coaching effectively. Combining a visual model of a skill or technique in combination with precise verbal information is a powerful tool for engaging most learners. Following this up with opportunities to practice provides the optimum opportunity for maximising learning in the pedagogic setting. Finally, if maximising learning is the objective of coaching science, then the following quote attributed to William Glasser could help coaches in developing the most appropriate coaching strategy:

We learn:

- *10 per cent of what we read*
- *20 per cent of what we hear*
- *30 per cent of what we see*
- *50 per cent of what we see and hear*
- *70 per cent of what we discuss*
- *80 per cent of what we experience*
- *95 per cent of what we teach others.*

William Glasser

Reviewing your coaching

It is essential that coaches review or evaluate their coaching performance. As a coach, you should learn from your coaching experiences. This is an important component of the coaching process (plan, deliver, and evaluate) and allows you to identify areas for your continued development as a coach. There are two principal ways in which you can gather information about your coaching. You can ask your participants to complete a brief questionnaire (Figure 7.4) or you can ask another coach to assess your performance (Figure 7.5). Completion of these proformas will enable you to find areas of your coaching performance that require improvement and subsequently you should produce a development plan based on the conclusions. Every coach should seek to improve their effectiveness at every stage of their career. To do this, the development plan should indicate specific goals that you have set yourself, for example:

- completing further academic and vocational qualifications
- working with a mentor
- observing sports coaches from a range of different sports
- observing sports coaches working with a range of different populations.

Performer Feedback Sheet

Please circle your answers.

Did you enjoy the session?

Did you enjoy the warm-up?

Did you enjoy the drills in the session e.g. the dribbling between the cones, the shooting into the hockey net?

Did the sports leader communicate clearly?

Did the sports leader demonstrate clearly what you had to do in the session?

Did you feel that your performance improved in the session?

What extra activities would you like to have done in the session?

....

....

Figure 7.4: An example of a questionnaire on a coach's performance

(a version of this questionnaire is available to download at www.pearsonfe.co.uk/foundationsinsport)

Assessment

Session Plan

Did the learner produce a lesson plan (prior to the start of the session/event?)	YES/NO
Was the session planned appropriately for the needs of the participants?	YES/NO
Will the session/event meet the aims and objectives of the session?	YES/NO

Targets

Did the learner set targets for participants?	YES/NO
Were these targets met during the session/event?	YES/NO
Before the session:	
did the learner carry out a safety check of the participants and of the venue and equipment prior to the session/event?	YES/NO
did the learner produce a risk assessment for the event/session?	YES/NO

Delivery

Did the learner communicate effectively throughout the session/event?	YES/NO
Did the learner use the facility and equipment effectively throughout the session?	YES/NO
Did the learner organise the session effectively?	YES/NO
Did the learner demonstrate effective application of the roles and responsibilities of a sports coach?	YES/NO
Did the learner demonstrate appropriate knowledge and language of the sport and the techniques and skills covered in the session?	YES/NO
Did the learner use an appropriate range of techniques to develop the performers within the session?	YES/NO
Did the learner wear appropriate clothing for the session?	YES/NO
Did the learner motivate the performers throughout the session?	YES/NO
Were the components of the session delivered effectively and appropriately?	YES/NO
Did the learner conclude the session with a summary and provide opportunities for feedback to all performers?	YES/NO

Which areas could be improved?

Signed _ (assessor)   Date _ _ _ _ _ _ _ _ _ _ _ _ _

Figure 7.5: An example of the observation record that another coach can use to assess your coaching performance.

Case study (for recommended answers, see www.pearsonfe.co.uk/foundationsinsport)

Nicolas is a coach who is working with a group of mixed ability participants. The participants all partake in weekly sessions, however Nicolas notices that the group are not progressing at the pace which they should. Nicolas favours autocratic coaching styles and maximising participant activity in his sessions because this is what he feels more comfortable with.

1. Should Nicolas coach in a style that he feels comfortable with?

2. What coaching styles can Nicolas use that will be more democratic?

3. Tactically the participants are very naïve. What can Nicolas do to encourage tactical development?

4. Decision making in competitive situations is a real problem for his participants. What activities can Nicolas include in his sessions that would develop their decision making capabilities?

5. What coaching styles are conducive to developing the skills of Nicolas' participants?

Check your understanding (for answers, see www.pearsonfe.co.uk/foundationsinsport)

1. Give a definition of sport.

2. Give a definition of sports coaching.

3. List five sub-discipline areas of sports science that impact on coaching.

4. Explain what is meant by 'coaching is like teaching'.

5. What is coaching science?

6. What are the four main theories of learning?

7. What does the acronym VARK stand for?

8. What are the four main learning styles?

9. List five multiple intelligences that a coach needs to be aware of in their participants.

10. Explain what the difference is between coaching style and coaching strategy.

11. List Kirk et al.'s (1996) five coaching styles.

12. List the three communication channels in ascending order of the percentage contribution of information in a message.

Time to reflect

1. Using your broader understanding of sport, investigate the multiple reasons why participants in your coaching sessions are taking part (performance, health, enjoyment, social reasons, etc.). Think about the ways in which you can meet these diverse needs of your participants.

2. For each of the contexts in which you coach, write a philosophy statement that guides your practice. Look for similarities and differences in your philosophy statements and use these findings to refine your philosophy statements.

3. Investigate the National Occupational Standards (NOS) that form the basis of coaching qualifications. Identify key areas that you need to develop and produce an action plan for enhancing your skills and abilities.

4. Think about why it is important for participants to take responsibility for sections of their coaching session. Consider how you can build this into your own coaching practice.

5. Think about the participants in your coaching session as learners. Implement a variety of strategies and styles aimed at maximising the effectiveness of your coaching. Reflect on what worked well and what didn't to guide your future practice.

6. Use the Internet to investigate current job vacancies in sports coaching. Use the findings of your investigation to map out your coaching development journey.

Useful resources

To obtain a secure link to the websites below, see the Websites section on page ii or visit the companion website at www.pearsonfe.co.uk/foundationsinsport

- Birmingham Grid for Learning (multiple intelligences questionnaire)
- British Cycling
- British Gymnastics
- Coachwise
- English Basketball Association
- International Journal of Sports Science and Coaching
- Sociology of Sport Journal
- Sports Coach UK
- Sport England
- Sports Leaders UK
- The British Olympic Association
- The Football Association
- The Lawn Tennis Association
- The Rugby Football Union
- The Sport Psychologist
- UK Athletics
- UK Sport

Further reading

Armour, K. (ed.). (2011). *Sport pedagogy: an introduction for teaching and coaching*. London: Prentice Hall.

Cain, N. (2004). 'Question time for the coaches: the six men plotting their countries' fortunes on the best and worst of their jobs'. *The Sunday Times*, Sport Section, p.9.

Cassidy, T., Jones, R.L. and Potrac, P. (2009). *Understanding sports coaching: the social, cultural and pedagogical foundations of coaching practice*, 2nd Edition. London: Routledge.

Chambers, F. (2011). Learning theory for effective learning in practice. In: K. Armour (ed.). *Sport pedagogy: an introduction for teaching and coaching*. London: Prentice Hall, pp.39–52.

Denison, J. (ed.). (1997). *Coaching knowledges: understanding the dynamics of sport performance*. London: A&C Black.

Department for Culture, Media and Sport (DCMS). (2002). *The coaching task force: final report*. London: DCMS.

Dunn, R. and Griggs, S.A. (1988). *Learning styles: quiet revolution in American secondary schools*. Reston, VA: National Association of Secondary School Principals.

Fleming, N. and Bonwell, C. (2001). *How do I learn best? A student's guide to improved learning*. Christchurch, NZ: Fleming and Bonwell.

Gardner, H. (1993). *Multiple intelligences*. New York: Basic Books.

Honey, P. and Mumford, A. (2001). *The learning styles helpers guide*. Maidenhead, UK: Peter Honey Publications Ltd.

Jones, R.L., Armour, K.M. and Potrac, P. (2004). *Sports coaching cultures: from practice to theory*. London: Routledge.

Kidman, L. and Hanrahan, S. (2011). *The coaching process: a practical guide to improving your effectiveness*, 3rd Edition. Palmerston North: Dunmore.

Kirk, D., Macdonald, D. and O'Sullivan, M. (eds.). (2006). *The handbook of physical education*. London: Sage.

Kirk, D., Nauright, J., Hanrahan, S., Macdonald, D. and Jobling, I. (1996). *The sociocultural foundations of human movement*. Melbourne: Macmillan.

Lombardo, B.J. (1987). *The humanistic coach: from theory to practice*. Springfield, Ill: C.C. Thomas.

Lyle, J. (2002). *Sports coaching concepts: a framework for coaches' behaviour*. London: Routledge.

Martens, R. (2004). *Successful coaching,* 3rd Edition. Champaign, Illinois: Human Kinetics.

Mehrabian, A. (1968). Communication without words. *Psychology Today.* 2 (9), pp. 52–55.

Mosston, M. and Ashworth, S. (1986). *Teaching physical education.* First Online Edition 2008. http://www.spectrumofteachingstyles.org/ebook.

Robinson, P.E. (2010). *Foundations of sports coaching.* London: Routledge.

Skills Active. (2011). Sport and recreation [online]. Available from: http://www.skillsactive.com/sport [Accessed 23 March 2011]

The Telegraph. (2011). England v Ghana: all I need is 100 words of English, claims Fabio Capello [online]. Available from: http://www.telegraph. co.uk/sport/football/teams/england/8412466/ England-v-Ghana-all-I-need-is-100-words-of-English-claims-Fabio-Capello.html [Accessed 06 April 2011]

Chapter 8

Performance analysis

Introduction

Performance analysis is a newly developed sub-discipline of sport and exercise science that focuses on actual sports performance as opposed to laboratory-based investigations. It involves observational analysis of sports performance that often utilises audio-visual and information technology-based equipment, particularly at the highest level of sport performance. At a grass-roots level, performance analysis can be conducted through a more 'pencil and paper' method of analysis, but this method is generally limited by the accuracy of information that can be provided. Performance analysis can be completed using any methods that allow data from actual sports performance to be recorded and analysed; these include notational analysis, biomechanical analysis of technique, qualitative observation and the measurement of physiological and psychological variables during actual sports performance.

An understanding of the principles of performance analysis is crucial for the work of sports scientists. They are fundamental to understanding team and individual performances and the development of team and athlete profiles. This enables sports coaches and athletes to alter techniques where necessary and developing tactics or tactical awareness.

Learning outcomes

After you have read this chapter you should be able to:

- know the purposes of performance analysis at different levels of sport
- know the cycle of completing performance analysis in sport
- know the different performance criteria used in performance analysis
- know methods of performance analysis
- understand the use of technology in sport performance analysis
- know how to provide feedback after analysing sport performance.

Starting block

In basketball, player 1 has 15 successful shots at basket but player 2 has 20 successful shots at basket. Who has had the better game? Take it a stage further. Player 1 had the opportunity to shoot 30 times, but passed the ball 15 times, which led to 15 more baskets; player 2 had the opportunity to shoot 40 times and he missed 20/40 when he could have passed 10 to a different player in a better position.

- Who has had the better game now?
- What does this tell you about the use of statistics in performance analysis?

Performance analysis at different levels of sport

The overall role of performance analysis is to provide information that enhances the performance of individual athletes or teams. Performance analysis techniques that can be used after an event with players are important for sports coaches because research suggests sports coaches cannot often accurately recall what has happened during an event. For example Franks and Miller (1986) found that football coaches were less than 45 per cent correct in their post-game assessment of events during 45 minutes of a football game.

Within this over-arching aim of performance enhancement, there are a number of different purposes for performance analysis in sport. These vary depending on the level of performance you are competing at and your role within the game (e.g. player, coach, official). The purposes of performance analysis are:

- technique development, e.g. analysing a golf swing to identify faults and enhance driving distance
- tactical development, e.g. analysing an opponent's on-court tactics in tennis to formulate a match plan
- injury reduction/management, e.g. using a video of an incident that resulted in an injury during a game to treat the injury at pitch side

- talent identification, e.g. if a coach of an U7 footballer recorded that the player scored 53 goals in a season, when the league average for a player is 20 goals, they would identify the player as talented and recommend them for a higher level of sport
- fitness assessment, e.g. through completing fitness tests over time and motion analysis with players
- coach education, e.g. to help coaches develop a greater knowledge of techniques and tactics used in their sport, and how to transfer this knowledge to their athletes
- athlete education, e.g. giving athletes a greater understanding of their strengths and areas for improvement on a technical and tactical level
- modelling sport performance, e.g. producing the 'perfect' model of performance so that different elements of athletes' techniques can be compared against it
- squad selection, e.g. providing coaches with performance statistics, such as successful passes against a particular team or total playing time so that they can judge whether an athlete should play in the next game
- judging sports, e.g. in sports, such as boxing, where points scoring is based on a boxer successfully landing punches with the knuckle part of the glove, so a judge must analyse live performance to award points.

The different levels of sport are viewed on the sport development continuum (see Figure 8.1). The continuum starts with foundation level performance, where novice athletes are introduced to sport. Novice athletes are generally young children at primary school through to late secondary school age, but can include older people who are new to a sport. The focus of the foundation stage of performance is fun and encouraging involvement in organised sport. This is usually when the first stages of athlete development take place.

The participation stage of the continuum typically involves people taking part for fun, social reasons, health and fitness, and to take part in organised sport. Normally at this stage, players will have a range of basic skills that they use in a competitive situation and tactics will be introduced into game play. Often, there will be a coach who will aim to develop the technique and tactical awareness of the player so that they are able to compete at a desired level. A local Sunday league sports player is an example of this level of participation. Players that are at a higher level at the participation stage will often move onto the performance stage where they will compete in representative squads up to national standard. This level of the continuum normally provides access to a higher level of coaching staff and performance analysis. It requires an increased commitment to development as an athlete to be able to progress further.

Finally, the excellence stage of performance is the highest level of performance. This encompasses the highest level athletes at the best clubs and international athletes. This stage provides access to the highest qualified coaches and the most specific level of performance analysis.

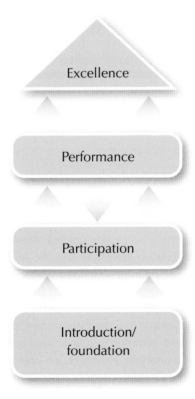

Figure 8.1: The sport development continuum. How do you think the purposes of, and resources required for, performance analysis will change at different levels of performance?

The purposes of performance analysis at different levels are the same, but the manner in which they are conducted is different. For example, at foundation level, the coach of a nine-year-old rugby player may count the number of passes that were successfully completed by the player and write this down on a piece of paper; whereas at excellence level, a team of performance analysts might use a specific IT programme to measure the successful passes of the whole team. The purpose in both instances is the same, i.e. to see if players were able to successfully execute skills, but the method of completing the analysis is very different.

 Remember

The purposes of performance analysis are broadly similar at each of the different stages of the continuum, but they will use different methods.

The cycle of completing performance analysis in sport

Figure 8.2 shows the general cycle of performance analysis and how this progresses to interventions that are aimed at improving performance. Figure 8.2 demonstrates that performance analysis is an ongoing process in sport that starts and ends with the performance of an athlete.

The performance analyst observes the athlete in their sport and records the necessary data from performance using one or more of the analysis methods (discussed later in this chapter). They will then analyse that data either qualitatively or quantitatively and interpret the data, extracting the key information that relates to the performance indicators in question.

The next stage is feedback to the coach, athlete or team regarding the analysis that has taken place. Then the support staff (such as, sports scientist or strength and conditioning coach) will start planning and preparing the intervention that they are going to use to try to improve performance.

Figure 8.2: The cycle of performance analysis

Different performance criteria used in performance analysis

Performance criteria are any aspects of performance that are used to analyse performance in sports. Performance criteria vary from sport to sport and can vary between different positions in different sports. For example, a striker in football would have different performance criteria from a goalkeeper in football. Common performance criteria used in sports include player movements, shots, passes, headers, saves, forced or unforced errors, dribbling attempts, crosses, strike rate and dismissal rate. Hughes and Bartlett (2004) offer an extensive list of performance criteria in a range of different sports.

 Stop and think

For your favourite sport or position within that sport, make a list of all the different performance criteria associated with that sport or sport's position.

When analysing performance criteria, a performance analyst may need to take their analysis further. For example, if analysing the performance of a goalkeeper in football, the performance analyst may look at the number of successful or unsuccessful saves. However, to get a greater depth of analysis, they may examine the successful saves further and look at what happened after the save, for example did the ball go out of play, did it remain in

play and go to a team-mate or did it remain in play and go to an opposing player?

 **Key term**

Performance criteria – aspects of performance that are used to analyse performance in sports. These are also referred to as performance indicators or key performance indicators in some literature

Methods of performance analysis, and the use of technology in sport

There are many methods of performance analysis that are used commonly in sport. They range from the most quantitative of methods through to more qualitative-based methods.

Analysing performance using notational analysis

Notational analysis is a method that provides a statistical account of the different performance indicators that have been targeted within a given analysis. With this in mind, there are five main applications of notational analysis (Hughes and Bartlett, 2008):

- tactical evaluation
- technical evaluation
- analysis of movement
- development of a database and performance modelling
- educating coaches and players.

Notational analysis can be conducted either by hand or through the use of specific software programmes. Given the extended use of performance analysis in elite sports in recent years, there are now specialised training courses designed for sports scientists to help them understand some of the different commercially available methods of notational analysis. However, the cost usually involved with IT-based programmes for notational analysis means that their use is often limited to the higher end of the sport development continuum. Those at the lower end of the continuum will be more dependent upon hand-based notation systems due to lower costs and less experience of technical equipment required. Through this section, you will be introduced to the methods of notational analysis but are advised to see Hughes and Franks (2004) for a comprehensive account of notational analysis.

Developing a hand-based notational analysis system

Regardless of the sport, all hand-based notation systems are developed and used through similar stages. Essentially, the performance analyst will decide on the performance indicators under investigation and justify these. They will design the notational analysis layout, check the accuracy of the information gained and present the results of the analysis. When considering the performance analysis, the analyst should take into account the athlete and positional demands, and consider time frames or the sequencing of events during an activity. Data will normally be collected using tally marks and these will be converted to descriptive statistics such as percentages or averages as part of the feedback process. Table 8.1 provides a hypothetical example of a simple hand-based notation system that indicates successful and unsuccessful performances of a centre midfield player in football during a 15-minute period.

Table 8.1: Example of a simple hand-based notation system

Performance criteria	Successful attempts	Unsuccessful attempts
Shots on goal	II	IIII
Passes	IIIIIIIIIII	IIIIII
Tackles	III	IIIII
Header	IIIII	IIIIII
Dribbles	IIII	II

More complex hand-based notation systems are sometimes used where a coach may want more complex information. For example, there may be a layout of a basketball court that is separated into segments so that positional play and ball transfer between court segments can be plotted. Another example is when players and sporting actions are attached to different codes, which are used to try to show which players attempted which actions and where (for example the point guard could be attached to the code 'PG', and a successful

dribble could be attached to the code 'DBL'). Predictably, this is a time consuming approach and can be inaccurate. These limitations have led to the development of video and IT-based notational analysis systems.

Stop and think

Use the performance criteria that you produced earlier to complete a hand-based notational analysis of a sporting event.

Video and IT-based notational analysis systems

Modern video and IT-based systems provide sports scientists with a quicker, more efficient and more detailed approach to notational analysis. They can also be conducted real-time if necessary and allow the sports scientist to use a recording of a particular event with their athletes, providing both qualitative and quantitative feedback, as well as allowing the sports scientist to play and replay the video to provide more information to athletes if required. The use of digital video technology allows live footage to be downloaded and transferred to software packages for analysis and can then be transferred into visual forms of feedback such as graphs, charts or onto a simulated playing area (such as an animation of a football pitch to show the number of different runs a player makes).

Video and IT-based systems work by coding or tagging players and sporting actions onto on screen buttons. Every time a particular action occurs, the performance analyst can press the button on screen. The system will store the number of actions or events ready to be viewed on that particular tag or button (see Figure 8.3 for an example). Other, more advanced, systems can track players and reproduce match play based on this tracking. This can be very useful in tactical analysis. In addition, systems are able to link videos of the events to a particular tag. So, if a player had scored three goals in a hockey game, the sports scientist would be able to click on the tag for the third goal and the video file could be viewed at the same time. These systems can be altered to meet the needs of different sports, positions and players; they have contributed heavily to modern performance analysis in sport.

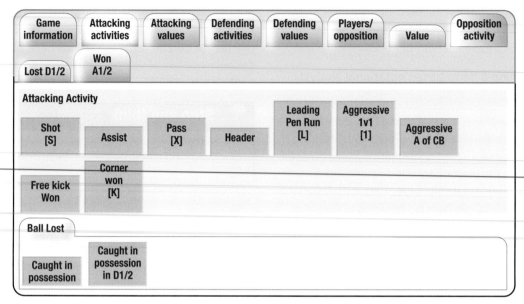

Figure 8.3: An example of a *Dartfish®* tagging system used in football

Stop and think

Research some popular performance analysis systems, such as *Focus X2* from Elite Sports analysis and *SportsCode Gamebreaker* from Sportstec. How can they be used in notational analysis?

Remember

Motion analysis is important for coaches and sports scientists when trying to understand how to shape coaching and training methods around competition demands.

Analysing performance using motion analysis

Motion analysis has provided a depth of information for sports scientists, including distance covered, speed of movements and the amount of time spent fulfilling activities in different sports. As a result of this it has contributed to the understanding of performance demands and fitness requirements of sport. The benefit of this contribution is coaches know how to shape their sessions to improve performance, based on this information. For example, motion analysis literature (e.g. Carling, Bloomfield, Nelson and Reilly, 2008; Carling, Reilly and Williams, 2009) has found that elite footballers sprint an average of 20 metres during games and that the average sprint duration is four seconds. The implication of these findings is that acceleration may be more important for football players than maximum speed and thus staff could use this information to plan sessions around developing these needs.

Bloomfield Movement Classification

The Bloomfield Movement Classification (BMC) (Bloomfield, Polman and O'Donoghue, 2004) was produced to allow analysts to measure the performance demands in sport and has since been adapted for use in a variety of team games (Bloomfield, Polman and O'Donoghue, 2007). This BMC involves 14 modes of timed-motion, three 'other' non-timed movements, 14 directions, four intensities, five turning categories and seven 'On the ball' activity classifications and is performed through video based motion analysis (see Bloomfield et al. 2004 for full details). The BMC has been used to analyse performance demands in different sports, such as soccer (Bloomfield et al. 2007) and netball (Hale and O'Donoghue, 2007), as well as injury risk in netball (Williams and O' Donoghue, 2005). Although there are advantages to using this approach because of the depth of information gained, the complexity of the method means that it can be difficult to use.

Video-based motion analysis

Video-based motion analysis has been used in many sports and involves cameras being placed around the playing area that allow all of the athlete's movements to be recorded. Until recently video-based analysis was recognised as the most accurate method for estimating distances; however there are now some limitations that have challenged this notion (Edgecomb and Norton, 2006). Whilst this method of analysis can track an athlete's movements, as well as using other information, such as playing shirt colours and numbers, some systems do require manual data inputting by a performance analyst where lots of athletes may be in the same place (such as defending an indirect free kick in football). Where this type of analysis is used in professional sport, the number of cameras required is dependent upon factors such as the size of the playing area and (where applicable) stadium dimensions. The feedback from video-based motion analysis can take 24 hours depending on the system that is being used, although the quality of information that can be gained from some tracking systems has been questioned (Carling et al. 2008; Edgecomb and Norton, 2006). Table 8.2 shows the different video-based tracking systems that are used in sport.

Table 8.2: Commercial video-based athlete tracking systems

Company	Software
Feedback Sport	*Feedback Football*
ProZone Holdings Ltd	*ProZone*
Sport – Universal SA	*AMISCO*

Stop and think

Use the websites of the companies in Table 8.2 to compile a summary of each of the tracking systems and their uses.

Electronic tracking-based analysis

Electronic tracking-based systems (sometimes referred to as electronic automatic tracking systems or automatic tracking systems) allow data to be collected in real-time and can record key performance indicators over one hundred times per second. This approach requires individual athletes to be 'tagged' and allows their movements to be tracked through radio transmitters and signal receivers, located around the playing area. More recently, global positioning systems (GPS) technology has been used to analyse performance in a range of sports, such as Australian football (Aughey and Falloon, 2010) and court-based sports (Duffield, Reid, Baker and Spratford, 2010). The use of GPS allows performance analysts to assess speed of movements, distances travelled, movement pathways, altitude and heart rate (although a heart rate transmitter must also be worn for this). GPS technology works by the receivers being located at a safe place on the athlete. The receivers locate signals that are sent at the speed of light by at least four satellites, orbiting the Earth. When the receivers draw on these signals, they calculate performance related data. The data can be downloaded later onto a PC for use by the sports scientist.

Various forms of electronic tracking systems, e.g. computer-based tracking systems and GPS tracking systems have comparable capabilities when analysing motion. However, depending on the GPS device used, there have been errors in measurement reported, ranging from 2–25 per cent (Duffield et al. 2010) and there is currently little information available regarding the validity and reliability of GPS devices for high-intensity, intermittent sports activities (Coutts and Duffield, 2010).

Whilst various tracking systems are becoming more common in professional sport, there are issues, including electronic interference and poor signal strength (Edgecomb and Norton, 2006) and cost (Carling et al. 2009). Given that this type of analysis can require an athlete's kit to be fitted with electronic equipment (usually a small chip) its use in competition is against the rules of some sporting governing bodies (Carling et al. 2009). This is partly because there are concerns over player safety. For a comprehensive coverage of the use of motion analysis in sport see Carling et al. (2008) and Carling et al. (2009). Table 8.3 provides details of different electronic tracking-based systems commercially available.

Table 8.3: Commercially available electronic tracking systems

Company	Software
Catapult Innovations	*Minimaxx*
GPSports	*SPI Elite*
Trakus Inc	*Digital Sports Information*

Stop and think

Use the websites of the companies in Table 8.3 (available at www.pearsonfe.co.uk/foundationsinsport) to compile a summary of each of the tracking systems and their uses.

Technique analysis

Technique analysis has often been used within coaching science to isolate differences in skill levels of performers, to enhance player performance or to identify injury risk. When analysing an athlete's sporting technique, video footage is usually taken from two dimensional or three dimensional perspectives, so that a performance analyst can highlight any faults in the technique compared to the desired performance. When recording two dimensional videos, the performance analyst must be careful with the camera placement, ensuring that they take into account the **field of view** and **perspective error**. When recording performance, it is also necessary to use **horizontal scaling** or **vertical referencing**.

Key terms

Field of view – area that the sports scientist is recording that contains the sporting action

Perspective error – error where objects appear larger or smaller than they actually are as they move towards or away from the camera; it is difficult to effectively judge their position

Horizontal scaling – providing a scale of measurement that will allow you to convert on screen measurements to real life measurements, for example 1 metre 'real' = 1 centimetre 'screen'

Vertical referencing – as for horizontal scaling, but vertically

Historically this technique analysis is done by 'an educated eye' (e.g. an experienced coach), subjectively analysing the technique against their ideal. But with advances in modern technology it has become possible to get a more objective and holistic assessment of movements with reference to variables, such as joint angles, using analysis packages (e.g. *Dartfish®*). For example, Judge, Hunter and Gilreath (2008) reported the use of *Dartfish® ProSuite* to measure release height, release angle and support phase duration in their work with a female hammer thrower, when analysing her technique to enhance performance. Modern analysis packages allow for several images to be viewed side-by-side, overlapped or sections of a selected technique to show how technique has developed. This will help the sports scientist to plan interventions to help athletes enhance their technique further. Figure 8.4 shows an example of the use of video analysis in swimming, to isolate an element of technique to feedback to the athlete.

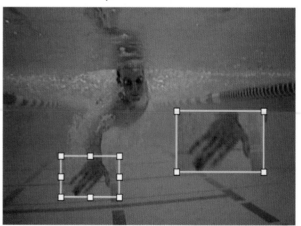

Figure 8.4: Using video analysis to isolate an element of technique. How can this level of analysis be used by sports scientists?

An athlete's performance will usually be measured against some form of standardised criteria for the particular technique, so that the sports scientist has performance related information that can be used with an athlete. When studying tackling in collision sports, Gabbet and Ryan (2009) used the following technical criteria to analyse the tackling performance of the players:

1. contacting the target in the centre of gravity

2. contacting the target with the shoulder

3. body position square/aligned

4. leg drive upon contact

5. watching the target onto the shoulder

6. centre of gravity forward of base of support.

Using clear technical criteria to analyse the technique of athletes helps with the consistency, clarity and transparency of information that can be provided and can help when translating research findings into practice.

Know how to provide feedback after analysing sport performance

Intrinsic feedback

Feedback is an essential part of the cycle of performance analysis and serves a number of important roles, including enhancing motivation and helping athletes to detect errors. A lot of feedback that an athlete receives about their performance comes from intrinsic sources of sensory feedback, such as tactile, visual and auditory senses. The most obvious example of this is when an athlete sees a shot miss a target – the athlete then knows that they have to change something about performance to change the end result. As the athlete becomes more experienced, they will learn to detect feedback from their senses with a greater degree of sensitivity. For example, an experienced golfer can judge the success of the shot through the feel of their swing and hearing the sound of the club head on the ball without seeing where the ball lands and will be able to make decisions about corrective action required to alter performance. A coach should encourage their athlete to concentrate on this **intrinsic feedback** as it is an essential element of skill acquisition.

Extrinsic feedback

Another important source of feedback is **extrinsic feedback**. This is feedback that comes from a source external to the athlete (such as a sports scientist) and is an essential part of enhancing learning and performance. One of the biggest problems for sports scientists is to decide on what information to feed back to the athlete as there is often masses of data (either in print, video or digital versions) which

would overwhelm an athlete if it was all given at the same time, so this should be considered prior to delivering feedback. Typically, feedback should be prioritised in order of importance (i.e. the biggest area for improvement will need to be developed first so feedback on this will be provided first) in order to enhance performance and will normally take the form of **knowledge of results (KR)** and **knowledge of performance (KP)**. KR and KP are both essential elements of the feedback process that complement each other – one is little use on a performance enhancement level without the other. For example, although it will be good for a young developing basketball player to notice that all of their shots keep bouncing off the backboard (KR), this is of little use to them if they do not know why this happens. As well as highlighting the areas for improvement and providing corrective feedback, it is also important for the sports scientist to provide a rationale for the identified areas and the methods for improvement (Mouratidis, Lens and Vansteenkiste, 2010). As well as KP and KR, there are a number of different types of extrinsic feedback: **concurrent feedback**, **terminal feedback**, **positive feedback** and **negative feedback**.

Key terms

Intrinsic feedback – feedback that comes from the athlete's senses

Extrinsic feedback – feedback from external sources, such as a sports scientist

Knowledge of results – feedback to the athlete about the outcome of an action or event

Knowledge of performance – feedback to the athlete about the actions that have caused the result and how these must be changed to alter the result in future

Concurrent feedback – ongoing feedback provided during an activity

Terminal feedback – feedback that happens after an event, rather than during the event

Positive feedback – feedback that occurs after successful completion of a task, used to reinforce performance

Negative feedback – feedback that happens after an unsuccessful attempt at a task, used to highlight and correct errors

143

Modes of feedback

Another key issue for sports scientists is how to present feedback to athletes. Feedback may be presented verbally to athletes or with different physical demonstrations. For example, when providing feedback to a young football player to explain why their shot has gone over the cross bar, a sports scientist may tell the player that they need to make sure that they do not lean back too far when they kick the ball and that they should keep their head over the ball. This could be accompanied by a demonstration of the desired action. Using this verbal and demonstrative feedback allows the athlete to concentrate on the chief features that have been identified the next time that they attempt the skill and can result in enhanced skill learning and performance (Kernodle, Johnson and Arnold, 2001).

Emerging technologies mean that sports scientists have a range of videos, game reconstructions, statistics and computer generated models that can be used and matched to the learning preference of the athlete. It is also possible to use a combination of different feedback methods to enhance performance. For example, Judge et al. (2008) showed how they combined video feedback, photograph sequences and different statistics that related to key performance criteria in hammer throwing (release angle, height and support phase duration). These were used to develop an intervention to improve the technique of a female hammer thrower. They reported that the use of the range of feedback mechanisms combined with the athlete working closely with the sports scientist, resulted in an American record being set for the women's hammer throw, even though the athlete did not possess the considered ideal physical make up for a hammer thrower.

Factors to consider when providing feedback

There are a number of factors to consider when providing feedback to athletes (see Figure 8.5). As well as the mode of feedback, the sports scientist should consider the depth and precision of feedback that they provide to the athlete.

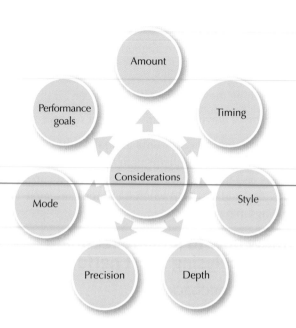

Figure 8.5: Factors to consider when providing feedback to athletes

Generally, more precise feedback is beneficial for athletes, although this can be dependent upon the skill level of the athlete. If the feedback that a sports scientist provides is too precise and technical for the athlete to understand, there is little chance that the feedback will help to enhance performance. In addition, the sports scientist must decide on the amount of feedback required. Larger amounts of feedback have been shown to enhance learning and development in novice athletes, but too much feedback later can be detrimental. It can result in athletes trying to change their technique unnecessarily. In addition, too much feedback from the sports scientist can cause the athlete to become dependent upon the feedback and prevents them from developing self-evaluative and reflective skills. These skills are important for self-development as an athlete. The timing of feedback is critical. If a sports scientist provides concurrent feedback the athlete may need to split their attention between performing the skill and listening to the feedback. The athlete is less likely to reflect on their skill development as they are constantly being guided by the sports scientist. This is likely to reduce the performance of the skill as well as the athlete not being able to process the information from the sports scientist. Finally, the style of feedback is an important factor in its effectiveness. In their study of 337 adolescent athletes, Mouratidis et al. (2010) found that autonomy-supported feedback can still be motivating for an athlete, can encourage an athlete to persist with training and can enhance perceived wellbeing; even if the sports scientist is delivering feedback that suggests they have a low level of competence.

Sandwich approach to feedback

A commonly used approach to providing feedback to athletes is the sandwich approach. It is a useful method of providing feedback to an athlete based on the live, subjective type of performance assessment that sports scientists often go through at pitchside (e.g. when watching a player have a shot on goal in football and the ball rises steeply after it is struck). The sports scientist must analyse the performance and produce feedback quickly. This approach has three stages.

1. The sports scientist provides a positive opening statement about something that the athlete has done well (e.g. 'That was a great strike, well done!')

2. The sports scientist then provides specific feedback to help the athlete to improve (e.g. 'Next time, keep your head over the ball, then you will keep the ball down.')

3. The sports scientist closes with a positive statement to encourage the athlete (e.g. 'Keep up the hard work, the goal will come!')

One word sports scientists should avoid using during the sandwich approach is 'but'. If it is used, often the athlete will forget everything that has preceded the 'but', which reduces the effect of the positive opening statement and places all of the emphasis on the corrective action. The feedback could then be seen as negative by the athlete.

Goal setting

Goal setting is an essential part of the feedback process as any **corrective feedback** will only be relevant to an athlete if it is linked to a performance goal (Liebermann et al. 2002). See *Chapter 6: Sport psychology* for details of goal setting in sports sciences.

Key term

Corrective feedback – statements that convey messages of how to improve after mistakes or poor performance

Case study (for recommended answers, see www.pearsonfe.co.uk/foundationsinsport)

Michelle is a long jumper, who is part of the Olympic developmental squad, aiming to succeed in the Olympic games trials. She has a higher maximum speed than most of the other people that she competes against in competition. She has a longer standing broad jump than most of her team mates and is not suffering from any injuries, but she rarely finishes first in competition. Michelle's coach is at a loss as to why she doesn't win more competitions. Michelle and her coach are both very receptive to feedback and are keen to improve.

1. What are the purposes of performance analysis in this case?
2. What techniques do you think you would use to analyse the performance of this athlete and why?
3. Which modes of feedback do you think would be useful for this athlete and why?

Check your understanding (for answers, see www.pearsonfe.co.uk/foundationsinsport)

1. What are the different purposes of performance analysis?
2. What are the different aspects of the sport development continuum?
3. What are performance criteria?
4. What are the applications of notational analysis?
5. What is the Bloomfield Movement Classification?
6. How does GPS tracking work?
7. What factors should a coach or sports scientist consider when filming techniques?
8. Why is it important to use established criteria when analysing techniques?
9. What are the different types of feedback?
10. What are the different factors to consider when providing feedback to athletes?

Time to reflect

1. How would the application of performance analysis techniques change with different levels of performance?
2. Why is it important for athletes to be actively engaged in the feedback process when their performance is being analysed?
3. What are the problems with a performance analyst being overly controlling when working with a client?
4. Do you think that performance analysis should be a stand alone discipline within sports science or that it should be integrated with others?

Useful resources

To obtain a secure link to the websites below, see the Websites section on page ii or visit the companion website at www.pearsonfe.co.uk/foundationsinsport

- *Dartfish®*
- Elite Sports Analysis
- GPS Sports
- International Association on Computer Science in Sport
- International Society of Performance Analysis of Sport
- ProZone
- Quintic
- Silicon Coach
- Sportstec

Useful journals

Coaching and Sport Science Review

International Journal of Performance Analysis in Sport

International Journal of Sports Science and Coaching

Journal of Quantitative Analysis in Sports

Journal of Sports Sciences

Further reading

Aughey, R.J. and Falloon, C. (2010). Real-Time vs. Post-Game GPS Data in Team Sports. *Science and Medicine in Sport*, **13**, pp. 348–349.

Bloomfield, J., Polman, R. and O'Donoghue, P.G. (2004). The Bloomfield Movement Classification: Movement Analysis of Individual Players in Dynamic Movement Sports. *International Journal of Performance Analysis in Sport-e*, **4**, pp. 20–31.

Bloomfield, J., Polman, R. and O'Donoghue, P.G. (2007). Reliability of the Bloomfield Movement Classification. *International Journal of Performance Analysis in Sport*, **7**, pp. 20–27.

Carling, C., Bloomfield, J., Nelson, L. and Reilly, T. (2008). The Role of Motion Analysis in Elite Soccer: Contemporary Performance Measurement Techniques and Work Rate Data. *Sports Medicine*, **38**, pp. 839–862.

Carling, C., Reilly, T. and Williams, A.M. (2009). *Performance Assessment for Field Sports*. London: Routledge.

Carling, C., Williams, A.M. and Reilly, T. (2005). *Handbook of Soccer Match Analysis*. London: Routledge.

Carron, A.V., Burke, S.M. and Shapcott, K.M. (2009). Enhancing Team Effectiveness. In B. Brewer (ed.), *Handbook of Sports Medicine: Sport Psychology,* pp. 64–74. West Sussex: Wiley Blackwell.

Coutts, A.J. and Duffield, R. (2010). Validity and Reliability of GPS Devices for Measuring Movement Demands of Team Sports. *Journal of Science and Medicine in Sport*, **13**, pp. 133–135.

Duffield, R., Reid, M., Baker, J. and Spratford, W. (2010). Accuracy and Reliability of GPS Devices for Movement Patterns in Confined Spaces for Court-Based Sports. *Journal of Science and Medicine in Sport*, **13**, pp. 523–525.

Edgecomb, S.J. and Norton, K.I. (2006). Comparison of Global Positioning and Computer-Based Tracking Systems for Measuring Player Movement Distance During Australian Football. *Journal of Science and Medicine in Sport*, **9**, pp. 25–32.

Franks, I.M. and Miller, G. (1986). Eyewitness testimony in sport. *Journal of Sport Behaviour*, **9**, pp. 39–45.

Gabbett, T. and Ryan, P. (2009). Tackling Technique, Injury Risk and Playing Performance in High-Performance Collision Sport Athletes. *International Journal of Sports Science and Coaching*, **4**, pp. 521–533.

Gould, D. (2010). Goal Setting for Peak Performance. In J.M. Williams (eds.), *Applied Sport Psychology: Personal Growth to Peak Performance*, 6th Edition, pp. 201–220. Boston: McGraw–Hill.

Hale, S.L. and O' Donoghue, P.G. (2007). Addressing turning and direction changes when using the Bloomfield Movement Classification. *International Journal of Performance Analysis of Sport*, **7**, pp. 84–88.

Hughes, M., and Bartlett, R. (2004). The Use of Performance Indicators in Performance Analysis. In M. Hughes and I.M. Franks (eds.). *Notational Analysis of Sport: Systems for Better Coaching and Performance in Sport*, 2nd Edition. pp. 166–188. London: Routledge.

Hughes, M. and Bartlett, R. (2008). What is Performance Analysis? In M. Hughes and I.M. Franks (eds.) (2008). *The Essentials of Performance Analysis: An Introduction*, pp. 8–20. London: Routledge.

Hughes, M. and Franks, I.M. (eds.) (2004). *Notational Analysis of Sport: Systems for Better Coaching and Performance in Sport,* 2nd Edition. London: Routledge.

Hughes, M. and Franks, I.M. (eds.) (2008). *The Essentials of Performance Analysis: An Introduction.* London: Routledge.

Judge, L.W., Hunter, I. and Gilreath, E. (2008). Using Science to Improve Coaching: A Case Study of the American Record Holder in the Women's Hammer Throw. *International Journal of Sport Science and Coaching*, **3**, pp. 477–488.

Karageorghis, C.I. and Terry, P.C. (2011). *Inside Sport Psychology.* Champaign, Illinois: Human Kinetics.

Kernodle, M.W., Johnson, R. and Arnold, D.R. (2001). Verbal Instruction for Correcting Errors Versus Such Instructions Plus Videotape Replay on Learning the Overhand Throw. *Perceptual Motor Skills,* **92**, pp. 1039–1051.

Liebermann, D., Katz, L., Hughes, M.D., Bartlett, R.M., McClements, J. and Franks, I.M. (2002). Advances in the Application of Information Technology to Sport Performance. *Journal of Sports Sciences*, **20**, pp. 755–769.

Locke, E.A., Shaw, K.N., Saari, L.M. and Latham, G.P. (1981). Goal Setting and Task Performance. *Psychological Bulletin*, **90**, pp. 125–152.

Mouratidis, A., Lens, W. and Vansteenkiste, M. (2010). How you Provide Corrective Feedback Makes a Difference: The Motivating Role of Communicating in an Autonomy-Supporting Way. *Journal of Sport and Exercise Psychology*, **32**, pp. 619–637.

Reilly, T. and Williams, A.M. (eds.) (2003). *Science and Soccer,* 2nd Edition. London: Routledge.

Smith, H.W. (1994). *The 10 Natural Laws of Successful Time and Life Management: Proven Strategies for Increased Productivity and Inner Peace.* New York: Warner.

Weinberg, R.S. and Butt, J. (2005). Goal Setting in Sport and Exercise Domains: The Theory and Practice of Effective Goal Setting. In D. Hackfort, J. Duda and R. Lidor (eds.), *Handbook of Research in Applied Sport Psychology,* pp. 129–146. Morgantown, WV: Fitness Information Technology.

Williams, R. and O'Donoghue, P. (2005). Lower limb injury risk in netball: a time-motion analysis investigation. *Journal of Human Movement Studies*, **49**, pp. 315–331.

Chapter 9

Study skills

Introduction

Study skills are the approaches you apply to your learning, including your ability to take in new information, retain it and perform well in assessments. The development of good study skills will improve your chances of success in your foundation degree.

At school or college you might have received substantial direction on how to approach your study, including what books to read, which chapters, how to interpret your reading, what information to include in assignments and how to construct your answers. At degree level you are expected to discern much of this on your own and act as an independent learner. This might be quite challenging to begin with, but if you develop good study habits from day one of your programme and use the resources and support available to you, you will begin to reap the benefits.

This chapter introduces you to study skills that will support your personal and professional development within the field of sports science, including listening skills, note-taking skills and becoming an effective, independent and confident learner.

Learning outcomes

After you have read this chapter you should be able to:

- identify your existing study skills and learning style

- develop your study skills, including reading, listening, note-taking and making the most of resources available to you

- understand the importance of critical thinking and how to develop as a critical thinker

- prepare for assessment.

Identify your study skills and learning style

Your foundation degree is likely to involve some sessions and/or resources to help you develop your research and study skills. These might be delivered through a personal tutor programme or through modules on personal and professional development.

An audit of your study skills

To begin, be clear about the skills you already have as well as the ones you need to develop. Reflect on your experiences of learning to date. What have you found easy, what has presented challenges, how have you learnt to overcome them? What might be your potential barriers to successful study?

Top tip

· Establish good study habits from the very start of your programme. Monitor and review these regularly to ensure they are working optimally to support your learning. Check your college or university website for web-based study skills resources including further information on the skills discussed in this chapter, hints and tips, diagnostic tests and self assessment exercises.

Identify your learning style

You will experience two types of learning throughout your foundation degree – **pedagogy** and **andragogy**. Pedagogy is teacher-led education; your lecturer will decide your learning content and best method of delivery. Andragogy is learner-focused education; this is where you are responsible for your own learning. This method is apparent in your own study and in your work experience module. To help you with your own studying you need to decide on your preferred learning style.

One of the most widely used methods to identify different learning styles is the VARK model (Leite et al., 2009). It includes a series of questions and you choose the answer which best describes your preference. Your preferred learning style will be shown, and advice given about specific study strategies. Understanding your preferred learning style means you can use appropriate techniques to facilitate your learning.

Key terms

Andragogy – learner-focused education

Pedagogy – teacher-led education

Table 9.1: Five learning styles

Learning style	Tools and activities	Suggested activities
Visual learners (learn best through seeing)	• Use visual images – pictures, models, videos, flow charts, graphs and textbooks • Use different colours, highlight key information and underlining	• Select lecture notes and highlight key information in colour • Can you display the information in a visual manner such as a flow chart?
Aural learners (learn best through listening)	• Attend lectures • Replay the lecture and fill in any gaps in your lecture notes • Active participation in discussions and tutorials • Explain information to others • Describe visual information	• Ask permission from your lecturer to record a lecture using a dictaphone • Now replay the lecture and fill in any gaps in your lecture notes
Read/write (learn best through reading and writing)	• Read textbooks, journals and definitions • Write lecture notes up in full • Use headings, lists and definitions • Read lecture notes aloud	• Read several journal articles in relation to a lecture topic
Kinaesthetic (learn best through experience)	• Focus on learning through moving, touching and doing • Work experience placements • Shadowing other professionals	• Seek a placement in which you can shadow a sports scientist working
Multimodal	• Learn via a combination of two or more learning styles	

To obtain a secure link to an online learning styles questionnaire, see the *Useful resources* list on page 161.

Fleming (1995) suggests there are five learning styles, as shown in Table 9.1.

Developing your study skills

Listening

In order to maximise your performance and make the most of lectures you need to be a good listener. Taught programmes are heavily reliant on the delivery of information and your ability to listen. Listening is a cognitive act that requires you to pay attention, think about the information delivered and mentally process it.

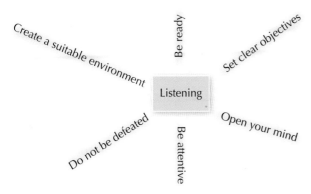

Figure 9.1: Key components to ensure you are a good listener. How can you achieve each of these?

- **Be ready** – prepare for each lecture by reading any notes and required reading beforehand. Consider how much you already understand about the topic that is due to be delivered. Make a conscious effort to find the topic useful and interesting. Take everything you need for making notes during the lecture.

- **Clear objectives** – have a clear idea of what you expect from the lecture and the topic to be delivered. Ask questions if you are unsure of anything or if you think something has not been covered. Your lecturer may highlight that your question will be addressed in the next lecture.

- **Open your mind** – question what you are being taught but allow enough time for information to be covered. Your question may be answered as

the lecture progresses. If it isn't, ask at a suitable interval, not in the middle of the lecture. Be receptive to new ideas and points of view.

- **Be attentive** – turn off your mobile phone so you are not tempted to surf the Internet or check for text messages. Focus, and maintain eye contact with your lecturer. Sit in a position where you can fully engage in the lecture and will not be distracted by others. Make additional notes, listen attentively and ask questions to clarify wherever you are unsure. Try to understand the main message of the lecture and the links and ideas presented. Write down key information quickly, particularly anything the lecturer has highlighted as important to your assessment or exam. If you know something requires further research, add a question mark to draw your attention to it after the lecture.

- **Do not be defeated** and stop listening when you feel challenged or find a topic hard. This is the time to increase your focus and listen very carefully while opening your mind. If you are struggling to understand, say so – others are probably feeling the same.

- **Environment** – if the room is too hot, sit by an open window and if you know the room is cold, wear extra clothing. Be proactive and think how you can best cope with the environment to limit the distraction.

Note-taking

You will generally be faced with two types of note-taking: those that you take during taught sessions and those that you make as a result of independent study. When it comes to note-taking the best approach is the one that works for you. Differing approaches can be equally effective but one secret to success is to remain actively engaged with the material you are reading or listening to whilst taking notes. If all you do is copy down what you read or hear then learning is less likely to occur.

Don't copy out sentences or passages of text verbatim or get frustrated if your lecturer appears to have whizzed though the content on a presentation slide without leaving time for you to copy everything down. It is likely that these are prompts for their delivery of information and you need to create your own means of synthesising that for yourself.

The most important aspect of note-taking is that your notes should be useful for future reference. *Do* be concise and summarise, use headings and numbered points, create your own shorthand and abbreviations and be sure to leave space in your notes to go back and add or amend. Review your notes before your next lecture on the topic to expand on your knowledge and understanding. Discuss these with your peers.

In lecture settings take an active approach to learning. Make a note of questions or tasks to follow up after. If reading has been recommended, undertake this and consider setting up a study group or journal club where you can get together in smaller groups to discuss and explore ideas, interpretation and understanding.

Develop a note-taking system which works for you, and ensure you file all your notes in an organised way. Your notes will be a valuable resource when preparing for exams, assignments and further reading. Investing time now will save time during the assessment period and will develop your understanding of the subject.

> ### Top tip
>
> Do not limit yourself to words when making your notes. Use drawings, maps and colour to help you connect ideas and themes to add understanding and for future ease of reference.
>
> Make a note to read any key references signposted by your academic tutors during lectures.

Reading

Reading is an important part of your course. When you embark on your foundation degree you may be surprised at the amount of reading that is expected of you, possibly within relatively short time periods.

It is highly likely that your tutors will have recommended reading. These are often seen as the bare minimum of reading that you are expected to engage with around a subject or topic area.

Added to that you will be typically asked to 'read around your subject' by sourcing material beyond that which is signposted by your tutor, often with limited guidance on how to tackle this. Try not to feel overwhelmed by this. Aim to select your reading material carefully by keeping the purpose in mind and trying to tune yourself in to cues from your academic tutors during your lectures. It is highly likely that these will signpost further reading or concepts for you to explore. These may be as explicit as independent study tasks that you are expected to complete in your own time, but later reflect on in future contact with your academic tutors. You may hinder your learning if you fail to complete such tasks.

> ### Remember
>
> Students who read effectively, as well as widely, are more likely to achieve higher grades.

Your academic reading should:

- enhance your understanding of your subject
- help you to understand theoretical concepts
- expand your applied knowledge of your subject
- help you explore possible alternative viewpoints in order to consolidate your own views and challenge those of others.

Active reading helps to keep the mind focused on the task in hand. If you own the book, or have printed out a journal, highlight or underline important details as you read. It will help to keep you focused. You may also wish to annotate the reading to reinforce information and make points for revision.

> ### Top tip
>
> If you want to write well you need to read extensively. Research the meaning of words that are unfamiliar to you but central to your understanding of the material you are reading and create a glossary of key terms.

Study reading
- Use when reading more complex material
- Read more slowly than your normal reading pace
- May need to read more than once to understand the complexity

Scan reading
- Use to quickly locate a specific piece of information
- Scan a paragraph or list to identify a specific piece of information

Reading

Skim reading
- Use when you need to quickly obtain a general idea
- Identify the main ideas of each paragraph
- Read a large amount of material in a short time
- Lower level of comprehension required

Figure 9.2: The three reading styles: study reading, skim reading and scan reading. Identify where you can use each of these reading styles in your study.

Critical thinking

Your ability to think critically will be a valuable asset to your study of sports science, but also your employability. Employers seeking graduates will often state the ability to think critically, innovatively and independently as essential criteria in a job specification.

The crucial elements of developing as a critical thinker are:

- asking questions

- weighing up information and deciding what is relevant

- making reasonable and logical judgements based on evidence

- establishing assumptions

- taking an honest approach and resisting manipulation

- being willing to subject your own viewpoint to further scrutiny

- being open to new evidence and the persuasion of others, sometimes in the context of making difficult decisions.

Remember

In essence critical thinking is about being able to ask appropriate questions and to identify relevant and valid information to reach sound judgements.

Writing

The written word is still the most common form of communication, and one you are most likely to use to answer your assignment tasks, whether they are essays, articles, reports, case studies, projects or posters. Writing skills, like any other skill, can be learned. View the development of your writing skills as an ongoing process, and one that you should reflect on frequently and use feedback to achieve your potential. There are some general guidelines that can be applied whatever the finished product, which will be covered here.

To be successful you need to understand the 'purpose of writing'. This will generally focus around the need to meet the assessment requirements of your course, demonstrating your knowledge and understanding of a topic area. Think about an assignment as an opportunity to:

- get to grips with the key theories and concepts in your subject area

- develop different viewpoints and perspectives that stretch your knowledge and understanding

- obtain feedback on your performance and review your approach to your study skills and subject area.

Generally, an essay, article or report is constructed using coherent paragraphs, which are connected in a logical way. An introduction is used to introduce the topic, with the main body developing an argument, linking point 1 to point 2, to point 3, etc. You should then always end with a conclusion. This should conclude your argument and summarise the main points.

A piece of writing can take time to develop. For a 2500 word essay allow a minimum of three weeks; for longer essays allow more time. You need this time not just to write the essay, but for researching, planning, drafting and redrafting, as well as editing and refining your work, paying particular attention to your spelling, grammar and referencing. The essay-writing process can be broken down into stages as shown below.

1. **Understand the topic** – ensure you fully understand the essay topic and the requirements of your work. Identify the key words within the essay title and make sure you understand their full meaning. You need a full grasp of the topic in order to ensure that all the information you include is relevant. You may decide to formulate your argument to the topic in question, in order to provide direction for the planning process. You can always amend your argument as your knowledge develops. Highlight key information on the assessment brief you have been given.

2. **Brainstorm** – this will allow you to put down all your ideas. Think laterally and document all information, even if something seems irrelevant (you may make a connection later on in your work). A brainstorm will help you to focus on your plan and reading.

3. **Essay plan** – produce a plan for your essay. Think about the structure and order, and which topics you are going to put where.

4. **Reading** – read a wide range of sources related to your essay topic and plan – use books as well

as academic journals. The Internet is a good source to develop thoughts and ideas and gain a quick understanding but should rarely be used as an academic reference. Academic references should form the basis of your research; these include books and journals.

5. **Amend essay plan** – on completion of your reading you will have a better understanding of the topic. Review your plan and make any amendments. Do you need to move or add a topic? Your plan should help you to write analytically. Consider the following and amend your plan as necessary:

- clearly identified main proposal, hypothesis or argument

- reasoned argument considering evidence, examples and research

- reasoned opposing argument – again considering evidence, examples and research.

6. **Justification of your perspective** – address weaknesses and flaws in opposing arguments using evidence, examples and research.

7. **Draft 1** – you need to write your essay based on your plan and the reading you have completed. If you feel there are gaps, or you do not have sufficient information, make a note and address these when you have completed the first draft.

8. **Additional information** – your first draft will have allowed you to ascertain weaker areas, and areas which require further understanding. Focus your additional reading on these areas and revisit the criteria your work will be measured against.

9. **Draft 2** – amend your first draft to address any weak areas or gaps in your work.

10. **Break** – take a break from your work. Fresh eyes and thought will enhance the next stage.

11. **Final version** – review your work, focusing on the flow and logical structure. You may need additional sentences or paragraphs to improve the links. Is there any irrelevant information? Focus on each sentence. Could you write the sentence with fewer words or with a clearer structure?

12. **Proofreading** – this is the final read through, paying particular attention to details such as spelling, punctuation and referencing. A friend might be able to help with this stage of your essay. Referencing within the text as well as including a full reference list is often overlooked by many students. The section on referencing below includes full details.

Referencing

In order to inform your knowledge and understanding, you will need to refer to academic sources. The material you read and research will form the substance of your work. Making reference to another author's work is known as citing (or citation) and you must give a full detailed list of all sources used in a reference list at the end of your work. You must fully reference your work; if you do not you may be guilty of plagiarism (see page 156).

Stop and think

Take a look at one of your assignment titles and ask yourself the following questions.

- What is expected?
- What is the most appropriate structure and format? Is one prescribed? If so stick to it.
- Is there a recommended length or word limit? If so don't exceed it.
- Is there a target audience for the end product?
- Am I encouraged to make reference to relevant academic literature? This is almost always an expectation at this level.

Remember

You may have been given a reading list; as a minimum you would be expected to engage with this.

Top tip

Good writing doesn't usually happen without a great deal of preparation. Get started on your assessments the day they are set. Talk to others, share your thoughts and ideas and consider setting up a study group focused on the assessment task.

You will generally have some marking or assessment criteria that should also give you significant clues as to what is expected. Make sure you make frequent reference to these throughout your assessment preparation and completion process.

Researching for your writing will usually involve taking a systematic approach to searching for the material you will use to support the production of your assessment and investigating this material critically in the process. To identify appropriate sources of information to help in the production of your assessment pieces you may have:

- tutor handouts or web-based materials
- topic guidance notes or handbooks
- your own notes from lectures, seminars and reading
- feedback from previous assessment pieces.

Always pay attention to any assessment or marking criteria that have been assigned; and do not forget to review the feedback you have been given on previous assessment pieces.

Top tip

When reviewing relevant academic literature look for current up to date sources of information. In your field of sports science this is most likely to be published in scientific journals.

Your university or college will have their own referencing guide which may differ slightly from the examples below. Pay particular attention to detail. This can be a time consuming process so on completion of your assessment, allow time in your planning to address this properly.

When you are making direct reference to an author's original idea, or a study they have conducted, reference as follows:

Whyte (2006) states that…

Powers and Howley (2009) propose that…

If there are more than two authors for the publication you should cite them as follows:

Sewell et al. (2009) state that…

When you are not directly making reference to an author(s), although you have used their concepts or ideas, you should reference as follows:

Nutritional knowledge is understood to play a central role in an athlete's nutritional intake and subsequent performance (Abood et al., 2004).

If you have identified two sources, which support this idea you should reference as follows:

Despite desire to succeed there remains a widespread lack of knowledge of optimal nutritional practices amongst athletes (Hoogenboom et al. 2009; Jessri et al. 2010).

The references at the end of your essay should be in alphabetical order. To reference a book, follow this format:

Sewell, D., Watkins, P. and Griffin, M. (2005) *Sport and Exercise Science; An Introduction*, London: Hodder Arnold.

To reference a journal, follow this format:

Hoogenboom, B.J., Morris, J., Morris, C., Schaefer, K. (2009) Nutritional knowledge and eating behaviour of female collegiate swimmers. *North American Journal of Sports Physical Therapy* Vol 4, (3) pp. 139–148.

> ## Top tip
>
> If you have two publications from the same author you should distinguish by placing an 'a', 'b' after each of the years. For example, Burke (2010a) and Burke (2010b).

> ## Remember
>
> Plagiarism is the term used to describe 'passing off the work of others as your own' and is regarded as an offence of serious misconduct by universities and colleges. You might commit plagiarism by using extracts from an article or book without using quotation marks or by not acknowledging a paraphrased section of work. To avoid plagiarism be careful with your note-taking and cite and reference all of your sourced material in the production of your assessed work. Try to develop your skills at evaluating and synthesising information from multiple sources as you'll be much more unlikely to plagiarise this way. Most universities and colleges now use anti-plagiarism software, such as Turnitin, that can be used to check your assessment work against other published resources such as journals, books, websites and student dissertations.

> ## Top tip
>
> Take some time to investigate the resources available to you to ensure you avoid falling foul of plagiarism.

Effective time management

Good time management is essential if you are to produce good quality work and achieve your goals. In higher education you will spend most of your time studying on your own without tutor support. You will be expected to manage your own study timetable.

If you are studying full-time you should expect your total study time to account for around 40 hours per week and think of it as a full-time job. Good time management is about making the best and most effective use of time to accomplish the things we need and want to. The challenges to good time management include knowing what you want and need to do and being able to establish and stick to priorities along the way.

> ## Top tip
>
> Make use of small windows of time that might otherwise be wasted, for example reviewing your lecture notes on the train or reading a journal article between lectures.

> ## Top tip
>
> Studying with others makes studying more enjoyable and provides the opportunity to gain from different perspectives, as well as the opportunity to share the load in terms of searching for resources and provides a sense of mutual support. It is better to view your peers as facilitators not competitors in your journey towards graduation.

Stop and think

To develop effective time-management skills you need to be aware of how you use your time at present. To do this record how you spend your time for a typical week in a personal time log.

- On completion of your log identify activities undertaken during the week; for example, watching television, studying, working, playing sport, going for coffee, socialising, etc.
- Calculate the total time spent on these activities.
- Now consider if you have the balance of these activities appropriate to achieving your goals.

Knowing what time of the day you are most productive will be crucial to using your time well. Take another look at your time log and consider the following questions:

- Which days of the week were you busiest/least busy?
- What hours of the day were you most/least productive?
- What were the most/least productive uses of your time?
- How much of your time was under/out of your control?
- What influences why you waste time or use it effectively?

To organise your time well:

- set yourself realistic goals and objectives
- identify what needs to be done to achieve them
- prioritise, plan and organise the actions required
- allocate appropriate time to actions required
- review and revise your time management strategies frequently.

Remember

Good time management will:

- reduce stress
- lead to improved productivity and performance
- allow more time for reflection
- build personal satisfaction and confidence
- allow for quality leisure time.

Getting on top of assessment

The purpose of assessment is to measure your performance in relation to set learning outcomes. Assessment methods for your course will vary and are likely to include a variety of formal and informal, summative and formative:

- essays
- case studies
- presentations
- project work
- examinations
- reports
- practicals or simulations
- observations and viva examinations
- peer and self assessment
- personal development plans and evidence portfolios.

Keep a diary and record all assessment deadlines as they are given to you. You will be expected to meet these deadlines unless mitigating circumstances are evident and you have abided by the rules in reporting these.

Preparing for a presentation

At some point during your career you will be expected to present information. You need a good understanding of your presentation topic to be able to communicate effectively with your audience and answer any related questions.

Preparing for exams

Give yourself plenty of time in order to prepare effectively for examinations. Implement good time management throughout the process, make a concerted effort and persevere through any difficulties.

Table 9.2: Top tips for an effective presentation

Preparation	Carry out research and understand your subject area thoroughly. Practise your presentation a number of times before your assessment. You could video yourself and reflect on your performance, or practise with colleagues and ask for feedback. Answer the task you have been given, and time yourself to ensure you stay within the time limit.
Presentation slides	Prepare your slides using a suitable IT package, for example PowerPoint® or www.Prezi.com. Ensure your material is presented with clarity, referenced and has visual aids. Do not overload your slides with lots of text which you are tempted to read word for word.
Your presentation	Dress appropriately. Present a positive attitude conveying enthusiasm, professionalism and confidence.
Examples/reference sources	Provide a range of examples and reference sources to help explain aspects, ensuring they are related to the subject.
Audience	Connect with your audience by maintaining eye contact with them. Scan all participants.
Interest	Make your presentation interesting by using visual aids. Ask questions to involve the audience (ensuring they are at an appropriate level). If you use video clips keep them short (20–30 seconds maximum) and clearly state their purpose or relevance.
Voice	Speak at an appropriate speed and vary the tone of your voice.
Reference list	Like other forms of written assessment a reference list will be expected.

Top tip

Remember KISS: **K**eep **I**t **S**imple and **S**traightforward. Start with the basics and progress to more complex information.

Stop and think

Look to your submission dates for your assignments. Allow yourself enough time to go through the stages of researching, planning, drafting and reviewing before submitting your assignment. Create an assessment calendar and set aside blocks of time to allow for these. Set yourself an action plan for completing your assignments and regularly reflect on your progress with this.

You should first write down the exam date, time and location on your semester calendar and work out a realistic revision schedule to meet the exam deadline. When revising, refer back to the list on page 151 under 'Listening'.

Maintain a routine before the exam, including regular meals to keep up your energy levels. If your exam is in the afternoon do not 'cram' in the morning – just refresh your memory with key points. Make sure you get a good night's sleep before a morning exam, and have a final read through of your revision notes. Ensure you have all your equipment and arrive in plenty of time for the start of the exam.

During the exam you should read the instructions carefully, and read all the questions first to identify those which are compulsory and those which are optional. Plan how much time you will allocate to each question, allowing a proportion of time to read through your answers. Clearly identify your answers within your answer book and start with the question you feel most confident with.

Use all your time effectively – never leave an exam early. Ensure you have answered the correct number of questions and your answer matches the question number. Read through your answers and edit where necessary, but remember that it is about the quality of your work, not the quantity. If you are running short of time, list the key information. Take care that your handwriting is legible – if the examiner cannot read your work they cannot mark it.

Preparing for practical assessments and *viva voce*

Practical assessments are likely to feature in foundation degrees in sports science. With an essay or written exam you have access to many resources which you can collate, and you have time to reflect and amend your work. With a practical assessment it is crucial you understand your subject area and are able to operate and communicate information competently and confidently at the time of assessment.

Practical assessments may also include a *viva voce examination* (commonly known as a viva), a question and answer style of assessment.

You need to prepare thoroughly for practical assessments and *viva voce*.

Understand the requirements of your practical and *viva voce* and draft possible questions you may be asked – you can then rehearse your answers.

Revise and practise the practical techniques to be assessed with other students.

Making the most of resources available to you

Your academic tutors

The amount of support offered to you by your academic tutors may vary a great deal between and across different programmes of study. What is consistent though is that you will be expected to take the lead in identifying what support you need, looking for ways of solving problems that arise, finding out what information and support is available to you and making best use of it.

Your academic tutors will provide guidance within course and topic handbooks, tutorial programmes, within lecture and seminar material and in the feedback they provide on your assessed work. If you run into difficulty in understanding what is expected of you most tutors will be willing to assist in your learning development but will expect you to have done the following before you take your problem to them:

> ## Top tip
>
> - Be prepared and wear appropriate clothing for your practical assessment – unless you are instructed to wear smart professional attire.
> - Stay calm and professional and maintain an appropriate manner and attitude.
> - Listen carefully to any questions. Do not be afraid to ask the examiner to repeat them if necessary.
> - If asked to evaluate your own performance in elements of your practical assessment be honest, if something does not go to plan it is better to acknowledge this and describe how you would rectify it.
> - If you do not know the answer to any questions, do not bluff – acknowledge that you do not know and move the assessment on.
> - Do not worry if parts of the viva voce were difficult. The examiner will ask a range of questions differing in complexity and difficulty in order to ascertain your knowledge and grade.

- reviewed all other sources of information thoroughly before seeking support
- worked through the problem and identified possible solutions to be discussed with the tutor
- prepared a list of questions to ask in order of importance.

Arrive on time and make the best use of your time with the tutor.

Your fellow students

It will be expected that you develop your own support networks. There are various ways you can approach this such as:

- reading groups or journal clubs to discuss theories and concepts that arise from recommended reading
- action learning sets to provide mutual support on assignments and projects
- social networks to help balance the 'work' and 'play' elements of student life.

Remember

- Set up good study habits from the start of your programme.
- Audit and review your study skills frequently.
- Become time aware and time efficient.
- Make good use of feedback and set yourself clear goals for improvement.

Check your understanding (for answers, see www.pearsonfe.co.uk/foundationsinsport)

1. Use an online questionnaire to identify your learning style. Describe the methods that will help you to learn more effectively. To obtain a secure link to an online learning styles questionnaire, see the Useful resources list on the next page.

2. Briefly describe the purpose of academic reading.

3. Define plagiarism.

4. Briefly describe two strategies which you could use to improve your listening skills.

5. What is the purpose of assessment?

6. Discuss three aspects to consider when preparing for a presentation.

7. Identify the 12 stages of writing an essay.

8. What are the crucial elements of developing as a critical thinker?

9. How can you study effectively and make the most of the resources available to you?

10. As a study skill, what are the benefits of good time management?

Time to reflect

1. Why is it important to establish good study habits from the start of your programme?

2. How do you intend to make the most of the resources available to you during your programme of study?

3. To produce your assessed material you will have to search for source material. Why is it important to take a systematic and critical approach to searching for material you will use to support the production of your assessed work?

4. Think about how you can successfully use feedback to improve your assessment outcomes.

5. Reflect on your assessment action plan. How can you ensure that you stick to your plan and achieve the assessment outcomes you would like?

Useful resources

To obtain a secure link to the websites below, see the Websites section on page ii or visit the companion website at www.pearsonfe.co.uk/foundationsinsport

- Dyslexia at College

- BRAINHE

- EPAX

- LearnHigher

- VARK

- skills4study – Palgrave Macmillan

Further reading

Dascombe B., Reaburn P., Reed R., Weyers J., Jones A. (2011) *Practical Skills in Sport and Exercise Science – Practical skills*. Prentice Hall.

Boulay, D. (2009). *Study Skills for Dummies*. Chichester: John Wiley & Sons.

Cotterall, S. (2008). *The Study Skills Handbook*. Basingstoke: Palgrave Macmillan.

Cotterall, S. (2008). *How to Write Better Essays*. Basingstoke: Palgrave Macmillan.

Cotterall, S. (2008). *Critical Thinking Skills*. Basingstoke: Palgrave Macmillan.

Fleming N. (1995) "VARK – a guide to learning styles", available at: www.varklearn.com/english/index.asp

Leite W.L., Svinicki, M. and Shi, Y., *Attempted Validation of the Scores of the VARK: Learning Styles Inventory with Multitrait–Multimethod Confirmatory Factor Analysis Models*, p. 2. SAGE Publications, 2009.

Chapter 10

Work placement

Introduction

Working and learning are often viewed as two discrete activities, with learning having to happen before working can commence. In reality, we never stop learning and the workplace is a rich environment for learning to occur. Your foundation degree should involve learning in the workplace as well as at university or college. Work-based learning (WBL) is a distinctive feature of foundation degrees, giving you the opportunity to link theory to practice, work on real projects in a relevant workplace and pick up technical and practical skills along the way. You may already have a workplace, but if not your academic tutors should have engaged with employers to provide this opportunity as part of your programme.

You will be required to complete a minimum number of hours of work experience as documented in your university or college module specifications; the number of hours may differ between institutions.

By their very nature, workplaces will offer differing experiences for WBL and you should expect to have different experiences from your peers. Your personal programme of WBL should assist you with career planning, allow for your development and practice of work-related skills and build your self-awareness and confidence in the process.

This chapter explores employment opportunities, possible roles you may undertake, as well as the skills you will need to apply for a placement and use in the work environment.

Learning outcomes

After you have read this chapter you should be able to:

- discuss employment opportunities for sports scientists
- develop a learning agreement to inform your work experience programme outcomes and influence your career decisions
- demonstrate appropriate communication and personal skills for employment
- write a letter of application and curriculum vitae
- understand how to develop as a reflective practitioner.

Employment opportunities for sports scientists

The career prospects for sports and exercise scientists are expanding all the time. A foundation degree in sports science should begin to open the doors to a range of employment opportunities not only in sport but also the healthcare, fitness and leisure industries, including:

- sports science officer
- sports nutritionist
- exercise physiologist
- exercise consultant
- physical activity promotion officer.

Most sports now recognise the role of sports science as an integral part of development and success; most athletes, particularly those involved in professional and elite sport, consider the application of sports science as an essential part of their training and competition programmes.

Usually the sporting world focuses on achieving the best results possible. Athletes and coaches alike now view the sports scientist as a useful resource. As recently as the early 1990s there was relatively limited scope for athletes to engage with sports scientists in terms of detailed physiological assessment, monitoring and feedback. Today, however, the impact that sports science can have on the performance of our very best athletes is more clearly recognised. Collectively, across the disciplines, sports science has the potential to add a percentage or two to the athlete's performance, which might not sound a great deal but when you are performing at world class level, that might just be the difference between winning a championship medal or not.

Successful sports scientists take opportunities whilst studying their degree to volunteer in a range of projects and activities to gain additional experience, build their **curriculum vitae** and network of contacts, gain confidence and get a feel for what aspects of the work enthuse them. In addition, many professional sports clubs now offer internship opportunities to new graduates. These are often voluntary posts or offer minimal pay but you can expect to claim reasonable expenses.

Key term

Curriculum vitae – document which provides an overview of your qualifications, employment and relevant life experience

Figure 10.1: Types of employment – how would your role as a sports scientist differ between employment opportunities?

Roles a sports scientist may undertake

Your role as a sports scientist will vary according to your chosen employment. As a foundation degree student of sports science you will have developed a background across a number of subjects related to sports performance. These areas will include sports biomechanics, physiology, psychology, nutrition, coaching science and performance analysis. You may decide to develop your knowledge, skills and employment experience in one of the discipline strands of sports science, such as that of a sports nutritionist or exercise physiologist, or you may want to have a broad role across disciplines such as a sports science officer. If you work for a larger organisation or a professional team, you are more likely to work as part of a multi-disciplinary team. Your role will be more specific and you will be expected to liaise with different colleagues, who might include other sports scientists, physiotherapists, sports therapists, technical and strength and conditioning coaches. If you find employment in the field of exercise and health you may work as an exercise consultant or physical activity promotion officer. Many of these roles are likely to require further training and development beyond your foundation degree.

Figure 10.2: Examples of activities a sports scientist may undertake

Stop and think

Take a look at the British Association of Sport and Exercise Scientists Guide to Careers in Sport and Exercise Science. It is available to download free at the BASE website and investigate the range of career opportunities in sports science and exercise science.

Developing a learning agreement

In order to ensure maximum benefit from a work placement it is common practice to draw up a learning agreement outlining the clear roles and responsibilities of the student, the work placement provider and academic institution in relation to learning and assessment. Well-planned activities

and work-based projects should provide positive outcomes for both you and your employer.

Your learning agreement learning outcomes might relate to key transferable skills such as: working with others or effective communication, module specific learning outcomes relating to core knowledge or the attainment of professional awards or occupational standards.

Remember

Work-based learning requires the identification and achievement of defined and related learning outcomes.

Learning agreements do not need to be long or detailed documents, but they should include:

- all relevant contact details (including your own, those of your work-based learning co-ordinator and work-based learning mentor)
- the duration of your work-based learning
- hours of work
- learning outcomes of your programme of study
- how you will be expected to achieve these and any identified review points
- how the proposed activities and projects to be undertaken by you will meet the business objectives of the employer/organisation and the learning outcomes
- the process of planning and negotiation undertaken to decide your learning agreement
- any relevant health and safety issues.

Your responsibilities

To ensure a successful work-based learning experience your responsibilities include:
- complying with the rules, regulations, and normal requirements of the employer or organisation, including confidentiality, timekeeping, codes of behaviour and dress
- performing tasks assigned by your work-based learning mentor, which are related to the learning outcomes identified in your learning agreement
- seeking regular feedback on your performance within the workplace and reflecting on your learning experience

- notifying your college or university work-based learning co-ordinator of any changes needed to the learning agreement or of any problems that may develop during your work placement.

Your learning agreement should be signed and dated by all parties and reviewed regularly.

Remember

Work-based learning involves actively using the workplace as a learning environment, and should be viewed as more than work experience or just 'being at work'.

You should also develop a Personal Development Plan (PDP) to reflect on your learning, performance and/or achievement and to plan for your personal, educational and career development. The primary objective of a PDP is to improve your capacity to understand what and how you learn, and to review, plan and take responsibility for your own learning, helping you to:

- become a more effective, independent and confident self-directed learner
- understand how you are learning and to relate that learning in wider contexts
- articulate your personal goals and evaluate progress towards their achievement
- improve general skills for study and career management
- develop a positive attitude to life-long learning.

Remember

Your learning agreement should help guide and structure your work experience placement and help you achieve clearly defined learning objectives from it.

Your Personal Development Plan should be used for continually reflecting on your learning and performance and identifying personal, educational or career development needs.

Skills for work placement and employment

Your foundation degree will develop your portfolio of transferable skills. These are skills which can be applied to a range of jobs. Examples include communication, problem-solving, leadership and time-management skills.

Communication skills

Whatever your job role as a sports scientist the development of good communication skills is essential if you are to develop successful relationships within your workplace whether these are with athletes, clients, colleagues or employers. Good communication helps you to convey your message to the recipient clearly and unambiguously. It is also essential that you receive information clearly.

Verbal communication

During all verbal communication you need to convey your message as clearly as possible to the recipient and avoid unnecessary jargon, such as complex medical terminology. You should speak clearly, concisely and at an appropriate speed. Words should be chosen which convey your intent and deliver succinct meaning in a logical manner. You should avoid creating resistance or a defensive mindset in your recipient. You should also try to avoid using words which are accusatory, judgemental, blaming or critical.

Non-verbal communication

Non-verbal communication, commonly known as body language, plays an important role in communication. Body language includes eye contact, facial expressions, gestures, posture, voice, touch and space – as discussed below.

Non-verbal communication is a powerful tool which you can use to help secure employment, build rapport with athletes, develop your client base and address challenging situations.

- **Eye contact** – to portray confidence ensure that you make frequent eye contact. When first approaching the recipient make gentle eye contact, and develop the gaze. Intense eye contact can be as detrimental as too little.

- **Voice** – think about the quality and projection of your voice, pace, expression and emphasis.
- **Posture** – move confidently, adopting a confident posture. This will make you feel more confident and also help to make others feel confident about you.
- **Facial expression** – your face is very expressive and communicates a wide range of emotions, such as happiness, sadness, anger, fear and disgust. You should be aware of your emotional state and ensure you only show a positive, confident and pleasing expression.
- **Gestures** – many people talk with their hands; some more than others. Ensure that any hand gestures you make are not misinterpreted.
- **Touch** is used as a way of communicating. A clear distinction should be made between personal and professional communication. A firm handshake is a professional reassuring approach upon first meeting. A warm hug would be far too familiar and unprofessional within the work environment (although an appropriate way to greet a good friend).
- **Space** – the need for personal space differs from person to person. Invading a person's space can communicate signals for intimacy, aggression or dominance, all of which are inappropriate. Maintain your personal space and respect the space of others.

Effective and successful communication will depend on your ability to self reflect, to be emotionally self aware and to critique your own non-verbal communication skills in relation to the message you are sending out. A good way to hone your skills is to observe yourself in action through a digital recording (ensure you have the consent of those who you are videoing – if they are aged under 16 parental consent will need to be sought). Watch your performance whilst identifying your strengths and any areas for improvement.

Personal skills required for employment

Figure 10.3 Personal skills required for employment

Enthusiasm

Enthusiasm is paramount. It is the energy that you create to bring about a successful outcome. To have enthusiasm you need to have an interest in your subject and a knowledge and belief in yourself. Always be enthusiastic, but also realistic about what you can achieve. People do not gravitate towards boring people. Enthusiasm can act like a magnet, and people tend to be drawn to those who are enthusiastic because they are upbeat and positive. However, over-enthusiastic people can be too intense; they tend to invade the space of others and may even repel them.

Self-discipline

Self-discipline is an important tool whether you are employed or self-employed. It is the ability, regardless of emotional state, to take action. Actions will vary from being punctual, carrying out professional practice and thorough preparation to developing new behaviour and thought patterns. It is your ability to use your willpower to accomplish an objective, despite wishing you were doing something else. Self-discipline can be developed and trained.

Self-motivation

Self-motivation is your ability to motivate yourself. You will have a reason to accomplish an objective and find the strength to achieve without the need for persuasion or support from others. It is the ability to be able to motivate yourself to overcome setbacks, unfair criticism, overcome others' negative attitude towards you and the general barriers in life and at work.

Organisation

Organisation is the ability to plan and co-ordinate your personal and professional schedules. Having good organisation skills will help to improve aspects, such as productivity, success, creativity, efficient working practices and cost effectiveness.

Leadership

A leader is someone who guides and inspires, and sets a new direction and vision for others. This is important within the workplace, particularly if you are working as part of a multi-disciplinary team. To be a good leader you need to make sure that the entire team understands their role, and is included when goals are being set.

Equality and diversity

Equality and diversity should be embraced and embedded. Equality gives every individual the opportunity to achieve their potential. This should be done without any prejudice and discrimination to develop a fairer society. Diversity is about recognising individual or group differences, treating people accordingly and valuing everyone positively.

Writing a letter of application

If you are not already in the world of work one of your biggest challenges might be securing an appropriate work placement. You should be heavily involved in the design and choice of location of your work-based learning and this should form an essential part of your personal and professional development plan (PDP) related to your career aspirations. It should enable you to take on appropriate roles within the workplace, giving you an opportunity to learn and apply the skills and knowledge you acquire in an integrated approach.

Good work-based learning opportunities will also contribute to the business objectives of the employer or organisation. This process involves the development of higher-level learning within both your academic institution and the workplace.

Potential workplace providers will receive many requests from students for placements, so you need to make sure your letter is noticed. See Table 10.1 for some key points to remember.

Table 10.1: Dos and don'ts when requesting work placements

Do...
• Make your message clear.
• Demonstrate a logical order representing your ideas and thoughts.
• Proofread your letter for spelling and grammar mistakes.
• Use the correct opening and closing phrase
• Ask someone else to read it.

Don't...
• Use terms such as 'read now', 'urgent' or 'help'.
• Provide too much information – this will overload the reader.
• Use slang or abbreviations.
• Be over familiar.

When you write a letter of application you should:

1. put your address at the top right-hand corner
2. place the address of the person you are writing to on the left hand side below your address
3. put the date below this on the right
4. always address your letter to somebody using their correct title, for example, 'Mr Cox' or 'Ms Cox'. Using first name terms to a person you do not know is over familiar and unprofessional. Using the title 'Mrs' or 'Miss' incorrectly can offend, therefore 'Ms' is preferable. If you do not know the name of the person you are writing to you should address the letter 'Dear Sir or Madam'
5. use your opening paragraph to convey the purpose of your letter; it is the most important element. Provide a clear, concise summary

of your message, no longer than a couple of lines. Your letter should then go on to give information to support your message

6. structure your letter in a coherent manner. This is achieved by putting forward your ideas in structured sentences. These allow the reader to clearly understand each element of information being delivered. The sentences should be constructed in a logical order to allow the reader to formulate a complete picture of the message you are delivering. Make sure you use accurate spelling and correct grammar and sentence structure. Read your letter out loud to ensure that it reads correctly and flows well. Get another person to proofread your letter

7. use the last paragraph of your letter to state what you would like the person to do as a result of your letter and thank them

8. end your letter correctly. Use 'Yours sincerely' if you know the name of the person to whom you are writing, or 'Yours faithfully' if you do not.

```
                                    The Firs
                                    10 Wintergreen Lane
                                    Milford
                                    Lancashire
Centre for Sports Performance
Sports Park
Green Road
Bedford
Bedfordshire
BE1 DG11                            18 June 2011

Dear Mr Cox or Dear Sir or Madam

Text of opening paragraph should provide a clear summary.

The main body of your letter should be well structured and
your last paragraph should state what you would like the
person to do.

Yours sincerely or Yours faithfully

Your signature

Your name typed
```

Figure 10.4: Template for a letter of application

Writing a curriculum vitae (CV)

A CV, sometimes also known as a resumé, is a logical overview of your working life. It is important to ensure your potential work placement provider notices you. It must be concise and accurate and needs to be thorough to highlight all relevant information. You should view your CV as your chance to sell yourself to your potential work placement provider. You are selling your skills, qualifications, experience and ultimately your ability to contribute to the organisation.

Many CV templates are available on the Internet for free but there is no perfect one. The CV format used will differ from person to person and situation to situation. The CV you construct for your work placement will be different from that of someone who has more years of experience and qualifications than you and who is applying for a job.

Consider how relevant information is when you are constructing your CV, and whether or not it will help you to sell yourself to the prospective organisation. What you must not do is draw attention to your weaknesses. For example, if you have a valid driving licence then this could be an advantage, so include it on your CV. However, if you do not have a driving licence or have failed your test twice, do not include the information.

What to put in your CV

Essential details to include in your CV are listed below.

Personal details

- Name
- Ensure contact details are personal details and not work details. Phone numbers included should be those which you are most accessible on. Email is a very accessible communication method.
- Nationality is not required.
- Marital status and family is optional.
- Date of birth is optional (age discrimination is illegal in the recruitment process under the Employment Equality (age) regulations 2006).

Education

- Include clearly the qualification and year of study (the institution is optional). Present the information starting with the most recent. For example:

  September 2008 – June 2011, FdSc Sports Science, Distinction, University name

- Include further education and school education. You may or may not wish to highlight GCSE grades.

- If you have additional qualifications, which are vocationally related, such as coaching, umpiring or first aid qualifications, you may wish to include a heading 'Vocational qualifications', particularly if you have a strong educational background. This will further sell your skills and abilities. If your education is weak and you have not entered into too much detail, you should include other qualifications here. This will enhance your education section and you will appear stronger to the prospective organisation.

Experience

- List all relevant experience you have gained. Include all employment and be prepared to be questioned on any gaps in your employment history.

- If you do not have an extensive employment history you should highlight experiences such as a gap year experience, part-time employment, voluntary work, charity work, summer camps, unpaid work, internships or association memberships. Provide a concise description of your experience for each.

- If your employment history is extensive and you have additional experiences to offer you may wish to use the headings 'Employment history' and 'Experiences' to strengthen your CV.

Additional information and sections you may want to include in your CV include the following.

Personal statement

This should grab the reader's attention. It should detail your attributes and goals and be no longer than 50 words. If you have a strong CV you could combine this section with your letter of application.

Skills

The skills you detail should be specific to the position for which you are applying and demonstrate that you would be a positive addition to the organisation. Provide a summary of job-related and transferable skills.

Job-related

These skills are related to the position for which you are applying and should be directly related to your placement.

Transferable skills

All foundation degrees have a wide range of transferable skills embedded into the programmes. Transferable skills include team work, synthesis and analysing information, presentation, communication and problem solving. Give examples where relevant.

Hobbies and interests

This section highlights you as a person. Your hobbies and interests can reflect your motivation, personality traits and personal skills. This section should still be related to the position applied for and sell you in a positive light. If it does not, then you should think about omitting it from your CV.

References

Do not provide any references on your CV. If the organisation wants this information they will ask you for it, or ask for it to be detailed on an application form. They should ask your permission to contact your referees either before an interview or upon appointment. You would not want your current employer to be approached for a reference when they do not know you have applied for another job – particularly if you are not appointed. For your placement you may wish to put your supervisor's contact details here as an exception to the rule.

> ### 🔖 Top tip
>
> Ensure your application is word processed and tailored for the position for which you are applying. If it is a more generic position highlight what you think are your unique selling points.

Reflective practice

Reflective practice is about developing purposeful learning. It involves you looking at your experiences in more depth in order to learn for next time. It will develop your personal and professional growth and develop your ability to link theory and practice.

For your placement you will be required to set targets and reflect upon your progress in achieving your targets, and your experiences during your placement. Reflective practice is essential to help you learn from your experience, and to develop. This process should be continuous, both on a personal and professional level.

There are many theories to facilitate your reflective practice. One of the most popular used by universities and colleges within the work placement module are Kolb's learning cycle and Gibbs' reflective cycle.

Remember

Work-based learning allows you to take responsibility for your learning. The close integration of academic and vocational learning adds value to your experience and qualification.

Kolb's learning cycle

In 1984 David Kolb published his learning styles model. This is known by various names, including Kolb's experiential learning theory, Kolb's learning styles inventory and the Kolb cycle. Kolb suggests four stages to his model which can be entered at any stage, although they must be followed in sequence thereafter to ensure learning takes place. The four stages are as follows.

1. **Concrete experience** – the 'doing' phase. This is your experience while completing your placement.
2. **Reflective observation** – the reflective process of your work experience. You will self reflect throughout the placement by keeping a log. You may also obtain feedback from your supervisor, colleagues, peers and clients. These aspects can be drawn together to give an overall reflection of your placement. Note that reflection on its own is not sufficient; you could complete this stage for the next 15, 20 or 30 years of your sports science career and not develop personally and professionally.
3. **Abstract conceptualisation** – this stage allows you to review and draw conclusions from your reflection. It is accompanied by you carrying out further research within the field of sports science and gaining more input from your lecturers, mentors and other developmental activities. This will help you to plan what you would do differently next time.
4. **Active experimentation** – this is where you implement your changes within your work experience and therefore continue the cycle into the concrete experience stage. This cycle is continuous and ongoing throughout your work experience.

Gibbs' reflective cycle

Developed by Professor Graham Gibbs, the Gibbs' reflective cycle (1988) consists of six stages. It is one of the few models to take emotion into account.

1. **Description** – describe exactly what happened during your work placement. You should keep a detailed log of each day.
2. **Feelings** – For each of your descriptions, document what you were *thinking* and *feeling* at the time. You may comment on how *confident* you felt – did you feel that you could not answer a question because of lack of knowledge nor communicate effectively in a given situation?
3. **Evaluation** – for each experience you should list points (both good and bad).
4. **Analysis** – analyse what sense you can make out of the situation. What does it *mean*? Using the example in point 3, you could analyse that your knowledge of dealing with injuries is poor and due to your lack of experience and the shock, you were unable to control the situation and deal with the injury.
5. **Conclusion** – conclude and document what else you could have done, or perhaps should have done, during that experience. Do you need to

complete a first aid course, or revise a course that you previously attended?

6. **Action plan** – if the situation arose again, what would you do differently, and how will you adapt your practice in the light of this new understanding? For example, if you witnessed an open fracture, you could set actions to gain more supervised pitch side experience and attend a refresher first aid course.

The cycle is only momentarily complete – should the situation arise again you will have developed personally and professionally to deal with the situation and the new event will become a focus of the reflective cycle. Development is a continuous process.

Assessment

As a work-based learner you will need to provide evidence to demonstrate that through your work-based learning you have met the learning outcomes of your programme of study. You should have an input into formulating and agreeing these within your learning agreement and the evidence format, which may take the form of:

- reflective journals and logs
- personal and professional development portfolios
- practical project reports or portfolios
- management and technical reports or portfolios
- presentations or exhibitions.

Figure 10.5: Gibbs' reflective cycle (adapted from Gibbs, 1988). Use the cycle to reflect on a recent incident within your work placement.

Time to reflect

1. Investigate four organisations where you could complete your work placement.

2. For each potential placement organisation identify the skills you have to offer.

3. Write a letter of application for your preferred placement. Proofread and make any necessary changes, then ask a peer, friend or family member to review it and suggest any changes you might need or want to make.

4. Construct a CV, using an appropriate CV template, and seek guidance from your work experience tutor or careers advisor on its content and format.

5. After successful completion of your work experience, reflect on your experiences and the significance this has on your career development plan.

Check your understanding (for answers, see www.pearsonfe.co.uk/foundationsinsport)

1. How would you define work-based learning?

2. What are transferable skills?

3. What potential does a workplace provide for learning opportunities?

4. How can you develop reflective practice in your work-based learning?

5. What is the significance of professional development planning in today's working environment?

Useful resources

To obtain a secure link to the website below, see the Websites section on page ii or visit the companion website at

www.pearsonfe.co.uk/foundationsinsport

- Business Link
- BASES

Further reading

Boud, D., Cressey, P. and Docherty, P. (eds.) (2005). *Productive Reflection at Work: Learning for Changing Organizations*. London: Routledge.

Brounstein, M. (2001). *Communicating Effectively for Dummies*. Chichester: John Wiley & Sons.

Field, S. (2010) *Career opportunities in the sports industry*. New York. Ferguson.

Gibbs, G. (1988) *Learning by doing: A guide to teaching and learning methods*. Further Education Unit. Oxford Polytechnic, Oxford.

Kolb, D. A. (1984). *Experiential Learning: Experience as the Source of Learning and Development*. New Jersey: Prentice Hall.

Leland, K. and Bailey, K. (2006). *Customer Service for Dummies*. Chichester: John Wiley & Sons.

Chapter 11

Case study: Sports scientist

Context

The Carnegie Centre for Sports Performance is situated on Leeds Metropolitan University's Headingley Campus, within the Carnegie Research Institute. The centre has designated sports science laboratories and consultation rooms. Its human performance laboratory is accredited by the British Association for Sport and Exercise Science (BASES), ensuring that all standards required for validity, accuracy and reliability in service delivery are met. In addition, a mobile testing facility is used to deliver field-based assessments.

The staff have extensive experience of applying scientific principles to the promotion, maintenance and enhancement of sport and exercise performance. Elite athletes from a range of sports regularly visit the centre to benefit from its services and facilities where it offers a client focused approach with the aim of maximising athletic potential, enabling athletes to train and compete at their best.

The centre offers a range of services:

- biomechanical analysis
- performance analysis
- physiological testing
- sports nutrition
- sports psychology
- strength and conditioning.

The centre currently provides sports science support for the university's sports teams and a variety of sporting partners. The centre has also supported a number of extreme challenges in the great outdoors including amongst others an ascent on Everest, an Atlantic row and a Polar challenge.

Elite performers know that before being able to compete with the best it has become necessary to address all aspects of performance. Making a championship or Olympic final is no longer just a product of hard training and good coaching; physiological testing, performance analysis, optimal nutrition, psychological preparation and recovery strategies are all part of the ultimate performance.

Meet Amy

Amy, 28, began employment as a sports scientist at Leeds Metropolitan University in September 2008.

Her qualifications include:

- B.Sc. (Hons) Sport and Exercise Science
- M.Sc. Sport and Exercise Science
- Health and Safety Executive 'First Aid At Work'
- Automated External Defibrillation Emergency Aid
- Level 2 Certificate in Fitness Instructing.

Since starting her role her continuous professional development has included:

- ISAK level 1 Anthropometry
- Safeguarding and Protecting Children
- BASES workshop: Kinanthropometry
- BASES workshop: Upper Body Physiology
- BASES workshop: Respiratory Assessment and Interpretation
- BASES conference: Abstract poster presentation and symposium presenter
- supporting research projects and publishing abstracts and journal articles.

Stop and think

The British Association of Sport and Exercise Sciences (BASES) is the UK professional body for all those with an interest in the science of sport and exercise.

The International Society for the Advancement of Kinanthropometry (ISAK) is an organisation whose scientific and professional endeavour is related to the practice of kinanthropometry; the quantitative interface between human structure and function.

Background

Amy began her studies in 2001. She has worked very hard over the years to gain a wide range of experience in the delivery of sports science support. Whilst studying sports science at Leeds Met she was a motivated, enthusiastic and dedicated student. She was proactive in securing work experience, shadowing a fitness consultant at Sheffield United football club during the second year of her undergraduate degree programme. This gave her valuable experience in strength and conditioning, fitness training and pre-match support specific to football. This was a good place to start, as she also had personal experience of playing this sport at a competitive level. This provided an insight into working in professional sport and within a multi-disciplinary environment. It allowed her to develop good communication skills and to understand the challenges of translating her theoretical learning into practice.

As she continued through her degree programme Amy continued developing and gaining work experience in sports science support, working under the supervision of accredited sports scientists to support talent camps for the rugby football league and schools programmes. She describes these experiences as invaluable to her personal, professional and academic development and enthusiasm for the area. She recalls her big break as coming in 2006 when she worked on a large scale mountaineering project, playing a key role in the delivery of physiological support. She was part of a multi-disciplinary team, supporting a group of Army Mountaineers, who were attempting to become the first British Summiteers of the notorious Everest West

Ridge. This opportunity presented itself as a result of the commiment, hard work and competence she had demonstrated in volunteering roles in sports science support, during her undergraduate degree programme.

Realising there was more to learn she went on to do a master's degree in sport and exercise science and at the same time was successful in gaining an internship in physiology support that ran alongside her studies for 12 months. This provided more opportunities to gain valuable applied experience. Since gaining her current position she has also had the experience of teaching seminars at undergraduate and postgraduate level. She has presented at sports science conferences and spent a season seconded to work as a sports scientist alongside the strength and conditioning team at a premiership rugby union club. During this time Amy seized the opportunity to shadow the sports scientist, working with the England rugby union team at one of their training camps.

Beyond the groups of performers already identified, the range of athletes Amy has worked with includes rugby league players, track and field athletes, cyclists, cricketers, netballers, sailors and individuals undertaking extreme challenges or challenges in extreme environments.

Job description, role and responsibilities

Amy's role involves providing sports science support services to athletes ranging in ability (high performance athletes, student athletes and members of the general public) and sports. She specialises in exercise physiology.

These services include:

- athlete screening
- heart rate monitoring
- blood sampling and analysis
- blood lactate profiling
- online gas analysis
- GPS tracking
- body composition analysis
- hydration monitoring

- field-based assessments such as speed and agility
- altitude and heat acclimatisation, using an environmental chamber
- lung function assessment.

Amy's responsibilities include:

- supporting the promotion, development and delivery of sports science support services
- supporting research-related activities in sports science
- coordinating and managing data collection through laboratory and field-based techniques
- organising and analysing data for the purpose of athlete reports and feedback
- ensuring the health and safety of athletes
- mentoring physiology internship students.

Amy understands that to be successful in working with top athletes as a sports scientist she needs:

- excellent communication, organisational and interpersonal skills
- a high level of competency in using information technology
- the ability to work confidently as part of a team and on her own initiative to deliver a high quality customer focused service
- the ability to work flexibly and confidently within busy working environments and to be prepared to work outside normal office hours.

A typical working day

As Amy's role is so varied she doesn't really have a typical day and could be involved in any of the above activities, but during her secondment to work in premiership rugby Amy effectively supported the strength and conditioning provision for the team. This involved working with the first team coaching staff and players both during training and on match days, where she supported the hydration analysis of players.

She undertook other activities, including weight training, conditioning and recovery sessions; return to training rehabilitation progressions; body composition assessment; hydration checks and the gathering and interpretation of heart rate monitoring and GPS tracking data.

Specific responsibilities that Amy fulfilled in this role included the implementation of GPS player tracking during competition and training. She created systems to monitor key indicators of intensity, volume and the quality of training stimulus provided. This system was also used to assess the readiness of injured players for return to competition. Using live heart rate telemetry during both rugby and conditioning sessions, Amy developed and made operational systems used to quantify the intensity and volume of training sessions. Associated data analysis focused on the monitoring of heart rate-related fitness parameters.

Within the club's regular body composition assessment programme, Amy carried out frequent skinfold measurements for first team players. As a supplementary measure of body composition Amy also carried out dual X-ray absorptometry (DXA) scans on three occasions during the year.

Amy understands that to be a successful sports scientist, working with top athletes, you need good training in your scientific discipline, an awareness of the other people that impact on the athlete and a passion for sport. You need to be flexible, approachable and have excellent interpersonal skills, so you can convey information clearly and in a jargon-free way that athletes and coaches can relate to and apply in practice.

Amy is currently involved in a research project looking at pre-acclimatisation to altitude. Above 2000 m exercise becomes more difficult than at sea level and at higher altitudes the decrease in air pressure causes a significant disruption in the oxygen supply to the brain and muscles. In regions of high altitude, such as the Himalayas, mountaineers find it difficult to complete simple physical tasks and have a high risk of developing acute mountain sickness (AMS). This can lead to more serious illnesses. The aim of the research project is to examine the use of artificial acclimatisation on exercise performance through regular exposure to high altitude in a state-of-the-art environmental chamber (a process known as intermittent hypoxia) and then throughout an expedition to the Himalayas.

At times Amy has to work unsociable or long hours, but particularly enjoys the variety within her role and the opportunity to apply knowledge and skills in different contexts, especially elite and extreme environments. One of the most challenging aspects of the job is the need to be very well organised, with the ability to plan for contingency. Her advice to current students is to gain as much experience from a variety of situations and contexts as possible, working both with teams and individual athletes. Demonstrate that you can work well within a team environment as well as on your own, using your initiative. Get experience of working in pressure situations and within tight deadlines, and most of all maintain a personal interest in sport and training. As a sports scientist you often need to give the same degree of commitment and determination shown by the athletes and coaches you work with. Knowing that you have had some influence in the success of the athletes you have worked with is very fulfilling and provides good job satisfaction.

Sports science scenario

The Everest West Ridge straddles the Chinese-Nepalese boarder and is one of the mountain's toughest routes. Due to the effects of altitude a period of acclimatisation is required in order for climbers to be in optimal physiological condition to attempt this route. In their meticulous preparation for this toughest of challenges the Army team, supported by Amy and a team of senior sports science colleagues from a range of disciplines, were put through their paces using the latest technological equipment and training principles. This ensured the team had the best chance of success on the mountain.

The team underwent a series of physiological assessments. The information collected and analysed from these assessments enabled the prescription of individually-tailored training programmes. Each team member had the opportunity to be in the best physical condition possible prior to departure for the Himalayas with the mountaineers advised on cross-training methods that included gym-based sessions, running and mountain biking.

Stop and think

What types of physiological assessment do you think were conducted on the mountaineers in order to provide individually-tailored training programmes to support their preparations for their attempt on the Everest West Ridge?

What other elements of sports science support do you think would have been useful in the preparation for this extreme challenge?

Training and development

The British Association of Sport and Exercise Sciences (BASES) is the UK professional body for all those with an interest in the science of sport and exercise. They have developed a Career Guide for prospective and current students providing a comprehensive overview of the careers that you might pursue. It is free to download from their website. Qualified sports scientists can join BASES and, by presenting evidence of relevant work, can gain accreditation that is recognised across the UK. This additional recognition may be beneficial when job hunting or looking for career progression. To help keep abreast of current research and industry developments, BASES members can participate in workshops and conference programmes.

As mentioned, most athletes now view sports science as an integral part of effective training and preparation but gaining a job in this field, especially at the very elite end of sport, remains highly competitive. With the increasing awareness of the health benefits of exercise, exercise science

could be another avenue to pursue. In this area you would work with doctors to improve health through exercise in areas such as health promotion or cardiac rehabilitation.

Many students of sports science have not decided on a career path whilst studying their programme. A foundation degree in sports science will give you a good broad foundation in a range of scientific disciplines which can impact on sport. It is helpful to have had a personal background in sport, to really understand the athlete lifestyle and demands of training. In order to further your career you will need to take responsibility for your own professional development. Keeping up to date with current issues and new research will be very important for your employability.

Stop and think

Sports science internships

Many professional sports teams are now offering internships within their sports science departments. Internships usually run for a year and involve providing sports science and strength and conditioning support to athletes, often academy level athletes. Successful applicants should expect to be involved in continuing professional development programmes and gain valuable applied experience.

Consider what you might anticipate such a role to require and the essential and desirable job criteria that might be expected.

Time to reflect

1. Consider what the aim of sports science support is and how its application might change with different levels of performer.

2. How could you use BASES to develop your career as a sports scientist?

3. What do you think might be some of the most challenging aspects of working in performance sport and how might you overcome these?

4. As a sports scientist working in elite sport you are likely to liaise with a number of other professionals on a regular basis; what are the benefits and challenges of working in multi-disciplinary teams?

5. Why is it important to keep up to date with current issues in sports science?

6. What are the benefits of gaining additional qualifications and experience during your programme of study?

7. What opportunities and activities are available to you to enhance your career prospects?

8. Use the Internet to investigate current job opportunities in sports science. Find out the key personal attributes that would be expected of a good sports scientist.

9. Identify a continuing professional development plan for the next 2–3 years as you begin your career journey in sports science, including work experience opportunities and relevant further training.

10. If you were unsuccessful at securing a role in sport, what other career avenues would be open to you?

Useful resources

To obtain a secure link to the websites below, see the Websites section on page ii or visit the companion website at www.pearsonfe.co.uk/foundationsinsport

- American College of Sports Medicine
- Australian Institute of Sport
- British Association of Sport and Exercise Science
- English Institute of Sport
- British Journal of Sports Medicine
- Journal of Sport Sciences
- Journal of Applied Physiology
- Medicine in Sport and Exercise Science
- UK Sport

Further reading

Australian Sports Commission (2000). *Physiological Tests for Elite Athletes*. Champaign, Illinois: Human Kinetics.

BASES (2007). *British Association of Sport and Exercise Sciences Physiological Testing Guidelines, Volume 1: Sports Testing*. Leeds: Routledge.

Eston, R. and Reilly, T. (2008). *Kinanthropometry and Exercise Physiology Manual: Tests, Procedures and Data*, 3rd Edition. *Volume 1: Anthropometry*. Routledge.

Eston, R. and Reilly, T. (2008). *Kinanthropometry and Exercise Physiology Manual: Tests, Procedures and Data*, 3rd Edition. *Volume 2: Physiology*. Routledge.

McArdle ,W.D., Katch, F.I. and Katch, V.L. (2010). *Exercise Physiology: Nutrition Energy and Human Performance*, 7th Edition. Philadelphia: Lippincott, Williams & Wilkins.

Wilmore, J.H., Costill, D.L. and Kenney, W.L. (2008). *Physiology of Sport and Exercise*, 4th Edition. Champaign, Illinois: Human Kinetics.

Glossary

Absorption – the movement of digested food from the stomach and small intestine into body tissues and blood.

Activities of daily living – the things that you normally do in daily living at home or at work

Adenosine triphosphate (ATP) – high energy compound used for energy in the human body

Adrenalin – a hormone that increases heart rate and constricts blood vessels

Aerobic endurance – the ability of the cardiovascular and respiratory systems to supply the exercising muscles with oxygen over a prolonged period of time

Aerobic metabolism – the process of energy production with oxygen

Aerodynamics – fluid dynamics where the fluid is air

Agonist – the muscle producing the action (movement)

Amotivation – condition where there is an absence of motivation in an athlete

Anaerobic capacity – the ability to sustain very high intensity exercise without the presence of oxygen

Anaerobic metabolism – the process of energy production without oxygen

Andragogy – learner-focused education

Angle of attack – difference between the flight path of the body's centre of gravity and the angle of the body to the ground

Angular momentum – product of the moment of inertia and angular velocity

Ankylosing spondylitis – an inflammatory arthritis affecting mainly the joints in the spine or the sacroilium in the pelvis. However, other joints of the body may also be affected as well as tissues, including the heart, eyes, lungs and kidneys

Antagonist – the muscle opposing the action (movement)

Anteriorly – towards the front

Aponeurosis – a flat, broad tendon

Appendicular skeleton – all the parts that are joined to the head and trunk (axial)

Articular cartilage – (also known as hyaline cartilage) is smooth and covers the surface of bones

Articulation – the contact of two or more bones at a specific location

Athlete – a person who competes in organised sporting events

ATPase – enzyme that causes the reaction that releases energy from ATP

Autocratic – coach controls the learning environment

Axial skeleton – the head and trunk of the body

Axis – straight line around which we rotate when we move

Biomechanics – branch of sport and exercise sciences that examines the causes and consequences of human movement; and the interaction of the body with apparatus or equipment through the application of mechanical principles in sporting settings

Boundary Layer – layer of fluid that is adjacent to the surface of the body travelling through it

Calorie – the energy required to raise 1 g of water by 1°C

Cardiac hypertrophy – enlargement of the heart due to increases in muscle mass and/or chamber size

Cardiac output – the volume of blood ejected from the heart in one minute

Centre of gravity – the point at which gravity acts through a body. This changes every time you move but is at about 55–57 per cent of standing height when in the anatomical position

Coaching environment – the physical space in which sports coaching activities take place

Coaching philosophy – the guiding principles that shape a coach's behaviour in the coaching environment

Cognitive anxiety – negative thoughts, nervousness or worry experienced in certain situations. Symptoms of cognitive anxiety include concentration problems, fear and bad decision making

Concentric – muscle contraction generates force, which causes muscle shortening

Concentric contraction – muscle is shortening whilst producing force

Concurrent feedback – ongoing feedback provided during an activity

Control centre – determines the set point at which the variable is maintained

Corrective feedback – statements that convey messages of how to improve after mistakes or poor performance

Costal cartilage – hyaline cartilage which connects the sternum to the ribs

Curriculum vitae – document which provides an overview of your qualifications, employment and relevant life experience

Curvilinear motion – movement in a curved line (e.g. 200 metre sprint race in athletics)

Democratic – participant controls the learning environment

Diaphysis – main shaft of the bone

Diastole – cardiac cycle period when the heart is relaxing

Diet – a particular pattern of eating habits or food consumption

Digestion – the process by which enzymes in the gut break down larger chemical compounds in foods so that they can be absorbed by the body.

Direct method – a term used when a test measures the desired variable

Discipline – a branch of learning or scholarly activity that is taught and researched at university level

Diurnal variations – fluctuations which occur each day

Dorsiflex – move the top of the foot towards the body, showing the sole of the foot

Drag – resistive force that opposes the motion of a body and is created by the fluid that the body is travelling through

Eccentric – muscle lengthens due to the opposing force being greater than the force generated by the muscle

Eccentric contraction – muscle is lengthening whilst producing force

Effector – provides the means to respond to the stimulus

Ego orientated – people who judge success on social comparisons, determining whether they are better than other athletes

Electron transport chain – a process that uses hydrogen to form ATP

Endomysium – connective tissue, encasing individual muscle fibres

Epimysium – connective tissue, which encases all the fascicles surrounding the whole muscle

Essential amino acids – amino acids that must be obtained from the diet and cannot be synthesised by the body

Evert – move the sole of the foot away from the midline of the body

Exercise – activity that maintains or enhances physical fitness

Exergaming – the term used for video games that also incorporate physical activity

External imagery – imagining yourself doing something as though you are watching it on a film so that you can develop an awareness of how the activity looks. This can help athletes to correct errors in performance and develop correct movement patterns.

Extrinsic feedback – feedback from external sources, such as a sports scientist

Extrinsic motivation – external factors that drive an athlete, such as money and trophies

Facilitative – to assist in making things easier or less difficult

Fascia – fibrous tissue, binding together or separating muscles

Fascicular arrangement – the arrangement of fascicles, which ultimately affects power output and range of movement

Fatty acids – contain chains of carbon atoms to which hydrogen atoms attach. The number of hydrogen atoms relative to the number of carbon atoms determines if a fatty acid is classified as saturated or unsaturated. Unsaturated fatty acids may be monounsaturated or polyunsaturated. All fats consumed in our diet are a mixture of these different fatty acid types. Fatty foods containing a majority of saturated fatty acids are generally solid at room temperature, while fats composed of mainly unsaturated fatty acids are usually liquid at room temperature.

Fibrocartilage – this cartilage is very rich in type 1 collagen and is strong and durable. It can be found, for example, in the menisci of the knee and intervertebral disc

Field of view – area that the sports scientist is recording that contains the sporting action

Fixator – provide stabilisation at the proximal end of the limb

Force – mechanical action or effort applied to a body that produces movement

Force platform – device that measures forces

Force transmission – impact forces transmitted through the body

Free radical – an atom or compound with an unpaired electron, thought to cause cellular damage

Friction – resistive force produced when one body moves across another and their surfaces are in contact

Frontal axis – imaginary line drawn from left to right

Frontal plane – separates the body into imaginary front to back halves

Glycaemic Index (GI) – classification system for carbohydrate foods based on the blood glucose response they elicit

Glycogen – the principal storage form of carbohydrate in animals stored in the liver and muscles

Glycolysis – a process used to convert glucose to pyruvic acid

Ground reaction force – equal and opposing force that is exerted by the ground on a body

Health-related activities – activity aimed at improving the health and well-being of an individual

Holistic – dealing with the whole of someone and not just a part

Homeostasis – tendency towards relatively stable equilibrium between physiological processes

Horizontal scaling – providing a scale of measurement that will allow you to convert on screen measurements to real life measurements, for example 1 metre 'real' = 1 centimetre 'screen'

Hydrodynamics – fluid dynamics where the fluid is water

Hypervolemia – an increase in blood volume.

Impulse – product of the size of the force and the duration of the force application

Indirect predictive method – a term used when a test does not actually measure the desired variable but measures another variable which is used to predict the desired variable

Inertia – tendency for a body to remain in its state of motion

Insertion – the attachment of a muscle usually via a tendon to bone. The insertion on the bone is moveable as a result of muscle contraction

Internal imagery – imagining an activity from the first-person perspective and concentrating on how the activity feels. This is beneficial as it can generate the same type of muscular activity as physically performing the activity, but to a lesser extent.

Intervertebral disc – a fibrocartilage disc which lies between each adjacent vertebrae of the spine

Intrinsic feedback – feedback that comes from the athlete's senses

Intrinsic motivation – internal factors that drive an athlete, such as fun and satisfaction

Inverse dynamics – process of calculating net force from multiple forces

Invert – move the sole of the foot towards the midline of the body

Isometric – force generated by the muscle without changing length

Joule – one joule of energy moves a mass of 1 g at a velocity of 1 metre per second. Approximately 4.2 joules = 1 calorie

Kilocalorie – the energy required to raise the temperature of 1 kg of water by 1°C. Equal to 1000 calories and used to convey the energy value of food. Kilocalories are often simply referred to as calories

Kilojoule – a unit of measurement for energy, but like the calorie the joule is not a large unit of energy; therefore kilojoules are used more often

Kinematics – description of movements without reference to the forces involved

Kinetics – assessment of movement with respect to the forces involved

Knowledge of performance – feedback to the athlete about the actions that have caused the result and how these must be changed to alter the result in future

Knowledge of results – feedback to the athlete about the outcome of an action or event

Krebs cycle – a series of aerobic reactions that break down acetyl CoA to release energy

Lactate threshold – the point at which the body's energy demand exceeds the supply from the aerobic processes and the muscles rely on the anaerobic processes to supply the energy

Laminar Flow – smooth flow of fluid over a body

Learning – the activity of obtaining knowledge

Lift – fluid force that acts perpendicular to the relative motion of a body with respect to the fluid it is passing through

Ligament – a band of tough fibrous tissue connecting bone to bone

Lipolysis – the process of splitting triglycerides into glycerol and free fatty acids

Lordosis – exaggerated curvature of the lumbar spine

Macronutrient – nutrients that are required by the body in daily amounts greater than a few grams

Maximal oxygen consumption (VO2max) – the highest rate of oxygen consumption achieved during maximal exercise

Method – the style of coaching adopted by the coach

Mitochondria – a structure in cells where, in the presence of oxygen, food molecules are broken down to form energy

Moment of inertia – tendency for a rotating body to remain in its present state of motion

Momentum – product of a body's mass and its velocity

Monosaccharide – single sugar units, the most common of which is glucose

Motivation – direction and intensity of one's effort. Athletes will choose whether to try to achieve a particular task (direction) and how hard they will try (intensity)

Motivational climate – situational induced psychological environment that influences achievement strategies of participants

Multi-dimensional – being made up of a number of different dimensions (or factors)

Myoglobin – a singular chain globular protein, with a high affinity to oxygen

Negative feedback – feedback that happens after an unsuccessful attempt at a task, used to highlight and correct errors

Negative self-talk – self-critical statements that can distract attention, reduce confidence and self-efficacy levels and make it harder to achieve goals

Newton – force required to move a mass of 1 kg at a rate of $1\,\text{ms}^{-2}$

Noradrenalin – hormone that acts alongside adrenalin to increase heart rate, blood flow to the muscles and stimulates glucose release

Nutrition – the process by which chemicals from our environment are taken up by the body to provide the energy and nutrients needed to sustain life and maintain health

Occipital condyles – kidney-shaped with convex surfaces, there are two occipital condyles located either side of the foramen magnum. They articulate with the atlas bone

Origin – the attachment site of a muscle to bone (in a few exceptions muscle). The origin is a fixed location

Partial pressure – the pressure a gas exerts on a mixture of gases

Participant – a person who takes part or becomes involved in an activity

Pedagogical encounter – learning experience that takes place in the coaching environment

Pedagogy – the principles and practices designed to enhance learning in an individual

Performance criteria – aspects of performance that are used to analyse performance in sports. These are also referred to as performance indicators or key performance indicators in some literature

Perimysium – connective tissue, encasing fascicles

Perspective error – error where objects appear larger or smaller than they actually are as they move towards or away from the camera; it is difficult to effectively judge their position

Phosphorylation – the process of adding a phosphate group to ADP

Plantarflex – point the toes away, pushing the sole of the foot away

Positive feedback – feedback that occurs after successful completion of a task, used to reinforce performance

Positive self-talk – positive statements used to arouse and direct attention or to motivate people towards achieving goals

Power – the ability to generate muscular strength quickly

Pressure – amount of force applied over a given area

Pressure gradient – the difference between the partial pressures of two gases

Pubic symphysis – a cartilaginous joint articulating the superior rami of the left and right pubic bones

Pulmonary circuit – the circuit of the right side of the heart that transports blood to the lungs

Radius of gyration – relative distribution of mass in relation to the axis of rotation

Receptor – monitors the environment and detects changes (stimulus) to the variable

Rectilinear motion – movement in a straight line (e.g. 100 metre sprint race in athletics)

Resynthesis – the combining of simple compounds or elements to form a more complex one

Sagittal axis – imaginary line drawn from your back to your front

Sagittal plane – splits the body into imaginary left and right halves

Sarcolemma – cell membrane of the muscle fibre

Sarcoplasm – a gelatine like substance which fills the spaces between myofibrils; it is comparable to the cytoplasm found in cells

Scalar quantities – quantity that only has a magnitude (e.g. speed)

Somatic anxiety – relates to the awareness and perception of physiological changes (such as increases in heart rate, sweating and increased body heat) when you play sport

Speed – the ability to cover a distance in the shortest possible time

Sport(s) science(s) – umbrella term for academic programmes that focus on the application of scientific principles and techniques with the aim of improving sporting performance

Sports nutrition – the influence of nutrition on human performance during the preparation for, participation in and the recovery from sport and exercise

State anxiety – temporary, changeable mood state that is an emotional response to any situation considered threatening

Strain gauge – device used to measure force or torque in sport settings

Strategy – the actions taken by the coach in response to identified priorities for coaching

Streamlining – altering a body to reduce the disturbance to the fluid flow and drag

Strength – the ability of a muscle group to exert force to overcome a resistance

Stretch reflex – an automatic response to a sudden stretching of a muscle

Stroke volume (SV) – the volume of blood ejected from the left ventricle

Style – the way in which the coaching is performed

Sub-discipline – a field of specialised study within the discipline of sports science

Submaximal – exercise intensity below 100 per cent of maximum heart rate

Supinated – when the forearm is supinated the palm of the hand is facing forward when in the anatomical position

Sutural bone – extra piece of bone which appears in the suture in the cranium

Synergist – synergist muscles assist the agonist muscles and provide stabilisation to prevent any unwanted movement

Systemic circuit – the circuit of the left side of the heart that transports blood to the body

Systole – the contraction of the heart that forces blood out of the ventricles

Task orientated – people who judge success based on self-improvement and development

Tendon – a band of inelastic tissue connecting a muscle to bone

Terminal feedback – feedback that happens after an event, rather than during the event

Thermogenesis – the process of heat production

Torque – turning effect created by a force around an axis

Trait anxiety – aspect of personality and part of an individual's pattern of behaviour. Someone with a high level of trait anxiety is likely to become worried in a variety of situations; even non-threatening situations

Transverse plane – splits the body into imaginary top to bottom halves

Turbulent flow – disturbed flow of air around a body

Variable – the factor or event being regulated

Vasoconstriction – the process of narrowing of blood vessel diameter

Vasodilation – the process where the blood vessels increase in diameter

Vector quantities – quantity that has a magnitude and a direction (e.g. velocity)

Vertical axis – imaginary line drawn from your head to your toe

Vertical referencing – as for horizontal scaling, but vertically

Index